Introduction to Information Science and Technology

Introduction to Information Science and Technology

Edited by Charles H. Davis and Debora Shaw

ASIST Monograph Series

Published for the
American Society for Information Science and Technology by

Information Today, Inc.

Medford, New Jersey

Third printing, March 2018

Introduction to Information Science and Technology

Copyright © 2011 by American Society for Information Science and Technology

Publisher's Note: The editors and publisher have taken care in preparation of this book but make no expressed or implied warranty of any kind and assume no responsibility for errors or omissions. No liability is assumed for incidental or consequential damages in connection with or arising out of the use of the information or programs contained herein.

Many of the designations used by manufacturers and sellers to distinguish their products are claimed as trademarks. Where those designations appear in this book and Information Today, Inc. was aware of a trademark claim, the designations have been printed with initial capital letters.

Library of Congress Cataloging-in-Publication Data

Introduction to information science and technology / edited by Charles H. Davis and Debora Shaw.
     p. cm. -- (ASIS&T monograph series)
    Includes bibliographical references and index.
    ISBN-13: 978-1-57387-423-6
    ISBN-10: 1-57387-423-X
    1. Information science. 2. Information technology. I. Davis, Charles Hargis, 1938- II. Shaw, Debora.
Z666.5.I665 2011
020--dc23

                  2011023688

President and CEO: Thomas H. Hogan, Sr.
Editor-in-Chief and Publisher: John B. Bryans
ASIST Monograph Series Editor: Samantha Hastings
VP Graphics and Production: M. Heide Dengler
Managing Editor: Amy M. Reeve
Editorial Assistant: Brandi Scardilli
Book Designer: Kara Mia Jalkowski
Cover Designer: Dana J. Stevenson
Copy Editor: Bonnie Freeman
Proofreader: Penelope Mathiesen
Indexer: Beth Palmer

www.infotoday.com

Contents

Collaborators and Contributors

This collaborative undertaking would have been impossible without the instigation and cheerleading of Samantha Hastings, who wears, among other hats, that of ASIST monographs editor. John B. Bryans, editor-in-chief and publisher of the book publishing division at Information Today, Inc., was also an early supporter and voice of reason and encouragement. Russ Evans, who set up the wiki for our online collaboration, provided useful guidance, especially for our first steps. Bob Williams and his students at the University of South Carolina (USC) agreed to test-drive a first draft of the book. Bob Williams, Sam Hastings, and three valiant doctoral students at USC, Christopher Cunningham, Lisa Hudgins, and Yao Zhang, undertook copy editing, while Bob created the glossary. Most importantly, the following people helped write, edit, and occasionally gnash teeth over what has emerged as this *Introduction to Information Science and Technology*. The book would not exist but for these contributors:

Bill Albing	Lawrence J. McCrank
David Bawden	Michel J. Menou
Gerald Benoit	Michael Middleton
Jill Breznican	T. Patrick Milas
Pascal Calarco	Stefano Mizzaro
Donald Case	Allyson Mower
Shan-Ju Chang	Sue Myburgh
Yungrang Cheng	Diane Neal
Michele Cloonan	Jeppe Nicolaisen
Charles Cole	Sunny Pai
Christine Connors	Jay Paraki
Dave Cooksey	Shampa Paul
Christopher Cunningham	Anis Pervez
Ed Dale	Gabe Peterson
Charles Davis	David M. Pimentel
Anne Diekema	Serhiy Polyakov
Susan Doran	Devendra Potnis
Lorraine Eakin	M. Asim Qayyum
Sanda Erdelez	Haleh Raissadat
Frank Exner, Little Bear	W. Boyd Rayward
Jeffrey Forrest	Alma Rivera
Jane Greenberg	Lyn Robinson
Raf Guns	Nancy Roderer
Carole Hafner	Alenka Šauperl

Samantha Hastings
Suliman Hawamdeh
Ken Himma
Birger Hjørland
Marico Howe
Sharon Hu
Lisa Hudgins
Richard Hulser
Judy Jeng
Rafal Kasprowski
Sherry Koshman
Joseph Kraus
Bill Kules
Sean M. Lind
Christopher Lueg
Paola Maderna
Christine Marton
Terrence A. Maxwell

Steve Sawyer
Debora Shaw
Scott Simon
Diane Sonnenwald
Stacy Merrill Surla
Deborah Swain
Donghua Tao
Laurel Tarulli
Mike Thelwall
Donna Trivison
Ray Uzwyshyn
Shelly Warwick
Robert V. Williams
Mary M. Williams
Dave Yates
Jane Zhang
Yao Zhang
Lisa Zilinski

Major contributors by chapter are:

Chapter 1 Our World of Information: Robert V. Williams (initial draft)

Chapter 2 Foundations of Information Science and Technology: Robert V. Williams (initial draft) with W. Boyd Rayward

Chapter 3 Information Needs, Seeking, and Use: Birger Hjørland (initial draft), Laurel Tarulli, Yungrang Cheng, David Bawden, and Lyn Robinson

Chapter 4 Representation of Information: Charles H. Davis, Sue Myburgh, Birger Hjørland, and Diane Neal (initial drafts) with Birger Hjørland and Laurel Tarulli

Chapter 5 Organization of Information: Birger Hjørland, Diane Neal, Alenka Šauperl, and David Bawden (initial drafts) with Laurel Tarulli, and Raf Guns

Chapter 6 Computers and Networks: Lisa Zilinski (initial draft) and Sharon Hu

Chapter 7 Structured Information Systems: Debora Shaw (initial draft) and Sean M. Lind

Chapter 8 Information System Applications: Charles H. Davis, Birger Hjørland, Rafal Kasprowski, and Ray Uzwyshyn (initial drafts)

Chapter 9 Evaluation of Information Systems: Diane H. Sonnenwald and Judy Jeng (initial drafts)

Chapter 10 Information Management: Deborah Swain, Birger Hjørland, and Paola Maderna (initial drafts) with Laurel Tarulli

Chapter 11 Publication and Information Technologies: Laurel Tarulli, Jeppe Nicolaisen, and Mike Thelwall (initial drafts)

Chapter 12 Information Policy: Gabriel Peterson (initial draft)

Chapter 13 The Information Professions: Laurel Tarulli, Debora Shaw, and Paola Maderna (initial drafts) with Birger Hjørland

Chapter 14 Information Theory: Scott Simon and Birger Hjørland (initial drafts)

Introduction to Information Science and Technology has also benefitted from support and advice from many other people, including:

Hamid Ekbia
Kathryn La Barre
Liliano Sergio Maderna (in memoriam)
Hanna M. Söderholm
Fred Sonnenwald
Chicca Stitt
Miles J. Stitt Jr.

The editors appreciate the advice, patience, and support of the many contributors to *Introduction to Information Science and Technology*.

Introduction

A Collaborative Book

Introduction to Information Science and Technology is a collaborative book. Volunteers with knowledge in their respective areas have provided draft chapters reflecting their perspectives and knowledge. These were reviewed and enhanced by the initial authors and other experts using a wiki hosted by the American Society for Information Science and Technology. This book is a product of that collaborative effort, edited to serve as an introductory text.

One might think that an introduction for such an important field would be easily written. This is not the case. Each type of information system (the web, online databases, libraries, etc.) has a largely separate literature. Attention is typically restricted by technology, usually to computer-based information systems, or is focused on one function, such as retrieval, disregarding the broader context. What is published may be specialized, technical how-to writing with localized terminology and definitions. For example, publications on theory are often narrowly focused on such topics as logic, probability, or physical signals. This diversity has been compounded by confusion arising from inadequate recognition that the word *information* is used by various people to denote different things.

This text attempts to alleviate these problems by encouraging contributors to write at an introductory level, engaging additional readers and editors to broaden and strengthen the work, and testing a draft with students in an Introduction to Information Science course. The wiki that supported the collaboration retains the more detailed and specialized contributions and has helped the editors focus this edition of the book as an introduction to the field.

The American Society for Information Science and Technology provides all members access to the wiki. It presents considerably more detail, opinions, and interpretations than could be included in this print edition. It is our hope that the wiki version will continue to evolve and that a second edition of this book will benefit from the interaction the wiki supports.

About the Book

We begin by setting the context for our world of information in Chapter 1 and discussing the basic terms used and history of information science and technology in Chapter 2. Chapter 3 considers what causes people to look for information and their behaviors as they seek and use it. Chapters 4 and 5 examine past and current practices regarding the effective representation and organization of information so that potential users can identify sources that might meet their needs. Chapter 6 presents computers and network technologies, and Chapters 7 and 8 examine how these technologies are used in information systems. Chapter 9 considers the roles of information system users. Information management is the topic of Chapter 10, which looks at how information technologies affect and are affected by the organizations in which they are used. Chapter 11 examines how information and communication technologies are used in scholarly and social communication; Chapter 12 considers policy aspects of information access and use; and Chapter 13 looks at how information professionals approach these and related issues. Chapter 14 examines underlying theoretical issues and connections between information science and communication studies and philosophy.

In Chapter 1, you will discover how many zettabytes of information the typical American encounters in a year. This book represents a tiny portion of that annual intake, but it can help you make sense of all the rest. We hope you enjoy thinking and learning about this vast and rapidly changing world of information.

Our World of Information

1.1. How Much Information?

Information is everywhere and in huge amounts. How much is there (can we find out)? Where does it come from? And how does all that information affect us as individuals? What can we do to find out what it's worth while providing some level of organization and control? This introductory chapter places each of us, as information producers and users, into the big picture.

In 2008, researchers Roger Bohn and James Short at the University of California–San Diego's Global Information Industry Center asked "How much information was consumed by individuals in the United States?" (2009, p. 8). They looked at only nonwork use of information, such as watching television or talking on a cell phone. Among their conclusions are the following:

- Each American spends, on average, half of each day of (11.8 hours) consuming information.

- Although we spend 41 percent of our "information time" in front of the TV, TV provides less than 35 percent of the bytes of information we consume.

- Computer and video games, because of their graphics, account for 55 percent of the information bytes we consume at home.

- Altogether, we gobbled up some 3.6 zettabytes of information at home in 2008.

How much is a zettabyte? It is 10^{21} bytes, or 1,000 exabytes. Bohn and Short (2009, p. 8) estimate that an exabyte, or 1 billion gigabytes, is the capacity of all the hard disks in home computers in Minnesota (population 5.1 million). So the nonwork information consumed in the U.S. in 2008 was equal to what could be stored on 3,600 Minnesotas' worth of hard drives. In other words, if all this information were "printed ... in books and stacked ... as tightly as possible across the United States including Alaska, the pile would be 7 feet high" (p. 13). Bohn and Short also found that radio is "a highly byte-efficient delivery mechanism." People listened to radio for 19 percent of their hours spent consuming information—this amounted to 10.6 percent of daily words received but only 0.3 percent of the total bytes of information received (p. 9).

In the 1980s, Ithiel de Sola Pool and his colleagues investigated the growth of information (measured in words) supplied by the media in the U.S. and Japan (Neuman & Pool, 1986; Pool, 1983; Pool, Inose, Takasaki, & Hurwitz, 1984). They analyzed the number of words supplied and consumed as well as the average price per word. They reported that available information was shifting from print to electronic media, the price per word was falling dramatically, and although the rate of consumption was increasing (at 3.3 percent per year), it was falling ever further behind the amount of information supplied. These findings have implications for information overload, information diversity, and the economics necessary to sustain vibrant, creative industries in journalism and popular and high culture.

Neuman, Park, and Panek (2010) extended Pool's work to cover the period from 1960 through 2005. They found a tremendous increase in the ratio of supply to demand. In 1960, 98 minutes of media were available for every 1 minute of media consumed: Choices had to be made, but the number of choices was within reason. By 2005, more than 20,000 minutes of mediated content were available for every minute consumed. This, they point out, "is *not* a human-scale cognitive challenge; it is one in which humans will inevitably turn to the increasingly intelligent digital technologies that created the abundance in the first place for help in sorting it out—search engines, TiVo's recommendation systems, collaborative filters" (p. 11). Neuman and colleagues also found a change from *push* to *pull* technologies: Traditional, one-way broadcast and publishing media push content, with the audience accepting the decisions of newspaper editors and network executives. Today, technologies are evolving to pull in audience members, who have more choice and more control than ever before over what they watch and read, and when. Search engines (especially Google) and social networking sites (e.g., YouTube, Facebook) are emerging as major influences on public opinion and popular culture.

1.2. Where Does Information Come From?

Philosopher Karl Popper (1979) found it useful to use a metaphor of three "worlds" to describe how knowledge exists and develops:

- World 1: the physical world

- World 2: subjective reality (how we see or experience the world)

- World 3: objective knowledge (accumulated and scientific knowledge)

Science, Popper says, is a process that takes place in all three worlds: In World 1, events happen; in World 2, we try to make sense of them; and in

World 3, we try to explain the events while others react to these explanations and try to improve on them. Thus, we bring the three worlds together to create information (or awareness) through a never-ending process that produces knowledge. Along the way we create tools and technologies that help this process.

To take a less philosophical, more practical view, information reaches us from records of historical events, scientific knowledge, religious or cultural knowledge, art and literature, personal knowledge and records, documentation of governments or organizations, business, commerce, and many other sources.

Information may arrive prepackaged from a variety of sources. Publishers, government agencies, and other organizations produce formal products such as books, journals, and databases. Individuals package information in email, blogs, wikis, and other forms. Various institutions handle these packages. Libraries customarily deal with books, journals, video and audio recordings, microforms, databases, and even manuscripts, papyri, and clay tablets. Archives typically house governmental records, personal papers, and manuscripts. Databases (some commercially compiled and others available for free on the internet) also provide access to books, journals, webpages, blogs, videos, and other sources.

All of these various "packages" of information can be considered to be information systems (micro and macro) created to achieve some purpose. They may also be considered to be (micro and macro) communications systems, so that the information in them can be satisfactorily transferred: from the package to someone who wants the information or from one package to another package. However, all communications systems have potential problems. Information science seeks to analyze, design, and evaluate these systems in order to understand and improve how they function.

1.3. The Effects: Information Overload

The world is filled with information, and we acquire it in various ways:

1. We discover it through our physical, mental, and emotional senses.

2. We seek it by asking questions and searching for it.

3. We obtain it through feedback from other people and from various types of information systems.

4. We organize it (in our heads and in our files) and may make new information.

For centuries people have noted (or complained) that there is too much information in the world. In 1755 French encyclopedist Denis Diderot wrote that the increase in published material would eventually make it easier to rediscover facts from observing nature than to find information "hidden away in an immense multitude of bound volumes" (Diderot, 1975/1755, pp. 234–235). Alvin Toffler (1970) described the technological and structural changes in society in his book *Future Shock*, which helped to popularize the term *information overload*, meaning having so much information that it is difficult to set priorities or make decisions. Richard Saul Wurman (1989) observed that people respond with *information anxiety* to this inability to cope with the perceived flood of information.

Consider the ideas of information overload and information anxiety on a personal level. Thinking historically, compare the amount of information (and the systems for accessing that information) available to you today for succeeding in college or finding a job with that available to your parents and your grandparents. Are you, your family, and your country better off (financially, psychologically, or in other ways) because you can know almost instantly what is happening around the world (say in Baghdad, Moscow, or Mumbai)?

1.4. Evaluating Information

As we attempt to screen information and reduce the amount with which we must contend, we ask two basic questions about information: its value (what is it worth?) and its quality (is it any good?). Ultimately, the value estimation must be considered in light of the cost of the information, which brings us to the familiar question of the relation between costs and benefits.

Calculating a cost-benefit ratio is not easy because there are many aspects of cost and because the notion of benefit may be difficult to assess. Costs are typically of two types. Fixed costs, which are moderately easy to determine, include labor (salaries), equipment, supplies, and software. Variable costs are more difficult to determine. Examples include delays by others involved, unexpected breakdowns (for whatever reason), and mistakes or errors. On the other side of the cost-benefit ratio, the following questions can be used to determine the benefit of information or an information system:

1. Did it save time?

2. Did it enhance effectiveness?

3. Did it give us an advantage over the competition?

4. Did it save money in the short run and the long run?

5. Did it help avoid costs of some type?

Quality is the second aspect we consider in evaluating information. Information scientists often consider the following factors in order to determine the quality of information:

- Accuracy

- Timeliness

- Age and obsolescence

- Completeness

- Source availability and ease of use

- Ease of understanding

- Trustworthiness of source

From the perspective of the legal research service Virtual Chase (2008a), the following criteria are valuable for assessing the quality of information:

- Scope of coverage: Is it inclusive or limited?

- Authority: Who said it?

- Objectivity: Is it limited or is there no bias?

- Accuracy: Has it been checked or verified?

- Timeliness: Is it out of date or up-to-date?

Evaluating information quality is especially important for web-based information. Useful steps identified by Virtual Chase (2008b) include the following:

1. Identify and check the source.

2. Discover the source's expertise.

3. Determine the level of objectivity.

4. Establish the date of publication.

5. Verify factual statements.

It is usually much easier to evaluate so-called factual information than subjective (opinion-based) information.

1.5. Managing Your Information

We are said to be living in an information society—even though historians disagree as to when it began and definitions of information vary. We can easily see some impacts of information on society (such as information overload, described in section 1.3), but others are hard to identify. We cannot say what the economic impacts of information are because we have trouble differentiating an information worker from a noninformation worker. This complication holds for many products today: Which are information intensive and which are not? Even if it is difficult to define, the notion of an information society is so common that we need at least a brief list of its major characteristics:

- Major changes occur in information technologies.

- Large portions of the economy deal with information.

- Many occupations now are information intensive.

- Information networks are a major feature of our lives.

- Information available for our use is extensive—and continually growing.

Who manages this information? Information professionals! And who are they? Their professional titles include database managers, webmasters, information systems staff, librarians, systems librarians, records managers, archivists, and many more.

What happens to information after it is created? A large portion is destroyed (by plan), such as online course materials that are removed after a specified time. Quite a bit of electronic information self-destructs, such as the data we generate while playing a video game. Some information is saved in archives (which may be personal, corporate, or governmental), and some is stored in libraries (and may eventually be destroyed or discarded). The web retains some information; for example, the Internet Archive's Wayback Machine (www.archive.org) shows earlier versions of websites. And some information is destroyed.

What can you do about the impact information has on you? Some options include managing it better; using new technologies to improve your control; creating better indexes, classification systems, and archival systems; and just getting rid of the information you no longer need.

References

Bohn, R. E., & Short, J. E. (2009). *How much information? 2009 report on American consumers.* San Diego, CA: Global Information Industry Center, University of California–San Diego. Retrieved November 11, 2010, from hmi.ucsd.edu/pdf/HMI_2009_Consumer Report_Dec9_2009.pdf.

Diderot, D. (1975–1995). Encyclopédie. In *Oeuvres complètes* (H. Dieckmann et al., Eds.) (vol. 7, pp. 174–262). Paris: Hermann. Original work published in 1755.

Neuman, W. R., Park, Y. J., & Panek, E. (2010). *Tracking the flow of information into the home: An empirical assessment of the digital revolution in the U.S. from 1960–2005.* Ann Arbor, MI: University of Michigan. Retrieved November 11, 2010, from www.wrneuman. com/Flow_of_Information.pdf.

Neuman, W. R., & Pool, I. S. (1986). The flow of communications into the home. In S. Ball-Rokeach & M. Cantor (Eds.), *Media, audience and social structure* (pp. 71–86). Beverly Hills, CA: Sage.

Pool, I. S. (1983). Tracking the flow of information. *Science, 211,* 609–613.

Pool, I. S., Inose, H., Takasaki, N., & Hurwitz, R. (1984). *Communications flows: A census in the United States and Japan.* Amsterdam: Elsevier North Holland.

Popper, K. (1979). *Objective knowledge: An evolutionary approach* (rev. ed.). New York: Oxford University Press.

Toffler, A. (1970). *Future shock.* New York: Random House.

Virtual Chase. (2008a). *Criteria for quality of information.* Retrieved November 11, 2010, from virtualchase.justia.com/quality-criteria-checklist.

Virtual Chase. (2008b). *How to evaluate information—Checklist.* Retrieved November 11, 2010, from virtualchase.justia.com/how-evaluate-information-checklist.

Wurman, R. S. (1989). *Information anxiety.* New York: Doubleday.

CHAPTER 2

Foundations of Information Science and Technology

2.1. Basic Concepts

Reflect for a moment on the importance of technology in your life every day. How do you

- Keep in touch with people across campus, across town, or around the world?

- Find information to answer a trivia question or prepare a research paper?

- Create the soundtrack for a walk or workout?

- Provide an evening's entertainment?

- Present information about yourself to friends, family, or future employers?

All of these information-related tasks are increasingly assisted by or reliant on technology. And the equipment we use continues to change rapidly and dramatically, even if the basic functions performed and kinds of information we seek and exchange are essentially what they were a century ago.

Studying information science and technology allows us to move from living in this complex world to observing and improving our understanding and mastery of it. This book considers fundamental aspects of human information processing, and how various abilities and limitations affect our uses and potential applications of evolving communication and information technologies. We will trace historic roots and theoretical foundations while keeping in mind their consequences and possibilities for applications and services now and in the near future.

This chapter provides background and definitions for terms and concepts that are basic to the field. Examining answers to the question, What is information? introduces this basic concept and demonstrates the three dominant approaches to studying and understanding information science and technology. Next, we consider how information can be physically manifested and disseminated. The following section briefly examines what *information science* means, and the chapter concludes with an account of the field's intellectual and historical roots.

2.2. Defining Terms

Information

Defining *information* is an obvious first step in understanding information science and technology. Buckland (1991) observed that *things* can be informative. A tree stump contains in its rings information about its age, as well as information about the climate during the tree's lifetime. In similar ways, *anything* can be informative.

Some theorists hold that information is an objective phenomenon; others say that it depends on the receiver. Parker (1974) took the objective approach: "Information is the pattern of organization of matter and energy" (p. 10). Bateson (1972) took the subjective view: Information is "a difference that makes a difference" (for somebody or something or from a specific perspective; p. 453).

Note, first, the similarities between the two perspectives. Both the objective and the subjective views agree that any "pattern of organization of matter and energy" may inform somebody and thus be considered information. Information is thus a very broad term that is not limited to text or human products.

The basic difference should also be mentioned. If information is objective, then the representation of information is independent of context and purpose. If, on the other hand, information is understood as subjective, then its representation in information systems must consider who is to be informed and about what. These two perspectives, which Ellis (1992) labeled the *physical* and *cognitive paradigms*, have both provided useful bases for thought and development of information science.

Recently, researchers have added a third perspective: the *socio-cognitive approach*, which holds that individual cognitive or subjective understanding is conditioned by society and culture. Hjørland (1997), for example, holds that information "users should be seen as individuals in concrete situations in social organizations and domains of knowledge" (p. 111).

Some writers contrast information with the notions of *data* and *knowledge*.

Data

Data is the plural of *datum*, derived from Latin *dare* (to give); hence, data is "something given." Some style manuals insist that data be used only in the plural; it may, however, be used as a collective noun: a plural noun used in the singular to denote a set of items. Machlup (1983) wrote:

Data are the things given to the analyst, investigator, or problem-solver; they may be numbers, words, sentences, records, assumptions—just anything given, no matter in what form and of what origin. This used to be well known to scholars in most fields: Some wanted the word *data* to refer to facts, especially to instrument-readings; others to assumptions. Scholars with a hypothetico-deductive bent wanted data to mean the given set of assumptions; those with an empirical bent wanted data to mean the records, or protocol statements, representing the findings of observation, qualitative or quantitative. ... One can probably find quotations supporting all possible combinations of the three terms [*data, information,* and *knowledge*] or of the concepts they are supposed to denote. Each is said to be a specific type of each of the others, or an input for producing each of the others, or an output of processing each of the others. Now, data from the point of view of the programmers, operators, and users of the computer, need not be data in any other sense. (pp. 646–647)

Spang-Hanssen (2001) discussed data as well in a 1970 speech:

Information about some physical property of a material is actually incomplete without information about the precision of the data and about the conditions under which these data were obtained. Moreover, various investigations of a property have often led to different results that cannot be compared and evaluated apart from information about their background. An empirical fact has always a history and a perhaps not too certain future. This history and future can be known only through information from particular documents, i.e. by document retrieval. The so-called fact retrieval centers seem to be just information centers that keep their information sources—i.e. their documents—exclusively to themselves.

We may conclude that what is considered data is relative: What some consider the given (or input), others may consider the output. From the perspective of information science, it is important to represent and communicate not just data but also its background, its reception, and the theoretical assumptions connected with data, which makes the concepts of *knowledge* and *document* important.

Knowledge

The classical definition goes back to Plato: Knowledge is verified true belief. This definition is problematic, however, because knowledge is always open to modification and revision, so that very little (or nothing) can be considered knowledge in Plato's sense. This is why pragmatic and materialist theories consider the concept of knowledge in relation to human practice: Knowledge expands the actors' possibilities to act and to adjust to the world in which they live. Pragmatism and materialism consider human practice the final criterion of knowledge and see experimentation as an integrated component.

The *Oxford English Dictionary* definitions of knowledge include 1) "skill or expertise acquired in a particular subject ... through learning;" 2) "that which is known;" and 3) "being aware or cognizant of a fact, state of affairs, etc." (OED Online, "knowledge").

The Data-Information-Knowledge-Wisdom Hierarchy

Ackoff (1989) saw the *information pyramid* (Figure 2.1) as a progression:

1. Data are facts that result from observations.

2. Information is collections of facts provided with context.

3. Knowledge is generated when people supply meaning to information.

4. Wisdom results from shared insights and knowledge.

For example:

1. Contributors to the World Wide Web post results from their empirical research in the sciences or new insights into historical events or literary research. These contributors create links from one page to another. Each link could be considered a piece of data (a datum).

2. By tracing the links, we can create a structure or map of the web. This organized collection of links is information.

3. Analyzing the map of the web allows us to see areas of dense linking and identify sites that receive links from many others (hubs). This knowledge of web structure results from our understanding of the information.

4. The occurrence of many links to a website is often believed to indicate that the site has value and potential utility for other web users. Search engines such as Google take advantage of this "wisdom."

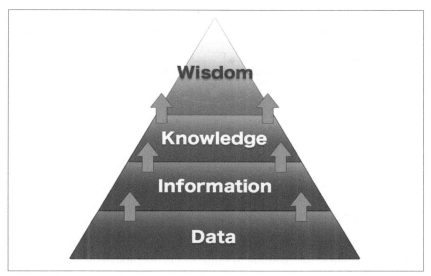

Figure 2.1   Data-information-knowledge-wisdom pyramid

Braganza (2004) suggested a top-down perspective rather than the traditional bottom-up approach. Rather than assuming that data is the basic unit of information and knowledge, information professionals, in order to provide more useful insights into information work, should consider beginning with a focus on the creation and communication of knowledge.

The pyramid model does a reasonable job of reflecting the evolution of thinking about the concept of information. Early research focused on the base of the pyramid: how to send, receive, and manipulate bits of data. The Shannon-Weaver model of communication (Figure 2.2) from 1949 shows this focus (and is discussed in more detail in Chapter 14).

In the 1940s, Claude Shannon was working for the telephone company at Bell Labs. While investigating how to transmit a message both efficiently and effectively, he realized that noise, from any source, could keep the destination (the person on the other end of the telephone line) from receiving the message that the information source had sent. Shannon's analysis also demonstrated that there is a theoretical limit to bandwidth.

In 1949, Shannon and Warren Weaver wrote *The Mathematical Theory of Communication*, which demonstrates how redundancy helps to compensate for noise in the transmission of a message. If you are directing a colleague to a site on the web, you might give the internet protocol (IP) address, such as 209.85.129.99. However, if you mistype just one numeral, your friend might be directed to the wrong location. By using a URL in natural language, your friend can compensate for errors (noise) that might creep into the message:

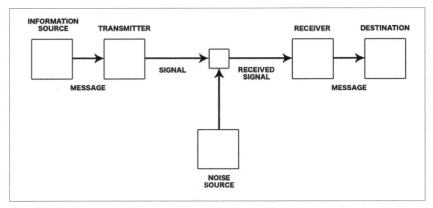

Figure 2.2   Shannon-Weaver model of communication

www.google.com is the redundant, human-understandable version of an IP address.

Shannon and Weaver (1949/1964) identified three aspects of information:

1. Technical aspects, concerned with problems of transmission

2. Semantic aspects, related to the meaning and truth of a message

3. Influential aspects, concerned with how a message affects human behavior

The definition of information used in their mathematical theory considers only the first level, the technical concerns in transmission; this is the base of the information pyramid. The Shannon-Weaver model has been criticized for its *conduit metaphor*, emphasizing the channel, rather than the source and destination of the message.

Interest in the semantic aspects of information had gained ground by the 1980s. Researchers noted that different people had different understandings of the same item of information. This led to research on the cognitive aspects of information (the mental processes of knowing), including how people assess information (Machlup & Mansfield, 1983). Requiring consideration of the human perspective means that information can no longer be understood objectively; what is informative will depend on the person assessing the meaning and truth of a message, as Shannon and Weaver would say. Recent research has also considered social aspects of how information is understood. This approach notes that how each of us understands an item of potential information is influenced by our social environment: societal conventions (such as language), history, and interactions with other people. This view has been labeled the *socio-cognitive approach to information* (Hjørland, 2002).

2.3. Disseminating Information

Documents

Before information science was termed *information science*, it was called *documentation*, and documents were considered the basic objects of study for the field. Buckland (1991) has described the history of the concept of *document* in information science. Early in the 20th century, researchers felt a need for a generic term for the object of their work: not only texts, but also natural objects, artifacts, models, objects reflecting human activities, objects of art, and human ideas. The term document (or *documenting unit*) was used with a special meaning in order to include informative physical objects. Buckland noted that the word document comes from Latin *docere*, meaning to teach or inform, and the suffix -*ment*, meaning a tool. Originally, then, the word meant a tool for teaching or informing, whether through lecture, experience, or text. Only later was it narrowed to mean objects carrying texts.

In information science today, the concept of document is understood as "any concrete or symbolic indication, preserved or recorded, for reconstructing or for proving a phenomenon, whether physical or mental" (Briet, 1951, p. 7, as cited in Buckland, 1991, p. 355).

Information and Communication Technologies

For the past half century we have used the term *information technology* to note the use of computer hardware and software for handling information. Kline (2004) traces the origin of the term to the business world, where "management information systems" were developed in the 1960s. The term information and communication technologies (ICTs) has been adopted more recently, acknowledging the increasing importance of telephones, cable, and satellite transmission in effective use of information technologies. Figure 2.3 uses data from the U.S. Census to show the rates of adoption for several ICTs.

Alan Kay, who worked at Atari, Xerox, Apple, and Disney, has defined technology as "anything that was invented after you were born." His assertion expresses the common feeling that new technologies are being introduced and adopted with increasing speed. Figure 2.3 suggests that U.S. residents born in the 21st century will view broadband internet as a natural part of life, but it will always be a "technology" for many of their parents. As we design, use, and evaluate systems that rely on ICTs, we should be aware of new developments and also mindful of the "long tail" of technologies that some users will approach as novel or challenging even as others accept them as an inseparable part of life.

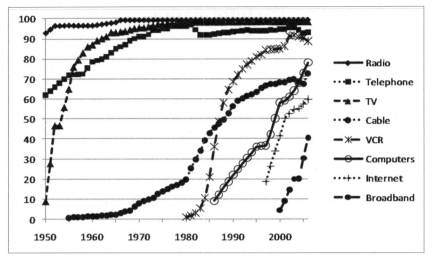

Figure 2.3 Percentage of U.S. households using information technologies, 1950–2006

2.4. Information Science

Information science emerged as the name for this field in about 1960. The Institute of Information Scientists was established in 1958; the American Documentation Institute changed its name to the American Society for Information Science in 1968, and in 2000 changed its name again to the American Society for Information Science and Technology.

Borko's (1968) definition of information science provides a list of tasks the field should address: "the origination, collection, organization, storage, retrieval, interpretation, transmission, transformation, and utilization of information" (p. 3). *The Online Dictionary for Library and Information Science* (Reitz, 2007) uses similar terms: "The systematic study and analysis of the sources, development, collection, organization, dissemination, evaluation, use, and management of information in all its forms, including the channels (formal and informal) and technology used in its communication."

Sometimes the plural, information sciences, is used. Machlup and Mansfield (1983), for example, suggested that one should speak about the information sciences as one speaks of the social sciences.

The term *informatics*, which was proposed independently by Walter F. Bauer and Phillipe Dreyfus in 1962 (Bauer, 1996), has a similar meaning. Redmond-Neal and Hlava (2005) say it "represents the conjunction of information science and information technology" (p. 63). Reitz (2007) continues, "It is the formal study of information, including its structure, properties, uses, and functions in society; the people who use it; and in particular the technologies developed to record, organize, store, retrieve, and disseminate it" ("informatics"). WordNet (2006) defines both information science and informatics as "the sciences concerned with gathering, manipulating, storing, retrieving, and classifying recorded information." Both information science and informatics can be used with subject-specific modifiers, as in *geographic information science* (studying geocoded information) or *bio-informatics* (using information technology to study biological information).

2.5. Intellectual Foundations of Information Science and Technology

Arguments About Origins

Information science has been variously described as interdisciplinary, transdisciplinary, metadisciplinary, and multidisciplinary. Each term is partially accurate but not entirely adequate. Information science has intellectual roots in a number of disciplines and applied fields of study and practice.

These disciplines and applied fields have been well described and explored in a now classic series of articles in *The Study of Information: Interdisciplinary Messages*, edited by Fritz Machlup and Una Mansfield (1983). The discussions attribute the origins to bibliography, library science, documentation, and developments in the 1950s in the handling and retrieval of scientific documentation. Ultimately, the discussants agree to disagree, but all generally acknowledge the merits of each other's arguments. The brief review presented here represents a primarily Western perspective on the history of information science and technology since the invention of printing.

Major Developments in the Early History of Information Science

To a significant extent, all societies are information societies. Even before the technologies of literacy were developed, a rich oral tradition of information existed in most societies. Ong (2002) has described how difficult the transition was from an oral to a literate society. He maintains that learning the technologies of literacy was the first fundamental shift in the way humans thought and processed information, a transition from a world of sound to a world of sight.

Even though archives and libraries have existed since the beginning of civilization, practitioners gave little attention to issues regarding their administration, arrangement, description, access, and related concerns until the 18th century. Archival materials and library materials are now viewed as distinctly different but were often treated similarly, and few principles were developed for their handling. For both archives and libraries, the custodian of the documents was usually a noted scholar in one or more subjects and only minimally concerned with the development of principles regarding management and use. The *Encyclopaedia Britannica* ("Library," 2010) puts it concisely: "Although the traditional librarian acted primarily as a keeper of records, the concept of an active service of advice and information eventually appeared as a legitimate extension of the role of custodian."

Just as rudimentary rules and methods for arranging and describing library and archival materials had begun to emerge prior to the 18th century, so had the art of bibliography, usually with attention to completeness in some subject or type of materials. Conrad Gesner's (1516–1565) *Bibliotheca Universalis* (published in 1545) provides an excellent example. Gesner developed and expanded general principles of inclusion, arrangement, and indexing (Jackson, 1974). Indexing principles, or at least techniques, had even earlier origins, particularly in dealing with sacred texts. Most of these early techniques and practices were well described in Gabriel Naudé's (1600–1653) *Advice on Establishing a Library* (1627), a work that became influential in its time on issues regarding bibliography, library management, classification, cataloging, and related topics.

The bibliographic "urge" of Gesner and others was matched by the desire of scholars to understand and organize all of human knowledge. Plato and Aristotle were likely the first to state this goal; during the 17th and 18th centuries, many others began work on such endeavors. A classification system of the world's knowledge and the draft of an encyclopedia to contain it, produced in 1620 by Francis Bacon (1561–1621), were foundations for later developers. Gottfried von Leibnitz (1646–1716), librarian, philosopher, mathematician, and logician, followed in Bacon's footsteps with his classification system, again with attention to organizing all of the world's knowledge. Others, such as Denis Diderot (1713–1784) and Jean d'Alembert (1717–1783), continued this work ("Library," 2010). The idea of compiling, classifying, and making available the world's knowledge would later greatly influence those in library science, documentation, and information science.

By the 18th century, a number of advances in the library arts began to appear: national and subject bibliographies, printed library catalogs, new schemes for subject arrangement of materials on shelves, and principles for bibliography. Also, the first museums were opened to the public in this period. Formerly, these commonly called "cabinets of curiosities" were the private collections of royalty. The British Museum opened to the public in 1753 and was soon followed by the Louvre Museum in Paris in 1793.

The rapid expansion of the number of libraries of all types during the early 19th century led to more extensive writings about libraries and library management. Martin Schrettinger (1772–1851), a German librarian, was the first person to use the term *library science*; in 1808 he employed the term

Bibliothekswissenschaft to describe the science that dealt with cataloging, classification, shelving and shelf arrangement, and library management. Friedrich A. Ebert (1791–1834) and Christian Molbech (1783–1857) expanded on his work. Molbech emphasized that "librarianship is a matter of theory and practice, and it consists of two principal branches, organization and administration" (as cited in Jackson, 1974, p. 324). Schrettinger, Ebert, and Molbech presented the types of skills and knowledge needed by a librarian, essentially destroying the long-dominant idea that being a scholar is sufficient background for a librarian (Jackson, 1974). The first journal devoted to libraries, librarianship, and library science issues, titled *Serapeum: Journal of Library Science, Manuscript Information, and Older Literature*, focused on scholarly libraries; it began publication in 1840 in Germany (Jackson, 1974).

Considerable progress was made in the development of the techniques and content of library science between 1850 and 1900. In the U.S. this trend included the following milestones:

- The 1876 founding of the American Library Association

- The 1876 publication of a comprehensive statistical report on libraries, which also contained Charles A. Cutter's chapter on library catalogs and his *Rules for a Dictionary Catalog*, an introduction to the study of library science, and Melvil Dewey's introduction to his decimal classification scheme

- The rapid adoption and use of Dewey's decimal classification system and Cutter's expansive classification system by libraries of all types; both employed subject arrangement systems and easy-to-use marking systems for shelf arrangement of documents

- The common deployment of card catalogs in all types of libraries

- The 1876 publication of the first journal devoted to library management concerns, the *American Library Journal* (later changed to *Library Journal*)

- The 1887 founding, at Columbia University, of the first formal, university-based educational program for librarians

In the U.K., Anthony Panizzi, librarian for the British Museum, developed 91 rules for author-title entries, bringing consistency to cataloging work. These rules, first published in 1841, continued to influence all developers of library catalogs through the remainder of the 19th century. In 1877, the Library Association of the United Kingdom was founded after an international conference of librarians.

In Europe, the *École des Chartes*, founded in France in 1821, improved the formal education and training of librarians, archivists, and bibliographers. Karl Franz Otto Dziatzko (1842–1903), a professor of library science at the

University of Göttingen (Germany), introduced library education classes in 1886. Informal courses and in-service education continued to dominate European library education through the remainder of the 19th century. Attempts to remove the "scholarly librarian" approach in the education of librarians continued to trouble European library education, ultimately leading to two different philosophies and types of library science: one focused on scholarly libraries and one on popular libraries (Davis, 1994).

Dewey's practice-centered philosophy eventually dominated library science. Columbia's School of Library Economy dealt with the practical problems of libraries, and most lectures were delivered by practicing librarians (Jackson, 1974, p. 399). Library education and training were slowly moving from an apprenticeship approach to one based on a formal technical education.

Major Developments in the Modern History of Information Science

By the beginning of the 20th century, the amount of published literature in all fields of study, especially the sciences, was growing rapidly. It was also becoming more technical, more difficult to acquire, and greatly in need of new approaches to summarization and subject access. The tools that developed—such as indexes, bibliographies, and abstracts—required someone who understood the subject matter of the literature and how to present it.

In 1895, Belgian attorneys Paul Otlet and Henri LaFontaine established what would become the International Institute of Bibliography with the objective of controlling the world's literature. Otlet and LaFontaine were greatly influenced by earlier encyclopedia efforts, as well as the desire to foster peace through the unification of knowledge. Over the next 40 years, Otlet and colleagues developed systematic principles, techniques, and technologies for what they called documentation. Otlet's key idea was that separating the book (or journal) from its author and his intentions should allow one to extract and index the work's new contribution to knowledge.

Researchers at the International Institute of Bibliography used the relatively new technology of cards and combined them with Dewey's classification scheme (which they soon revised extensively, creating the Universal Decimal Classification). They built a large bibliography and catalog, peaking at 15.6 million entries in 1942. Otlet called this approach the "mongraphic principle," so that bits and pieces (pages, paragraphs, sentences, etc.) of information were indexed and classified; essentially, these researchers were creating a database (Rayward, 1997). Combining the technologies of card, cabinet, and microfilm (Otlet and LaFontaine invented microfiche) with indexing that used the Universal Decimal Classification provided a complete information system. Otlet then added an information service via mail or telephone.

In the late 1800s and early 1900s, the number of museums, particularly in the U.S., expanded, and a professional cadre of museum specialists developed to support them. John Cotton Dana, director of the Newark Public Library, was a pioneer in this area. In 1925 Dana, one of the founders of the Special Libraries Association in the U.S., established the Newark Museum in the same building as the library and began an apprenticeship program that would foster in museum curators a broad knowledge, including familiarity with library processes. A key part of the expertise of these curators was the development of exhibitions and loan programs that met the needs of the local population (Given & McTavish, 2010).

By 1934, Otlet had systematized most of his ideas about the science of documentation into his text, *Traité de documentation* (Otlet, 1934/1980). For Otlet, documentation represented "the means of bringing into use all of the written or graphic sources of our knowledge" (as cited in Rayward, 1997, p. 299), as well as a new intellectual discipline. Although some scholarly librarians objected, the documentation idea had considerable influence in Europe; it was essentially unknown elsewhere in the world. Special librarians in the U.S. and the U.K. did pick up some of these ideas and approaches (particularly in the detailed indexing of a wide variety of documentary materials and specialized information services; Muddiman, 2005; Williams, 1997). The European documentation movement influenced Watson Davis, who founded the American Documentation Institute in 1937 to study the problems of the distribution of scientific information.

After World War II, Suzanne Briet, director of studies at the National Institute for Techniques in Documentation in Paris, expanded Otlet's ideas by defining documents broadly, to include much more than text. Buckland (2009) describes her views as "semiotic," treating documents as "indexical signs exposing an unlimited horizon of networks of techniques, technologies, individuals, and institutions" (p. 79).

In the early part of the 20th century, *library science* gradually gained acceptance as the preferred term to describe the study of the management of libraries and library services. University-level educational programs along the Columbia University model were established at several other institutions even though the predominant training approach remained within libraries. Charles C. Williamson's study of library education, published in 1923, strongly recommended moving library education to universities (Davis, 1994); in the U.S. this move was largely complete by the 1950s. Williamson's report also emphasized the importance of research in meeting the challenges of library science; in 1926 the University of Chicago established the first PhD program in library science.

As the Graduate Library School at Chicago took shape, the faculty debated the focus of the program. Pierce Butler's small booklet *An Introduction to Library Science* (1933/1961) emphasized the philosophical principles of librarianship rather than its scientific aspects. Between 1950 and 1970, education for librarianship moved from the expectation of an undergraduate degree to a requirement for a master's as the first professional degree. The establishment of the U.S. National Archives in 1934 gave impetus to the archival community's development of an archival science.

The explosion of scientific documentation during and after World War II challenged librarians and the scientific community. Scientists, dissatisfied with what they perceived as slow and cumbersome cataloging and classification processes and ineffective retrieval methods, introduced new technologies: punched cards and, later, computers. Scientists and special librarians collaborated in this work. Principles and techniques for coordinate indexing and searching were developed and adopted in many libraries and information centers. Automatic indexing and abstracting, machine translation, and remote searching of databases were tried, with both successes and failures. Initially, these pioneers called themselves scientific information specialists, but this cumbersome title was inadequately descriptive of what they were trying to do: develop a science of information.

A rich outpouring of new retrieval systems, new technologies for storage, and new ways of subject control took place between 1950 and 1970, much of it funded by the National Science Foundation, the U.S. Air Force, and other government agencies. Systems were developed that provided automatic indexing, machine translation, thesaurus construction, retrieval effectiveness, citation indexing, and online retrieval. These experiments and systems brought new participants to the new field, people with backgrounds in computer science, linguistics, behavioral sciences, mathematics, and communications. Textbooks for the new field called it information retrieval, information storage and retrieval, or information science. Documentation or information science was influenced by Vannevar Bush's idea of Memex (Buckland, 2006) and the information theory work of Claude Shannon, Warren Weaver, and Norbert Wiener on telecommunications systems. Definitions of this new field were offered (borrowed largely from the European documentalists) (e.g., Borko, 1968; Shera & Egan, 1950; Simon, 1947; Tate, 1950) but no definition seemed to suit everyone (Lipetz, 2005).

Recent Major Trends in the Development of Information Science

By the early 1970s, research extended to information use and information-seeking behavior. Researchers, primarily from the behavioral sciences, studied the information needs of researchers in various scientific fields. In the early 21st century, this has been one of the most active research areas in information science. Case (2007) points out the involvement of the communications sciences in studying information-seeking behaviors and the valuable contributions communication scientists have made to broadening the scope of information science.

From the 1960s to the 1980s, many archival studies programs in the U.S. and Canada became established in schools of library science and information science, with a few in departments of history or public history. Museum studies during the 1970s began to take a different approach from the one Dana had promoted in the early 1900s. Influenced by the Canadian Museums Committee, training of curators emphasized expert knowledge and the production of new knowledge. Exhibits of this new knowledge tended to focus on the scholar and not the general public. The debate about the training and responsibilities of museum staff continues, but recognition is gradually emerging that museums, like libraries and archives, are "memory institutions" (Hjerppe, 1994) and, as such, play multiple roles. As digitization of the collections in all three types of institutions increases, it is becoming evident that libraries, museums, and archives share many of the same issues about preserving their information and making it available to the scholar and the general public (Given & McTavish, 2010).

By the late 1980s and the early 1990s, both a significant bifurcation and a curious melding had taken place in information science. On one side were the computer and information science schools and people with major objectives centered on systems analysis, information processing, database design, and information theory. On the other side were the library and information science people, some with an orientation closely linked to computer science but most with a wide-ranging set of objectives complementary to their origins in library science or documentation programs. These objectives were centered largely on information seeking, use, or behavior; management of information; information policy; classification theory; and bibliographic control. The research and development work of both groups is increasingly oriented toward issues surrounding the internet and electronic documents. The computer and information science people often find a "home" in the various sections of the Association for Computing Machinery, and people from both groups find the American Society for Information Science and Technology a hospitable place for their research and educational interests.

In a recent assessment of the relationships, differences, and contributions of librarianship and information science to each other, Hayes (1994), a pioneer in both areas, stated, "Librarianship serves as one of the most visible and well-defined contexts for theoretical studies of information processes; conversely, information science serves as one of the foundations for library science" (p. 275). He concluded, "Together librarianship and information science share concerns with each of them [the various threads he discusses], but they approach them from different perspectives and with differing priorities" (p. 280).

Rayward (1997) concluded his article on Otlet and LaFontaine's work in documentation with a return to Machlup and Mansfield's (1983) themes, considering whether information science is narrow or broad, whether it is only a composite of disciplinary "chunks" and not a true discipline, and whether it will ever emerge as a true discipline on its own. Rayward did not answer these questions but suggested that the ultimate foundation of information science involves the interactions between information and society.

References

Ackoff, R. L. (1989). From data to wisdom. *Journal of Applied Systems Analysis, 16*, 3–9.

Bateson, G. (1972). *Steps to an ecology of mind.* New York: Ballantine.

Bauer, W. F. (1996). Informatics and (et) Informatique. *IEEE Annals of the History of Computing, 18*(2). Retrieved November 11, 2011, from www.softwarehistory.org/history/ Bauer1.html

Borko, H. (1968). Information science: What is it? *American Documentation, 19*(1), 3–5.

Braganza, A. (2004). Rethinking the data-information-knowledge hierarchy: Towards a case-based model. *International Journal of Information Management, 24*(4), 347–356.

Briet, S. (1951). *Qu'est-ce que la documentation?* Paris: Documentaires Industrielles et Techniques.

Buckland, M. (1991). *Information and information systems.* New York: Greenwood Press.

Buckland, M. (2006). *Emanuel Goldberg and his knowledge machine: Information, invention, and political forces.* Westport, CT: Libraries Unlimited.

Buckland, M. (2009). As we may recall: Four forgotten pioneers. *ACM Interactions, 16*(6), 76–79.

Butler, P. (1961). *An introduction to library science.* Chicago: University of Chicago Press. (Original work published 1933)

Case, D. O. (2007). *Looking for information: A survey on information seeking, needs, and behavior.* London: Academic Press.

Davis, D. G. (1994). Education for librarianship. In W. A. Wiegand & D. G. Davis (Eds.), *Encyclopedia of library history* (pp. 184–186). New York: Garland.

Ellis, D. (1992). The physical and cognitive paradigms in information retrieval research. *Journal of Documentation, 48*(2), 45–64.

Encyclopaedia. (2010). *Encyclopædia Britannica.* Retrieved February 18, 2010, from www.britannica.com/EBchecked/topic/186603/encyclopedia.

Given, L. M., & McTavish, L. (2010). What's old is new again: The reconvergence of libraries, archives and museums in the digital age. *Library Quarterly, 80*(1), 6–30.

Hayes, R. M. (1994). Information science and librarianship. In W. A. Wiegand & D. G. Davis (Eds.), *Encyclopedia of library history* (pp. 275–280). New York: Garland.

Hjerppe, R. (1994). A framework for the description of generalized documents. *Advances in knowledge Organization, 4*, 173-180.

Hjørland, B. (1997). *Information seeking and subject representation: An activity-theoretical approach to information science.* Westport, CT: Greenwood Press.

Hjørland, B. (2002). Epistemology and the socio-cognitive perspective in information science. *Journal of the American Society for Information Science and Technology, 53*(4), 257–270.

Jackson, S. L. (1974). *Libraries and librarianship in the west: A brief history.* New York: McGraw-Hill.

Kline, R. K. (2004). What is information theory a theory of? Boundary work among information theorists and information scientists in the United States and Britain during the Cold War. In W. B. Rayward & M. E. Bowden (Eds.), *The history and heritage of scientific and technological information systems: Proceedings of the 2002 Conference* (pp. 15–28). Medford, NJ: Information Today for the American Society for Information Science and Technology.

Library. (2010). *Encyclopædia Britannica.* Retrieved February 18, 2010, from www.britannica.com/EBchecked/topic/339421/Library.

Lipetz, B. A. (2005). Defining what information science is or should be: A survey and review of a half-century of published pronouncements. In R. V. Williams & B. A. Lipetz (Eds.), *Covert and overt: Recollecting and connecting intelligence service and information science* (pp. 187–198). Medford, NJ: Information Today and Scarecrow Press for the American Society for Information Science and Technology.

Machlup, F. (1983). Semantic quirks in studies of information. In F. Machlup & U. Mansfield (Eds.), *The study of information: Interdisciplinary messages* (pp. 641–671). New York: Wiley.

Machlup, F., & Mansfield, U. (1983). *The study of information: Interdisciplinary messages.* New York: Wiley.

Muddiman, D. (2005). A new history of ASLIB, 1924–1950. *Journal of Documentation, 61*(3), 402–428.

OED Online. March 2011. Oxford University Press. Retrieved May 8, 2011, from www.oed.com/view/Entry/104170.

Ong, W. J. (2002). *Orality and literacy: The technologizing of the word* (2nd ed.). New York: Routledge.

Otlet, P. (1980). *Traité de documentation. Le livre sur le livre: Theorie et pratique* (1980 reprint). Liege: Centre de lecture publique de la communaute française. (Original work published 1934)

Parker, E. B. (1974). Information and society. In C. A. Cuadra & M. J. Bates (Eds.), *Library and information service needs of the nation: Proceedings of a conference on the needs of occupational, ethnic and other groups in the United States* (pp. 9–50). Washington, DC: Government Printing Office.

Rayward, W. B. (1997). The origins of information science and the International Institute of Bibliography/International Federation for Information and Documentation (FID). *Journal of the American Society for Information Science, 48*(4), 289–300.

Redmond-Neal, A., & Hlava, M. K. (2005). *ASIS&T thesaurus of information science, technology, and librarianship* (3rd ed.). Medford, NJ: Information Today for the American Society for Information Science and Technology.

Reitz, J. M. (2007). *Online dictionary for library and information science.* Westport, CT: Libraries Unlimited. Retrieved November 11, 2010, from lu.com/odlis.

Shannon, C. E., & Weaver, W. (1964). *The mathematical theory of communication.* Urbana: University of Illinois Press. (Original work published 1949)

Shera, J. H. & Egan, M. E. (1950). Documentation in the United States. *American Documentation, 1*(1), 8-12.

Simon, E. N. (1947). A novice on "documentation." *Journal of Documentation, 2*(2), 238–241.

Spang-Hanssen, H. (2001). How to teach about information as related to documentation. *Human IT, 1*(1), 125–143. Retrieved November 11, 2010, from www.hb.se/bhs/ith/1-01/hsh.htm.

Tate, V. D. (1950, January). Introducing American Documentation. *American Documentation, 1*(1), 3.

Williams, R. V. (1997). The documentation and special libraries movement in the United States, 1910–1960. *Journal of the American Society for Information Science, 48*(9), 775–781.

WordNet. (2006). Princeton, NJ: Princeton University. Retrieved April 21, 2008, from wordnet.princeton.edu/perl/webwn?s=information+science.

CHAPTER 3

Information Needs, Seeking, and Use

3.1. Information Behavior

Information behavior research is part of the behavioral sciences and may be associated with the highly criticized behaviorist approach. Jerome Bruner (1990) suggested using the term *human acts*, rather than *human behavior*, to indicate the focus on meaningful rather than mechanical activities. The use of *actions* and *activities* also connects with the core concepts of *activity theory*. We might thus speak of *human information acts* rather than of *human information behavior*. However, because *information behavior* is still the most frequent term, we continue to use it.

Information behavior covers not only the active seeking of information but also a much wider range of activities. For example, an accidental encounter with information that was not sought and someone's attempt to avoid information are instances of information behavior. The term came into use as scholars moved away from an earlier focus on *library use and user studies*, which emphasized institutional sources and searches, to a broader investigation of how individuals encounter and make sense of their environments. Thus, information behavior encompasses information seeking, unintentional or passive behaviors (such as glimpsing or encountering information), and purposive behaviors that do not involve seeking, such as actively avoiding information. Whittaker (2011) extends the coverage to individuals' information *curation* practices—decisions about what to keep and how to find it.

Many theories and concepts are of potential relevance to research on information behavior; Fisher, Erdelez, and McKechnie (2005) briefly introduce 72 of them. Bates (2002) identified four modes of information acquisition (which she termed *information seeking*; see Figure 3.1).

When taking *directed* action, an individual seeks particular information that can be specified to some degree; the "undirected" seeker is more or less randomly exposing himself or herself to information. When *active*, the individual does something actively to acquire information; when *passive*, the individual is passively available to absorb information but does not seek it out. Bates (2002) contended that we humans absorb as much as 80 percent of our knowledge simply by "being aware" (Figure 3.1, cell d). Bates (2002) also pointed out that "browsing is the complementary opposite of monitoring.

	Active	Passive
Directed	Searching (a)	Monitoring (b)
Undirected	Browsing (c)	Being Aware (d)

Figure 3.1   Modes of information acquisition (Bates, 2002)

Here we have no special information need or interest, but actively expose ourselves to possibly novel information. … It can be said that monitoring and directed searching are ways we find information that we know we need to know, and browsing and being aware are ways we find information that we do not know we need to know" (first paragraph under "Browsing").

Case (2007) concluded his extensive review of the research and thinking on information behavior with eight lessons of information behavior research:

1. Formal sources and rationalized searches reflect only one side of human information behavior.

2. More information is not always better.

3. Context is central to the transfer of information.

4. Sometimes information—particularly generalized packages of information—doesn't help.

5. Sometimes it is not possible to make information available or accessible.

6. Information seeking is a dynamic process.

7. Information seeking is not always about a problem or problematic situation.

8. Information seeking is not always about *sense-making* either. (pp. 326–328)

Explaining Information Behavior: Activity Theory

Activity theory provides a good overall framework for considering information behavior. Wilson (2006) noted that activity theory is a conceptual framework, not a predictive theory, and thus allows researchers to use different theoretical perspectives. Typically, activity theory researchers employ multiple methods of data collection and extend their investigations for a long enough time that (nearly) all contextual issues can emerge.

Activity theory can provide a holistic view of information practices in which the individual subjects and their collective relationships, the objects used, and the tools or technology employed are treated as equally important and in which situated and historical context is taken seriously. Activity theory stresses the development of cognition as a unity of biological development, cultural development, and individual development. It has a strong ecological and functional-historical orientation. It focuses on the activity of the subject and the object orientation of this activity. Hjørland (1997) noted that activity theory "stresses the ecological and social nature of meaning. ... A person's use of a term may be determined not by his individual usage, but by the usage of some social group to which he semantically defers. Therefore, the content of a person's thoughts are themselves in part a matter of social facts" (p. 81).

Information Encountering and Information Avoidance

Information seeking is the most frequently studied information behavior; it is discussed below. Two other information behaviors merit brief comment: *information encountering* and *information avoidance.*

Information encountering is the "memorable experience of an unexpected discovery of useful or interesting information" (Erdelez, 1999). According to Erdelez, most people have some experiences of information encountering, although some "nonencounterers" have difficulty recalling any such experience. A small number of individuals are "super-encounterers," who rely on information encountering as a primary method for finding information even though they are aware that it is not the standard way to locate information one needs. Most people are "encounterers" or "occasional encounterers," who report that they frequently come across information while pursuing other tasks; libraries, bookstores, and the internet are often sites where information is encountered. Erdelez's super-encounterers reported that they found the amount of information on the internet overwhelming and they therefore tended not to use it.

Information avoidance has long been the subject of study in the fields of psychology and communication. As Case, Andrews, Johnson, and Allard (2005) have noted, "Sometimes people avoid information, if paying attention to it will cause mental discomfort or dissonance" (p. 354). Particularly with health-related information, researchers observe that some people adopt a *monitoring* approach—seeking additional information—but others use *blunting* strategies to ignore information or distract themselves from the problem. Case and colleagues noted that most models of information seeking assume that people want to find information and reduce their uncertainty; however, for some people and in some situations, information avoidance may be preferable, and additional information may actually increase uncertainty.

3.2. Information Needs

The concept of *information need(s)* (or *user need(s)*) comes from the field of library and information science. Miksa (2009) traced interest in users and their information needs back to the beginning of printing, with more attention in the 19th century as the library became the source of "mental cultivation" (p. 353) for not only the scholarly and well bred but the general population as well. The current understanding of information needs emerged as the field began to focus on empirical investigations of the use of library and information services. In this context, an information need arises when a person needs information in order to accomplish a goal; the library or an information system exists to fulfill users' and potential users' needs for documents and information. These needs may be related to educational, research, professional, recreational, or cultural activities, or to personal development.

An information need may be recognized or unconscious, and people may disagree about information needs: A student's perception and experience of an information need related to an assignment may differ from the teacher's understanding. Information need should be differentiated from *information demand*. For example, the demand for information or documents may be low if potential users see a library as inaccessible or unapproachable; still, the *needs* exist. Information needs may also exist in cases in which the individual remains ignorant of the need and thus cannot express it; for example, a student preparing a report may be unaware of useful information and therefore not request it.

Taylor (1968) presented one of the first analyses of information need, which he viewed as developing internally in the person seeking information. The information need develops from 1) an unexpressed, "visceral information need" to 2) a "conscious need" that can be expressed (often to a colleague), to 3) a "formalized need" that presents a more complete statement, and to 4) a "compromised need" that the information seeker has adapted to what he or she perceives the information system can handle.

Hjørland (1997) criticized Taylor's model because it views information needs as internal motivational states (a psychological condition) rather than lack of subject knowledge. What users *believe* they need is represented by their subjective understanding of their situations. This subjective understanding is reflected in their information seeking. Resolving the problem underlying users' information-seeking behaviors involves subject expertise at least as much as psychological knowledge.

Belkin (2005) proposed that information retrieval systems should be designed to consider and support the user's information need as it evolves during a search. Drawing on cognitive and communication perspectives, he described this need as an *anomalous state of knowledge*. The *anomaly* indicates that the user's state of knowledge is inadequate to resolve a particular problematic situation. The inadequacy might result from lack of knowledge or uncertainty regarding which concept would be appropriate in the situation.

Kinds of Information Needs

Information needs may be classified to reflect the kinds of information services that are relevant in relation to different situations:

- *Procedural information needs* concern how to do things: What do you need to know in order to bake a cake? to repair a car? to measure a melting point? to write a thesis? These kinds of needs may be partly satisfied by "how to" documents (or cookbooks).

- *Substantive information needs* relate to subject knowledge; for example, what is the atomic number of carbon or what were the causes of the Black Death? Such needs are often connected with scientific and scholarly research literature. Scholarship is developed through discourses (based on assumptions) about how to discover the truth or how to produce useful knowledge. Satisfying substantive information needs thus entails judgments about what constitutes authoritative information sources.

- *Muddled information needs* may occur, as when, for example, a user lacks subject knowledge and therefore is not in a position to formulate a precise question. Swanson (1986) posed the example of a search for mathematical analysis of how a child "pumps" a swing. The information cannot be found under *pumping* or *swings*, but in the literature on *parametric amplifiers*. Information needs may also be muddled, however, because a research field is without consensus—it is muddled itself. Theoretical improvement of the field is required.

- *Verificative information needs* seek evidence or confirmation. Some request bibliographic verification of sources that a writer plans to discuss. Library services and bibliographic databases have tools to deal with this kind of information need. Scientists also have verificative information needs for empirical data that confirm or weaken existing claims.

- *Educational information needs* occur when useful information exists, but the person in need is unable to understand it. Such needs are the province of educational systems; libraries and information services may be able to assist if good popularizations or translations exist to help the individual learn the material on his or her own.

3.3. Information Seeking

Information seeking is a conscious effort to acquire information in response to a need or gap in one's knowledge. The term indicates the common experience of needing, looking for, choosing, and using information of some kind. Such behavior is essential to human existence. Anticipating a driving trip, one looks for information about routes, distances, sights, and perhaps weather and lodging along the way. Similarly, a work assignment might require investigation of a topic and preparation of a report. Satisfying an information need could prompt a visit to the library or a web search.

Information seeking is so much a part of daily life that it is generally not a conscious activity unless a deadline is looming. Making a major decision (for example, buying a house) or completing a task (for example, writing a report) places people in information-seeking mode: talking to others, searching the web, reading journals, watching the news, and so on. The search generally proceeds through every conceivable avenue until either the need is satisfied or the information seeker runs out of time. It is commonly the latter as the demand for information is typically elastic: There is always more that one could know. After satisfying the information need (or giving up), one returns to a more passive state of monitoring the world.

When not concerned with an immediate task, such as buying or writing something, people observe and gather information in a different mode. Life is full of instances in which one becomes interested in learning more about a topic after accidentally encountering some bit of information about it. This sort of curiosity, unmotivated by an immediate goal, is a common aspect of human life. Bates (1989) was one of the first to notice the difference between the traditional information retrieval models, which focused on creating one set of documents that would answer a question exactly, and the actions of nonexpert searchers, who selected "individual references and bits of information at each stage of the ever-modifying search" (Bates, 1989, p. 410). She described the bit-at-a-time actions of online system users as *berrypicking*.

Confirmation Bias in Information Seeking

When people seek information, they tend to prefer sources that support, rather than conflict with, their existing opinions (Schultz-Hart, Frey, Lüthgens, & Moscovici, 2000). Conflicting, or dissonant, information tends to be avoided, which creates a *confirmation bias* in individuals' or groups' information preferences. The bias exists both before and after a decision has been made. It is evident in political decision making, where voters' preferences are often reflected in the news sources they use. When preparing a legal case, attorneys seek information that supports their argument; they also seek contradicting information in order to be aware of how the other side might present its case. Information professionals should not assume that people are neutral or objective when seeking information.

Schultz-Hart and colleagues noted that heterogeneous groups in which a minority has an "alternative" view tend to seek information more broadly and develop reports that reflect both views. The authors note that convergence and divergence draw on different cognitive and motivational processes. Divergence involves scrutinizing the problem and assessing the alternatives available, whereas convergence involves committing oneself to a particular perspective and upholding it against opposing forces. The underlying model of optimal decision making determines the approach used. Sometimes it is better to examine the alternatives deeply; in such cases, confirmation bias is problematic. In other cases, it is important to reach a decision quickly; in such cases, conformation bias is functional.

Models of Information Seeking

Several researchers have developed models of what people do when looking for information (Fisher et al., 2005). Typically, these models describe a sequence of steps in the information-seeking process; the models also identify variables involved in information seeking. Some models are sufficiently general to explain information seeking in various situations. Ellis's model of information-seeking behavior and Kuhlthau's model of the information search process are frequently used and provide good examples of the elements included in models of searching. Dervin's and Wilson's contributions attempt to provide theoretical perspective as well.

Ellis's Model of Information-Seeking Behavior

David Ellis (2005, p. 138) chose to focus on the behavior of scholarly researchers; he viewed the observation of behaviors as more "tractable" than attempting to study cognitive aspects of information seeking. Ellis observed that social science researchers' information seeking could be described by six types of activity (Ellis, 2005):

1. *Starting*: Activities characteristic of the initial search for information

2. *Chaining*: Following chains of citations or other forms of referential connection between material

3. *Browsing*: Semi-directed searching in an area of potential interest

4. *Differentiating*: Using differences between sources as a filter on the nature and quality of the material examined

5. *Monitoring*: Maintaining awareness of developments in a field through the monitoring of particular sources

6. *Extracting*: Systematically working through a particular source to locate material of interest (pp. 138–139)

Subsequent studies of humanities scholars, scientists, and engineers added seven more behaviors (Ellis, 2005):

1. *Surveying*: Familiarization with the literature of the area

2. *Verifying*: Checking that information is correct

3. *Selecting and shifting*: Deciding which references to follow up and which to cite

4. *Distinguishing*: Ranking information sources according to their perceived relative importance

5. *Filtering*: Use of criteria or mechanisms to make the information as relevant or precise as possible

6. *Assembling and disseminating*: Drawing together material for publication and dissemination

7. *Ending*: Information seeking at the end of a project (pp. 139–140)

Kuhlthau's Information Search Process

Carol Kuhlthau's model was initially developed in the 1980s and refined in the 1990s; it has been used in several empirical studies. Kuhlthau's model deals with six stages of the information search process and describes the information seeker's feelings, thoughts, and actions at each stage. It may be helpful to think about how students find information for a term paper, which was one of the areas first studied with this model (Kuhlthau, 2005):

- *Initiation*: A person becomes aware of a lack of knowledge or understanding, making uncertainty and apprehension common.

- *Selection*: A general area, topic, or problem is identified, and initial uncertainty often gives way to a brief sense of optimism and a readiness to begin the search.

- *Exploration*: Inconsistent, incompatible information is encountered, and uncertainty, confusion, and doubt frequently increase.

- *Formulation*: A focused perspective is formed, and uncertainty diminishes as confidence begins to increase.

- *Collection*: Information pertinent to the focused perspective is gathered, and uncertainty subsides as interest and involvement in the project increase.

- *Presentation*: The search is completed, with a new understanding enabling the person to explain his or her learning to others or in some way to put the learning to use.

Dervin's Sense-Making

Brenda Dervin's (1999) approach, although not strictly a model, provides a useful perspective on how interpretative or naturalistic research methods can be used to study information seeking (Case, 2007). Dervin criticized approaches that view information as an objective entity that exists apart from humans; she holds that information is not a brick that can be used to fill human "buckets" needing information. Instead, individuals construct information as they face gaps in their understanding of the world. Gaps occur in situations that are unique to the individual; bridging these gaps requires the individual to *construct* information, to make sense of the situation. Different people will perceive gaps (and bridges) differently. Research using this paradigm tends to focus on emotional (affective) perspectives as well as cognitive concerns.

Wilson's Model of Information Behavior

T. D. Wilson's model of information behavior has evolved since the early 1970s. Later Wilson (1981) distinguished among physiological, affective (emotional), and cognitive needs that might cause a person to seek information. Wilson also made a point of distinguishing the "person-in-context" (Wilson, 2005, p. 34) to emphasize the impact on the information seeker of the work role and the environment (physical, political, economic, social, and cultural). In the most recent model (Wilson, 1997), an information need arises for a person-in-context (role, environment), an activating mechanism prompts the decision to seek information, intervening variables (psychological, demographic, role-related interpersonal, environmental) affect the decision, and source characteristics come into play. The decision to search information resources is influenced by assessments such as self-efficacy and risk versus reward. Then information seeking occurs and may involve passive attention, passive search, active search, and ongoing search. Information is processed and used, affecting the person-in-context.

Summarizing Models of Information Seeking

A general view of information seeking emerges as more models are developed. In many cases information seeking involves a sequence of steps that can account for differences among information seekers. This can be presented via a model that is sufficiently general to explain information seeking in various situations.

A review of eight models of information seeking, including those discussed above, reveals that information seeking involves 11 types of variables:

1. Demographic characteristics

2. Personal experience and knowledge

3. Information needs

4. Thoughts (cognition)

5. Feelings

6. Criteria for source evaluations

7. Actions and queries

8. Information sources

9. Outcomes

10. Contexts (including barriers)

11. Criteria for evaluating information sources

3.4. Information and Digital Literacies

Information literacy, digital literacy, and similar concepts are frameworks for understanding and promoting effective use of information. *Information literacy* has been the more widely used term, particularly in school and college library contexts, since the 1980s. *Digital literacy* has gained popularity since about 2005. Numerous other information-related "literacies"—computer literacy, library literacy, media literacy, internet literacy, and so on—have also been suggested.

Information Literacy

Information literacy traces back to libraries' interest in *bibliographic instruction*, later known as *user education*. Grassian (2004) notes that bibliographic instruction is based in the physical library and is tool based, focuses on the mechanics of using those tools, and is tied to course assignments. Information literacy, however, has no physical constraints, is concept-based, helps people learn how to learn, and supports learning outcomes of academic programs. The American Library Association and Association for College and Research Libraries (2000) have adopted standards for information literacy:

1. The information literate student determines the nature and extent of the information needed.

2. The information literate student accesses needed information effectively and efficiently.

3. The information literate student evaluates information and its sources critically and incorporates selected information into his or her knowledge base and value system.

4. The information literate student, individually or as a member of a group, uses information effectively to accomplish a specific purpose.

5. The information literate student understands many of the economic, legal, and social issues surrounding the use of information and accesses and uses information ethically and legally.

UNESCO (2005) describes information literacy as an important tool for national and international development: It "is crucial to the competitive advantage of individuals, enterprises (especially small and medium enterprises), regions and nations; [and] provides the key to effective access, use and creation of content to support economic development, education, health and human services, and all other aspects of contemporary societies." Moreover, information literacy "extends beyond current technologies to encompass learning, critical thinking and interpretative skills across professional boundaries and empowers individuals and communities." UNESCO's Information for All Programme defines information literacy as people's ability to:

1. Recognize … their information needs.

2. Locate and evaluate the quality of information.

3. Store and retrieve information.

4. Make effective and ethical use of information.

5. Apply information to create and communicate knowledge (Catts & Lau, 2008, p. 7)

Information literacy focuses on understanding one's information needs, being able to find and evaluate relevant information, and using that information appropriately. The American Library Association and the Association for College and Research Libraries (2000) note, "Information literacy is related to information technology skills, but has broader implications for the individual, the educational system, and for society. Information technology skills enable an individual to use computers, software applications, databases, and other technologies to achieve a wide variety of academic, work-related, and personal goals. Information literate individuals necessarily develop some technology skills. Information literacy, while showing significant overlap with information technology skills, is a distinct and broader area of competence" (p. 3).

Digital Literacy

The term *digital literacy* was used in the 1980s, generally to mean the ability to deal with hypertextual information (in the sense of computer-supported, non-sequential reading) (Bawden, 2001). Gilster (1997) expanded the concept of digital literacy in his book of the same name. Rather than a set of skills, competencies, or attitudes, Gilster viewed digital literacy as an ability to understand and use information from a variety of digital sources—it is simply literacy in the digital age: the ability to read, write, and otherwise deal with information using the technologies and formats of the time. Other authors have used *digital literacy* to denote a broad concept linking together other relevant literacies and those based on communication technology competencies and skills, but they have focused on "softer" skills of information evaluation and knowledge assembly, together with a set of understandings and attitudes (Bawden, 2008; Martin, 2006, 2008).

In summary, we can say that digital literacy is the set of attitudes, understandings, and skills to handle and communicate information and knowledge effectively in a variety of media and formats. Some definitions include *communicating*; those with a records management perspective mention *deleting* and *preserving*. Sometimes the resolution is sharper, with *finding* broken down into subprocesses such as *choosing a source*, *retrieving*, and *accessing*. In an age when information comes mainly in digital form, digital literacy would seem essential; however, it must be adopted with the caveat that an important part of digital literacy is knowing when to use a nondigital source.

Digital literacy in this sense is a framework for integrating various other literacies and skill sets, although it does not need to encompass them all; as Martin (2006) put it, we do not need "one literacy to rule them all" (p. 18). Although it might be possible to produce lists of the components of digital literacy and show how they fit together, it is not sensible to try to reduce it to a finite number of linear stages. Nor is it sensible to suggest that one specific model of digital literacy will be appropriate for all people, or indeed for one person over a lifetime. Updating of understanding and competence will be necessary as individual circumstances change and as changes in the digital information environment bring the need for a fresh understanding and new competencies.

With these caveats, we can set out four components of digital literacy, as agreed to by most authorities in the field, in this way (Bawden, 2008):

1. Underpinnings

   • Literacy per se

   • Computer, information, and communication technology literacy

These underpinnings reflect the rather traditional skills, of which computer literacy is now one, that make up an older idea of literacy and an ability to function in society. Whether they should be regarded as a part of digital literacy proper or should be assumed, before digital literacy is grafted on, may be debatable. They are increasingly regarded as simply literacy in educational settings, or under headings such as *smart working* or *basic skills* in the workplace (Robinson, 2005).

These are the kind of basic skills needed to develop effective handling of information and knowledge. If traditional literacy is lacking, then however good the information technology skills, information will not be handled well. On the other hand, information and communication technology literacy is essential in dealing with the varied communication channels available to everyone.

2. Background knowledge

   • The world of information

   • The nature of information resources

This kind of knowledge was assumed for any educated person in the days when information came in books, newspapers, magazines, academic journals, professional reports, and not much else and was largely accessed through physical print-on-paper libraries. The well-understood publication chain—from author to archivist, passing through editors, publishers, booksellers, librarians, and the rest—lasted as a sensible concept well into the computer age. Now it seems outdated, and there is no clear model to replace it. Nonetheless, gaining as good an understanding as possible of what the new forms of information are and where they fit into the world of digital information has to be an essential start in being digitally literate.

3. Central competencies

   • Comprehension of digital and non-digital formats

   • Creation and communication of digital information

- Evaluation of information
- Knowledge assembly
- Information literacy
- Media literacy

These are the skills and competencies, building on the basic underpinnings, without which any claim to digital literacy has to be regarded skeptically. They are remarkably wide-ranging, and it would be sobering to try to assess to what degree they are possessed in the various countries of the world.

4. Attitudes and perspectives

- Independent learning
- Moral and social literacy

These attitudes and perspectives are perhaps what create the link between the new concept of digital literacy and an older idea of literacy, in vogue more than 200 years ago. It is not enough to have skills and competencies; they must be grounded in some moral framework, strongly associated with being an educated, or as our ancestors would have said, a "lettered" person. Of all the components of digital literacy, a moral framework may be the most difficult to teach or inculcate, but it comes closest to living up to the meaning of information in its Latin root *informare*—the transforming, structuring force.

Independent learning and moral and social literacy are the qualities attributed to a person with the motivation and mind-set to make best use of information. They provide the basis for understanding the importance of information and of "right dealing" with information resources and communication channels, as well as the incentive to continue to improve one's capabilities.

Taken together, these four components may seem to present a very ambitious set of competencies and attitudes to demand of anyone. Yet they seem to be what is needed to cope and to succeed in today's information environment. In particular, this form of digital literacy is a powerful aid in avoiding a number of the problems and paradoxes of information behavior—information overload, information anxiety, information avoidance, and the like (Bawden & Robinson, 2009).

References

American Library Association and Association for College and Research Libraries. (2000). *Information literacy competency standards for higher education.* Retrieved November 11, 2010, from www.ala.org/ala/mgrps/divs/acrl/standards/standards.pdf.

Bates, M. J. (1989). The design of browsing and berrypicking techniques for the online search interface. *Online Review, 13*(5), 407–424.

Bates, M. J. (2002, September). *Toward an integrated model of information seeking and searching.* Keynote speech at the Fourth International Conference on Information Needs, Seeking and Use in Different Contexts, Lisbon, Portugal. Retrieved November 11, 2010, from www.gseis.ucla.edu/faculty/bates/articles/info_SeekSearch-I-030329.html.

Bates, M. J. (2005). Berrypicking. In K. E. Fisher, S. Erdelez, & L. McKechnie (Eds.), *Theories of information behavior* (pp. 58–62). Medford, NJ: Information Today.

Bawden, D. (2001). Information and digital literacies: A review of concepts. *Journal of Documentation, 57*(2), 218–259.

Bawden, D. (2008). Origins and concepts of digital literacy. In C. Lankshear & M. Knobel (Eds.), *Digital literacies: Concepts, policies and paradoxes* (pp. 15–32). New York: Peter Lang.

Bawden, D., & Robinson, L. (2009). The dark side of information: Overload, anxiety and other paradoxes and pathologies. *Journal of Information Science, 35*(2), 180–191.

Belkin, N. J. (2005). Anomalous state of knowledge. In K. E. Fisher, S. Erdelez, & L. McKechnie (Eds.), *Theories of information behavior* (pp. 44–48). Medford, NJ: Information Today.

Bruner, J. (1990). *Acts of meaning: Four lectures on mind and culture.* Cambridge, MA: Harvard University Press.

Case, D. O. (2007). *Looking for information: A survey of research on information seeking, needs, and behavior* (2nd ed.). Amsterdam: Elsevier.

Case, D. O., Andrews, J. E., Johnson, J. D., & Allard, S. L. (2005). Avoiding versus seeking: The relationship of information seeking to avoidance, blunting, coping, dissonance, and related concepts. *Journal of the Medical Library Association, 93*(3), 353–362.

Catts, R., & Lau, J. (2008). *Towards information literacy indicators.* Paris: UNESCO.

Dervin, B. (1999). On studying information seeking methodologically: The implications of connecting metatheory to method. *Information Processing & Management, 35*(6), 727–750.

Ellis, D. (2005). Ellis's model of information-seeking behavior. In K. E. Fisher, S. Erdelez, & L. McKechnie (Eds.), *Theories of information behavior* (pp. 138–142). Medford, NJ: Information Today.

Erdelez, S. (1999). Information encountering: It's more than just bumping into information. *Bulletin of the American Society for Information Science, 25*(3). Retrieved November 11, 2010, from www.asis.org/Bulletin/Feb-99/erdelez.html.

Fisher, K. E., Erdelez, S., & McKechnie, L. (Eds.). (2005). *Theories of information behavior.* Medford, NJ: Information Today.

Gilster, P. (1997). *Digital literacy.* New York: Wiley.

Grassian, E. (2004) Building on bibliographic instruction. *American Libraries, 35*(9), 51–53.

Hjørland, B. (1997). *Information seeking and subject representation: An activity-theoretical approach to information science.* Westport, CT: Greenwood Press.

Kuhlthau, C. C. (2005). Kuhlthau's information search process. In K. E. Fisher, S. Erdelez, & L. McKechnie (Eds.), *Theories of information behavior* (pp. 230–234). Medford, NJ: Information Today.

Martin, A. (2006). Literacies for the digital age. In A. Martin & D. Madigan (Eds.), *Digital literacies for learning* (pp. 3–25). London: Facet.

Martin, A. (2008), Digital literacy and the "digital society." In C. Lankshear & M. Knobel (Eds.), *Digital literacies: Concepts, policies and paradoxes* (pp. 151–176). New York: Peter Lang.

Miksa, F. (2009). Information organization and the mysterious information user. *Libraries & the Cultural Record, 44*(3), 343–370.

Robinson, L. (2005). Healthcare librarians and learner support: Competences and methods. *Health Information and Libraries Journal, 22*(Suppl. 2), 42–50.

Schultz-Hart, S., Frey, D., Lüthgens, C., & Moscovici, S. (2000). Biased information search in group decision making. *Journal of Personality and Social Psychology, 78*(4), 655–669.

Swanson, D. R. (1986). Subjective versus objective relevance in bibliographic retrieval systems. *Library Quarterly, 56*(2), 103–118.

Taylor, R. S. (1968). Question-negotiation and information seeking in libraries. *College and Research Libraries, 29*, 178–194.

UNESCO. (2005). *Beacons of the information society: Alexandria proclamation on information literacy and lifelong learning.* Retrieved November 11, 2010, from archive.ifla.org/III/wsis.BeaconInfSoc.html.

Whittaker, S. (2011). Personal information management: From information consumption to curation. *Annual Review of Information Science and Technology, 45*, 3–62.

Wilson, T. D. (1981). On user studies and information needs. *Journal of Documentation, 37*(1), 3–15.

Wilson, T. D. (1997). Information behaviour: An interdisciplinary perspective. *Information Processing & Management, 33*(4), 551–572.

Wilson, T. D. (2005). Evolution in information behavior modeling. In K. E. Fisher, S. Erdelez, & L. McKechnie (Eds.), *Theories of information behavior* (pp. 31–36). Medford, NJ: Information Today.

Wilson, T. D. (2006). A re-examination of information seeking behaviour in the context of activity theory. *Information Research, 11*(4). Retrieved November 11, 2010, from informationr.net/ir/11-4/paper260.html.

CHAPTER 4

Representation of Information

4.1. What Is Representation of Information?

Working with even a modest collection of information sources—books you have enjoyed reading or pictures from your vacations over the past 5 years—often involves storing, retrieving, and organizing more pieces of information than the human memory can handle without assistance. *Representation* is the first step in providing support: The representation is commonly a shorter word, phrase, or image that brings to mind, stands for, or typifies the book, picture, or other source of information. For example, a nation's flag may represent that country's language version of a website; it may also represent your pictures from a vacation in that country.

After the collected information sources have been represented, they can be arranged or ordered so that it is easier to find a particular item in the collection. Tools to make the organization of information useful to many people include classification schemes (e.g., those used in a library), indexes (such as in the back of a book), and catalogs (in libraries or online retailers). Both representation and organization are fundamental to providing access to information. Information organization is discussed in Chapter 5.

4.2. Words and Meaning: Semantics

On the Origins of Language

Whether language is something we invented or something innate to humans is still being debated. Chomsky (1957) promoted the theory that humans have an innate ability to develop and use language. However, evidence of similar abilities is emerging for chimps, gorillas, and aquatic mammals that also have large brains.

It seems reasonable to assume that early human interaction involved gesturing and pointing, followed first by some kind of vocalization and then by a progression from visual mimesis to iconic representations of the external world. In ancient Egypt, hieroglyphs (pictographs) were followed by hieratic (priestly) and demotic (popular) writing, illustrating a progression from affairs of religion and state to a more practical form of expression that facilitated commerce. In the ancient Mesopotamian valley (Babylonia and

Sumeria in particular), cuneiform (wedge-shaped) writing was inscribed on clay tablets.

Interesting work by Schmandt-Besserat (1992) suggests that the earliest writing may have been closely tied to counting and mathematics. She suggests that some of the earliest tokens were in fact counters. Although used specifically for counting, the ancient Roman term *calculi* (pebbles) gave rise to our current terms *calculate* and *calculus*. The parallel is at the very least quite striking.

Alphabetic writing was an invention of the Phoenicians, who paved the way for the Greeks, the Romans, and the rest of the Western world in this respect. Oriental calligraphy progressed from pictographic to ideographic writing, showing a transition from literal to metaphoric symbolism. Interestingly, the very word *metaphor* is a metaphor, formed when Aristotle combined the Greek words meaning *beyond* (*meta*) and *to carry* (*pherein*).

Grammar and Syntax

Traditional grammar (the study of words and their use) and syntax (how words are used together to form phrases and sentences) provide a useful starting point to develop an understanding of language.

The first textbook on grammar is thought to have been written in the first century B.C. by the Greek scholar Dionysius Thrax. This seminal attempt at analyzing language served as a model, first for the ancient Romans and then for French primary schools. In fact, most modern grammars are quite formal, reflecting the early Greeks' penchant for adopting a scientific approach to their studies.

The English language poses additional challenges. Because English incorporates features from so many other languages, it provides useful and occasionally comic examples of grammar and syntax. Although its structure is basically Teutonic, approximately two-thirds of English words are of Greek and Latin derivation. This rich vocabulary introduces redundancy and ambiguity, making English at times a source of both mischief and humor; in addition, important distinctions preserved in other languages have either disappeared or never existed in English. English grammarians observe three basic cases: nominative, possessive, and objective. Although this is succinct and useful, it ignores nontrivial distinctions.

> "Call me a taxi," says the first speaker. "Okay," says the second, "you're a taxi."

This old joke exemplifies the inability to distinguish between a direct and an indirect object in English (except by context). Other languages (Latin and German, for example) use an *accusative* case to identify direct objects and a *dative* case for indirect objects. There can be no ambiguity, but neither can there be the same kind of humor—something of a trade-off. The dative and accusative cases are also used to differentiate between static and dynamic situations; in German, for example, "das Buch liegt auf dem Tisch" means "the book lies (or is lying) on the table" but "ich lege das Buch auf den Tisch" means "I lay (or am laying) the book on the table." The case is indicated by the form of the article following the preposition. Perhaps the reason many Americans have trouble distinguishing between *lie* and *lay* is the lack of inflection (i.e., ways to distinguish the case of a noun) in the language. Some have suggested that English speakers may also be reluctant to use the word *lie* because of its look-alike's meaning, prevarication.

German, the principal Teutonic language most closely related to English, has four cases rather than three: nominative, genitive, dative, and accusative. Nominative is virtually the same in each language, dative and accusative have been identified briefly already, and genitive is equivalent to possessive.

Latin is even more complicated, having seven cases: nominative, genitive, dative, accusative, ablative, vocative, and locative. The ablative case primarily preserves distinctions between and among different kinds of prepositional phrases. (For a taste of the importance possessed by Latin prepositions, consider that *de* implies *down from, ex* means *out of,* and *ab* suggests *away from.* Their impact on derivatives in English is profound: *descend* [climb down from], *extract* [draw out of], *absurd* [away from the rational].) Languages such as Latin are called *inflected* because the use of the words can be inferred from their form rather than their position in a sentence.

English and other modern languages often represent something of a hybrid between inflected and uninflected types. In addition, usage is constantly changing. American English differs substantially from British English—partly the result of geographic separation and partly the result of changing roles in the world. Both the U.S. and the U.K. have absorbed millions of immigrants from an extraordinary variety of countries. However, modern commerce and communication technologies have forced the interaction of all peoples as never before. Naturally, this has led to a considerable sharing of terms and may be causing greater linguistic homogeneity—not just among the English-speaking peoples, but globally.

Semantic ambiguity causes difficulty, whether the language is written or spoken. One needs to distinguish between *homographs* (words or other symbols that are written the same way but have different meanings) and *homophones* (words that sound the same but mean different things). The generic term is *homonym,* for words with different meanings but the same spelling or pronunciation. Although they are usually harmless when written (but embarrassing, as when one uses *there* for *their,* for instance), homophones can create considerably more confusion in conversations ("The oar/ore will not float.").

Although pronunciation is not normally considered a matter of grammar and syntax, its importance increases with the growth of voice recognition and text-to-speech synthesis machines. Compare, for example, the sound of *brought* with *drought* or *cough* with *dough* or *rough*, which essentially rhymed in Chaucer's 14th-century England. English consists of the detritus of many other languages, compromised by changing times and cultures, and the spelling of its words often reflects pronunciations of bygone eras. Because languages change over time, some linguists have suggested that we worry too much about conforming to standards. For example, the double or even triple negative, frowned upon in modern English, was a feature of Old English: "Ic ne can noht singan" (literally, "I not can nothing sing") was used for intensification. Something similar is still in use in French (McWhorter, 2001, p. 227).

Some of the rules of grammar and syntax may seem arbitrary, but they represent conventions that provide common ground for well-educated people. Moreover, they help foster understanding by reducing ambiguity and—to put it bluntly—to help people think straight. Change in language may be inevitable, but it should not be used as an excuse for capricious coinage or gross illiteracy. Properly educated people do not say such things as "just between you and I" or "It is up to you and I to do something." Prepositions are followed by the objective case: "just between you and me"; infinitive phrases take the objective case for their subjects: "It is up to you and me to do something about this situation." On the other hand, only a rigid purist would insist on "It is I" rather than "It's me" in a casual conversation, rules of predicate nominatives notwithstanding.

Machine Translation

In 1947, Warren Weaver became one of the first to propose that computers of the day, which were essentially large calculating machines, could eventually be used to translate text from one language to another. In a letter to cyberneticist and linguist Norbert Wiener, Weaver wrote, "When I look at an article in Russian I say, 'This is really written in English, but it has been coded in some strange symbols. I will now proceed to decode'" (Hutchins, 1997, p. 22).

Taken at face value, the implication is that machine translation should be a trivial matter of employing a substitution cipher, replacing, for example, a Russian word by its English equivalent. However, as Hofstadter (1997, p. 521) has noted, it is more likely that Weaver, who was fascinated by the subtleties of language, was merely trying to be provocative.

The difficulties of getting a computer to translate passages should be apparent, but successive generations of programmers have been unsuccessful. In addition to commercially available software for various natural languages, AltaVista, Babelfish, Google Language Tools, and other translation services are currently available on the World Wide Web. Such services work best with short, unambiguous passages but may produce inadequate translations of complicated text.

Hofstadter (1997) illustrated the pleasures and pitfalls of human translations of poetry, then remarked about machine translation:

> With a few exceptions ... the field of machine translation seems nearly bereft of an attitude of humility and respect for the subtlety and beauty of human language. Over and over again, one encounters articles and publicity claiming degrees of success that, if true, could only mean that all the mysteries of human language (and *a fortiori* all the mysteries of the human mind) had been fully understood.
>
> It is this stunning lack of humility, this regrettable level of hubris, that I find incomprehensible (and in this case also reprehensible). By no means does this imply, however, that I oppose the attempt to study or model human language and the act of translation by means of computers. ... I just think one should have the proper degree of respect for what one is tackling. (p. 522)

Stages of Information Representation

The information professional's work in representation builds on the author's expression and subsequent recording of the information. This progression moves through three stages. First, the author or creator generates an idea.

- An individual knowledge creator develops an idea. This idea can be based on experience, insight, or creativity; it forms only one part of that individual's total knowledge.

- The idea becomes distinct in the author's mind—conceptualized or even mentally verbalized, sometimes explained by an image. These ideas may be combined with or modified by other knowledge that the individual already has.

- For some reason, the author chooses to share the idea with others. To do so successfully, the idea must be represented in such a way that the person receiving the message in which it is contained is able to understand the meaning. This may be through movement, sound, or image, but more commonly the information is expressed in language.

- The author therefore expresses the idea in a language that is known to at least one other person; and this language, or sound patterning, will be controlled by linguistic rules of semantics, syntactics, and pragmatics.

In the second stage, the author records the information.

- If the author decides that the information needs a wider audience, he or she may record it in a more permanent form. Thus, the meaning of the information may be translated first into the sounds of words, for spoken language, and these sounds then further abstracted into a series of symbols, such as the letters of a particular alphabet, in order to be recorded. The meaning of the symbols or letters can be further enhanced through the design or pattern of their recording, such as by underlining and spacing.

- The nature of the document that contains this recorded or written information can provide contextual meaning: the document's components (introduction and contents page, for example), its physical presentation (single sheet of vellum, scholarly journal), and its context in general.

In the final stage, the information professional prepares a representation of the information.

- The information professional translates the author's expression, or the way in which the idea has been represented, into an intermediary system language. First the information professional determines the meaning of the information content of the document, and then he or she selects words that describe the information.

- The quality of description of the information content in terms of completeness and consistency depends on the method of identification of concepts. The subject matter must, therefore, be carefully analyzed.

- The information professional selects words (or terms) that best represent the concepts, bearing in mind not only the intrinsic subject matter or meaning of the information but also the possible ways in which such information may be requested by a user and the types of questions such information may answer.

4.3. Approaches to Information Analysis

Analysis is the investigation of the component parts of a whole and their relations in making up the whole. The term *information analysis* was introduced in the 1950s as a generic term for the study of all kinds of information objects, including texts, pictures, sounds, and objects.

Analysis is the first step in providing intellectual access to documents. Technical (computer-based) approaches to analyzing the subject or information content of a document may focus on *microstructure* or *macrostructure*. Microstructure analysis begins with syntactic analysis of sentences (parsing) and paragraphs, followed by semantic analysis; macrostructure analysis uses methods such as *data extraction* (conversion of knowledge from the textual format into a more structured representation, such as *frames*) A variety of theoretical perspectives have been developed to explain how to analyze documents or information objects.

Subjectivity, Objectivity, Contextuality

An element of subjectivity occurs in any analysis and coding of information. Subjectivity is particularly apparent in the analysis of nontextual documents. Consider how a single photograph might be interpreted as "a family on a picnic next to a river," "an old-fashioned picture," "a picture of my grandmother's 30th birthday party," "The Muddy Creek before the canal was built," or even an example of a particular photographic technique.

Context is evidently an essential consideration in information analysis. For example, a document about road building in the Roman Empire might be described in terms of technology, communication, political strength, history, archaeology, or cultural invasion. Deciding how to describe a document or piece of information in a database requires some sophistication: It is not simply a matter of reading self-evident properties from these items but a highly skilled interpretative activity "by which the properties of items are not only described, but stabilized and even created" (Levy, 1995, under "Cataloging as Order-Making").

Content Analysis

Content analysis focuses on the actual content of texts and seeks to describe their meaning objectively and systematically, within the context of communication. Krippendorff (2004) defines content analysis as "a research technique for making replicable and valid inferences from texts (or other meaningful matter) to the contexts of their use" (p. 18). To make such extrapolations, however, the context of the texts' creation is considered first.

The subject matter of the text is less important here than the recurrent themes and concepts it contains. The process of content analysis involves identifying the structures of, and patterns within, a text, which can then be used as a basis for making inferences to other states or properties (Krippendorff, 2004). Texts can be characterized and categorized by their predominant concepts and themes: Themes can be established only after concept analysis.

Affect extraction and analysis provide an emotional evaluation of concepts explicit in a text. It is problematic because emotion may vary across time and populations; there is clearly also a subjective element to such analysis.

Proximity analysis investigates the co-occurrence of explicit concepts. In this procedure, the text is defined as a string of words. A given length of words, called a *window*, is determined. The window is then scanned across a text to check for the co-occurrence of concepts. The resulting matrix, or group of interrelated, co-occurring concepts, might suggest an overall meaning.

Contextual Analysis

Context itself is a kind of text that can be interpreted, thus manifesting the shared concepts and meanings from which texts are constructed. Contextual analysis is a foundation for discourse, hermeneutic, and semiotic analysis.

Analysis considers the traditions, customs, and practices in which communication occurs; these may be considered from the perspective of cultural, social, ideological, organizational, disciplinary, epistemological, and professional strata. Boundaries between strata are not always clear because they influence each other. These strata are used to consider the texts, their creators, genres of communication, semiotic representation of concepts, and disciplinary discourses.

The content of a text is considered a social phenomenon shaped by its context, which includes the circumstances under which the text was created and its relationship with other texts. A text can be considered as a node in a network. Barthes (1977) sees a text as "a methodological field" that "exists in the movement of a discourse"(p. 156). Individual texts are involved in an intertextual and material weave that forms their context: Any text is thus an embodiment of connections across a literature base, linking various works, and displaying and articulating a particular discourse. Barthes (1977) describes the text as follows:

> woven entirely with citations, references, echoes, cultural languages (what language is not?), antecedent and contemporary, which cut across it through and through in a vast stereophony. The intertextual in which every text is held, it itself being the text-between of another text, is not to be confused with some origin of the text: to try to find the "sources," the "influences" of a work, is to fall in with the myth of filiation; the citations which go to make up a text are anonymous, untraceable, and yet already read: they are quotations without inverted commas. (p. 160)

Discourse Analysis

Discourse analysis seeks to identify the implicit assumptions in the use of language by identifying the relationships among a text, its discursive practices, and the larger social context that shapes both text and discourse. Discourse analysis assumes that the resources and strategies (lexis and grammar, rhetorical formations, typical cultural narratives, genres, the principles of constructing thematic formations, etc.) used in producing texts are characteristics of a community rather than unique to a discursive event in that community.

Pure semiotics does not encompass institutional frameworks or the social context of a text; these are examined in discourse analysis, sometimes known as *social semiotics*. In social semiotics, discourse is seen as involving the larger linguistic unit, or the text as a whole, and discourse analysis examines how meaning is made within a text by identification of the characteristics of the community that creates and uses the text. This method of analysis assists in discovering recondite meaning: It is broader, and yet more penetrating, than content analysis because the hidden or encrypted meanings of the texts are examined in order to discover intended or unintended social or political effects.

Language use within a discourse effectively constitutes social practice, action, and interaction, playing a role in the construction of the reality of a particular community—its identities, social relations, and power struggles. Language constructs reality or particular versions of an experienced world, positioning the reader to subscribe to particular beliefs, where some "truths" are accepted and others rejected.

Within a particular community, the use of certain metaphors, symbolic characterizations, and other assumptions can become naturalized (cf. Barthes's, 1994, "natural information") and are considered unproblematic, even transparent or "given." This naturalization, however, privileges certain attitudes or positions and, in so doing, precludes others. It is the task of discourse analysis to reveal the institutions and practices of power behind such naturalizations; this is accomplished by revealing the motivations and politics behind assumptions, or conceptualizations of an entity, and facilitating open and informed debate.

Hermeneutic Analysis

Hermeneutics provides the philosophical grounding for *interpretivism* because it is concerned with the discovery of meaning and coherence, particularly in texts, and how prior understandings and prejudices shape the interpretive process. Hermeneutics can be treated as both an underlying philosophy and a specific mode of analysis (Bleicher, 1980). As the latter, it provides a way of understanding textual data, in which the parts or the whole of a text can be examined in order to discover hidden meanings in individually or socially constructed realities.

Hermeneutic theory adopts the *social subjectivist* paradigm, in which meaning is inter-subjectively created (Berthon, Pitt, Ewing, & Carr, 2002). Hermeneutics acknowledges the subjectivity of the researcher and holds that meaning is made only by the researcher's insight and understanding of the text, which depends on an existing personal knowledge framework. Gadamer's (1976) definition of the task of hermeneutics is "a bridging of personal or historical distance between minds" (p. 95), which he describes as the "fusion of horizons" (p. 95); prior understandings and prejudices shape the interpretive process. Thus, interpretation is contextual, depending on the moment of interpretation and the horizon brought to it by the interpreter.

A *hermeneutic circle* refers to the dialectic between the understanding of the text as a whole and the interpretation of its parts, in which descriptions are guided by anticipated explanations. The movement of understanding, according to Gadamer (1976), "is constantly from the whole to the part and back to the whole" (p. 117), which he explains as "a circular relationship. The anticipation of meaning in which the whole is envisaged becomes explicitly clear in that the parts that are determined by the whole themselves also determine this whole" (p. 117).

Semiotic Analysis

Semiotics, literally the study of signs, seeks to establish the meanings of terms (or *signifiers*) used in a text, how meaning is determined, and consequently, how social reality is created and shared within a community. Content and discourse analysis can be considered types of semiotic analysis. Semiotic analysis considers the epistemological, theoretical, or disciplinary positions of the texts.

Texts are most often read only superficially, and the meaning of terms used is assumed at a lexical level. However, Barthes (1994) argues that by accepting terms at face value, "we take them for 'natural' information" (p. 158), not considering any hidden meanings they may suggest. Semiotics presumes that signifiers are located within the conventions of particular social and cultural contexts and that terms therefore have ontological meanings unique to a particular community. The various levels of semiotic analysis facilitate a deeper understanding of signs within a context because they are able to expose the conventions at work within a particular text and to reveal the implied or understood meanings of terms.

Barthes (1994) maintains that the first task of the semiological undertaking is to divide the texts into minimal significant units. The importance of an idea is revealed by the frequency with which a term signifying that idea appears in the text.

Semiotic codes are sets of practices that are familiar to a particular cultural community—these assist in communication of meaning within the community. Codes are themselves signifying systems, providing conventions for organizing signs into systems that correlate signifiers and signifieds; codes also transcend single texts by linking them into an interpretative framework. Knowledge of the framework or code is necessary for both the author and the reader of a text: They both provide and constrain meaning. Typically, external clues indicate what code is being employed; examples of such clues include the text's layout and progression of introduction, references, and tables.

What a term represents is considered and interpreted by the members of a community and matched against their mental models and ontological commitments. Terms may be used metaphorically or symbolically within the framework of a particular code, but such interpretations can be made clear only through consideration of the context of their use. Coding systems can be used effectively only if their users know how they are constructed and for what purposes.

Using the Analysis

Using one or more methods of analysis, the information professional determines the "aboutness" of a document. Sometimes this is a sentence ("This book is about ..."), and sometimes a few words (e.g., *losses, live sheep transport, Australia*) that summarize the potential (often quite different from actual) ways in which the information might be sought. The information can then be represented briefly in either of two ways:

- *Indexing* involves describing these concepts using either the language of the document itself or a controlled language that, it is hoped, will match with the expression of a user's request.

- *Classification* (see Chapter 5) involves using alphabetical, numeric, or alphanumeric systems that represent information and allow for sequential linear arrangement of physical documents.

The careful analysis of information resources underlies the information retrieval and visualization functions described in Chapter 8.

4.4. Abstracting

The international standard ISO 214-1976 defines the *abstract* as "an abbreviated, accurate representation of the contents of a document, without added interpretation or criticism and without distinction as to who wrote the abstract" (International Organization for Standardization, 1976, p. 1). According to the same standard, well-written abstracts "enable readers to identify the basic content of a document quickly and accurately to determine relevance ... and thus decide whether they need to read the document in its entirety" (p. 1) and are useful in computerized searching.

Abstracts may vary in a number of respects and may hence be categorized differently. They may differ, for example, in their length, varying from verbose and "literary" to very terse and "telegraphic"; according to their purpose; in the degree to which they are intended to replace the original document rather than point to it; in the extent of criticism and interpretation of the original; and in the extent to which they are targeted or slanted to a particular interest or type of user (for example, reflecting their intended users' needs by including items that are only briefly mentioned in the original).

Abstracts have by no means lost their importance over time. Nicholas, Huntington, and Jamali (2007) found that at least 20 percent of ScienceDirect users read only abstracts and relied on them for selecting relevant papers and acquiring information for their research. If, as the authors suggest, search engines tend to rank abstracts higher than full texts, then the content and structure of abstracts become even more important.

The Abstract's Content and Structure

For proper representation of information from the original document, standard ISO 214-1976 suggests that an informative abstract should include five elements:

- Purpose

- Methods

- Results

- Conclusions

- Collateral information from the original work if space permits

International standard ISO 214-1976, which has been adopted by the European Union, is very similar to the U.S. standard ANSI/NISO Z39.14: Guidelines for Abstracts, published in 1997 (American National Standards Institute/National Information Standards Organization, 1997). The standards describe three types of abstracts:

- Informative: Present the most important findings in the document by providing all of the information on purpose, method, results, conclusions, and background

- Indicative (or descriptive): Merely indicate the general topic of the document

- Informative-indicative: A combination of the two types and usually the only solution when space prohibits full report of findings

The different types of abstracts require different amounts of information from the original document and may vary in length. Different types of documents may also warrant different types of abstracts: Research papers would normally require informative abstracts (including all the structural elements), but review articles would usually be well represented by indicative abstracts, skipping methods and results. In their study of abstracts in various languages and disciplines, Šauperl, Klasinc, and Lužar (2008) confirmed several concepts. The authors demonstrated that abstracts vary with the writer's nation and culture and that a paper's purpose and scope influence the content and structure of abstracts (e.g., an abstract of a research report is different from an abstract of a literature review paper). The study also confirmed that a journal's role in a professional society influences abstract content and structure (does the journal stand as the record for original research or serve primarily as a channel for transferring new knowledge from research to a professional community?).

Automatic abstracting has been a goal for more than 50 years, since H. P. Luhn carried out the first tests at IBM in the late 1950s. Rush, Salvador, and Zamora (1964) approached the task by seeking to remove redundant information from the original text in order to produce a brief extract. Reflecting on a decade of research, Ashworth (1967, p. 477) noted that "abstracting is expensive because of the amount of intellectual effort required. It has therefore been an attractive proposition to investigate the possibility of replacing intellectual by mechanical effort." Chowdhury (2004) presented an overview of approaches to automatic abstracting and summarizing; work by Ou, Khoo, and Goh (2008) is a typical recent example. Nonetheless, most practical abstracting within information systems and services is still largely a task for human intelligence.

Instructions for Writing Abstracts

Abstracts are always brief; most consist of about 200 words. They should be written as a single paragraph in active voice, using clear and brief sentences. They do not contain references, illustrations, notes, or similar parts of original text, nor do they include information not found in the original document. Lancaster (2003) is one of many authors who provide advice on writing abstracts. Effective abstracting involves a variety of competencies and skills in the handling of information. Cremmins's *The Art of Abstracting* (1996) notes the subjectivity involved in the task. He suggests that the process of summarization takes four steps:

1. Analysis of document type: The abstractor determines whether the document is a book or a journal article, whether it is original research or an essay, whether the text is structured in chapters, how long it is. This is done by skimming the document.

2. Skimming the document: The abstractor identifies the parts that contain information that will be incorporated in the abstract. The abstractor also searches for clue words and terms, such as *method, result,* or *was found.*

3. Reading: Only now does the abstractor thoroughly read the identified parts of text and make an outline of the abstract.

4. Editing: The abstractor "polishes" the abstract, making sure no errors were made during the transfer of information from the paper to the abstract. The abstractor edits the text of the abstract and makes it an independent, self-contained, and clear document, closely representing the original text.

Abstracts, Extracts, and Summaries

Abstracts can be compared with summaries and extracts (Chu, 2003). Abstracts are prepared by human beings to represent the content of a document concisely and accurately. Summaries restate the main points of a document but assume that the reader will have access to the full text to develop a more complete understanding. Computer-created summaries are possible, especially for digital documents. Extracts use selected parts of a document to represent its content. Computer algorithms can be used to prepare extracts by, for example, selecting sentences that use words in the title or that begin or end a paragraph.

Examples of Abstracts

Two examples of abstracts are presented here. They are taken from Colorado State University's Writing@CSU Project (writing.colostate.edu/guides/documents/abstract/pop2c.cfm).

Descriptive abstract:
"Bonanza Creek LTER [Long Term Ecological Research] 1997 Annual Progress Report."
We continue to document all major climatic variables in the uplands and floodplains at Bonanza Creek. In addition, we have documented the successional changes in microclimate in nine successional upland and floodplain stands at Bonanza Creek (BNZ) and in four elevational locations at Caribou-Poker Creek

(CPCRW). A sun photometer is operated cooperatively with NASA to estimate high-latitude atmospheric extinction coefficients for remote-sensing images. Electronic data are collected monthly and loaded into a database which produces monthly summaries. The data are checked for errors, documented, and placed on-line on the BNZ Web page. Climate data for the entire state have been summarized for the period of station records and krieged to produce maps of climate zones for Alaska based on growing-season and annual temperature and precipitation.

Informative abstract based on experimental work:
Palmquist, M., & Young, R. (1992). The Notion of Giftedness and Student Expectations About Writing. *Written Communication*, 9(1), 137–168.

Research reported by Daly, Miller, and their colleagues suggests that writing apprehension is related to a number of factors we do not yet fully understand. This study suggests that included among those factors should be the belief that writing ability is a gift. Giftedness, as it is referred to in the study, is roughly equivalent to the Romantic notion of original genius. Results from a survey of 247 postsecondary students enrolled in introductory writing courses at two institutions indicate that higher levels of belief in giftedness are correlated with higher levels of writing apprehension, lower self-assessments of writing ability, lower levels of confidence in achieving proficiency in certain writing activities and genres, and lower self-assessments of prior experience with writing instructors. Significant differences in levels of belief in giftedness were also found among students who differed in their perceptions of the most important purpose for writing, with students who identified "to express your own feelings about something" as the most important purpose for writing having the highest mean level of belief in giftedness. Although the validity of the notion that writing ability is a special gift is not directly addressed, the results suggest that belief in giftedness may have deleterious effects on student writers.

4.5. Indexing

Indexing is the representation of a document (or part of a document or an information object) in a record or an index for the purpose of retrieval. Library catalogs, bibliographical databases, and back-of-the-book indexes are common examples.

The representation may identify the originators of the document, its publisher, its physical properties, and its subjects. Descriptive indexing emphasizes physical properties such as originator, publisher, and date and place of publication; subject indexing emphasizes what the document is about. Subject indexes may be prepared by human intellectual analysis or by means of computer-based statistical analyses of word frequencies. After analysis to determine the document's subjects, the subjects are "translated" into indexing terms (or other symbols, such as classification codes). Many indexes use natural language, often words taken from the document. In other cases the indexing is represented by controlled vocabulary or classification (see Chapter 5).

Keyword Indexing

Keyword indexing extracts words from a document in order to describe its subject. Early work in this area was conducted in 1958 by H. P. Luhn at the IBM research library. He created the keyword in context (KWIC) index, using titles of research articles. The keywords formed a column near the middle of the page, and portions of the author and title provided a snippet of context (Figure 4.1). Luhn soon reformatted the output to produce a keyword out of context (KWOC) index (Figure 4.2). Luhn's work was one of the earliest applications of computers for text processing (pp. 288–295).

Pre-Coordinate and Post-Coordinate Indexing

An indexer may combine the words describing a document's subject into phrases, such as *Learning Disorders* to specify that a document is about a particular aspect of learning and a particular kind of disorder. This is called *pre-coordinate indexing* because the words are combined by the indexer rather than by the person searching for the information. Pre-coordinate indexing is usually used in back-of-the-book indexes and many bibliographic databases and library catalogs. Although pre-coordinate indexing requires more work by the indexer, it is useful in helping the searcher locate information on a topic while avoiding documents that use the same words but with other meanings (*false drops*).

In *post-coordinate indexing*, the indexer identifies words that represent subjects in the document, but the combination of words is done when a searcher uses the database. The searcher uses Boolean logic (AND, OR, NOT; see Chapter 8) to combine words to express the information needed. Post-coordinate indexing allows searchers to choose words and combine them in ways an indexer may not have anticipated, which increases the flexibility of searching and often the number of documents retrieved (*recall*).

Stevens, M.. (1970)   * indexing* A state-of-the-art report. National Bureau [document 70-874]
Doyle, L. B. (1975).   * Information* retrieval and processing. Los Angeles: [document 75-005]
Keenan, S. (1973). C * information* data centers (pp. 97-104). Montvale, N [document 73-173]
Luhn, H. P. (1959).   * information* retrieval systems. In M. Boaz, Modern [document 59-302]
E. Tomeski, R. W. W * information* storage & retrieval proceedings of Feb [document 61-043]
Taube, M., & Woost   * Information* storage and retrieval: Theory, systems [document 58-306]
Luhn, H. P. (1961).   * intelligence* systems: Some basic problems and pre [document 61-659]

Figure 4.1   KWIC index

Indexing
70-874 Stevens, M. (1970). Automatic indexing: A state-of-the-art report. National Bureau of
Information
75-005 Doyle, L. B. (1975). Information retrieval and processing. Los Angeles: Melville.
73-173 Keenan, S. (1973). Progress in automatic indexing and prognosis for the future. In J. A.
59-302 Luhn, H. P. (1959). Auto-encoding of documents for information retrieval systems. In M.
61-043 Tomeski, E. R. & W. Westcott (Eds.) (1961). The clarification, unification &
58-306 Taube, M., & Wooster, H. (Eds.). (1958). Information storage and retrieval: Theory,
Intelligence
61-659 Luhn, H. P. (1961). Automated intelligence systems: Some basic problems and
prerequisit

Figure 4.2   KWOC index

Citation Indexing

The works cited in a scholarly document also provide clues to what the document is about (its subject). *Citation indexes* are databases of documents' bibliographic references; they allow searchers to search by *citation chaining*, locating newer documents that cite an older one. They also allow *forward chaining* (locating newer documents that cite the one in hand), as well as documents that have citations in common.

Citation indexes have been used for generations in legal research (Shepard's Citations were first published in 1873; Stevens, 2002). The principle was applied in other fields beginning in the 1960s, first with the *Science Citation Index* from the Institute for Scientific Information. Web-based versions, considering both bibliographic references and hyperlinks, are being developed (see Chapter 11).

Vector Space Model

Gerard Salton and colleagues developed the *vector space model* for use with the System for the Manipulation and Retrieval of Texts in the 1970s. In this model, each index term is defined as a dimension in space. A document is represented as a *vector* (or list of terms) in this space, showing the relative importance of each index term in describing the document. A query is also represented as vectors expressing the relative importance of each index term for the query. Retrieving information in vector space means locating the document vectors that are closest to the query vector: Documents similar to the query will have relatively small differences between the angles of their vectors.

Chu (2003, 2010) discusses strengths and limitations of the vector space model. This model relieves the searcher of understanding and applying Boolean logic. And because all documents are compared with the query, the vector space model can also provide a ranked list of documents considered most relevant (instead of listing all relevant documents in the system). The major criticism of the vector space model is its assumption that no relationships exist among the terms: that they are *orthogonal* to each other. This is demonstrably not the case; for example, *birthday* and *happy* would be expected to appear in the same document more often than *birthday* and *dictionary*.

Latent Semantic Analysis

Information retrieval researchers developed a computer-based technique called latent semantic analysis in 1990. Latent semantic analysis uses the vector space model to find connections (such as co-occurrence in a document and word proximity) among the words in a database (e.g., Ding, 2005; Dumais, 2004). Aggregating the contexts in which a given word does and does not appear provides a set of mutual constraints that largely determines the similarity of meaning of words and sets of words to each other. In this way, latent semantic analysis can represent the meaning of words and passages from analysis of text alone; for this reason it is sometimes called a "bag of words" analysis. "It makes no use of word order, thus of syntactic relations or logic, or of morphology. Remarkably, it manages to extract correct reflections of passage and word meanings quite well without these aids, but it must still be suspected of resulting incompleteness or likely error on some occasions" (Landauer, Foltz, & Laham, 1998, p. 261).

Being aware of the subjectivity of the information analysis process, of the information needs of different disciplines, and of linguistic or cultural differences, an information professional strives to prepare an adequate document representation to enable retrieval of relevant information. Information professionals must also continue to monitor users' information needs and customs in order to improve both manual and automated information representation.

The American Society for Indexing provides detailed information about indexing practices, software, and careers (www.asindexing.org).

References

American National Standards Institute/National Information Standards Organization. (1997). *ANSI/NISO Z39.14 – 1997: Guidelines for Abstracts*. New York: Author.

Ashworth, W. (1967). Abstracting. In *Handbook of Special Librarianship and Information Work* (3rd ed.) (pp. 453–481). London: Aslib.

Bar-Hillel, Y. (1960). The present status of automatic translation of languages. *Advances in Computers, 1*(1), 92–163.

Barthes, R. (1977). From work to text. In *Image, Music, Text* (S. Heath, Trans.) (pp. 155–164). New York: Hill and Wang.

Barthes, R. (1994). The kitchen of meaning. In *The semiotic challenge* (R. Howard, trans.) (pp. 157–159). Berkeley: University of California Press.

Berthon, P., Pitt, L., Ewing, M., & Carr, C. L. (2002). Potential research space in MIS: A framework for envisioning and evaluating research replication, extension, and generation. *Information Systems Research, 13*(4), 416–428.

Bleicher, J. (1980). *Contemporary hermeneutics: Hermeneutics as method, philosophy and critique*. London: Routledge & Kegan Paul.

Chomsky, N. (1957). *Syntactic structures*. The Hague: Mouton.

Chowdhury, G. G. (2004). *Introduction to modern information retrieval* (2nd ed.). London: Facet.

Chu, H. (2003, 2010). *Information representation and retrieval in the digital age*. Medford, NJ: Information Today, Inc.

Cremmins, E. T. (1996). *The art of abstracting* (2nd ed.). Arlington, VA: Information Resources Press.

Ding, C. H. Q. (2005). A probabilistic model for latent semantic indexing. *Journal of the American Society for Information Science and Technology, 56*(6), 597–608.

Dumais, S. T. (2004). Latent semantic analysis. *Annual Review of Information Science and Technology, 38*, 189–230.

Gadamer, H. G. (1976). *Philosophical hermeneutics* (D. Linge, Trans. & Ed.). Berkeley: University of California Press.

Hofstadter, D. R. (1997). *Le ton beau de Marot: In praise of the music of language*. New York: Basic Books.

Hutchins, J. (1997). Milestones in machine translation: Episodes from the history of computers and translation. *Language Today, 3*, 22–23.

International Organization for Standardization. (1976). *ISO 214-1976: Documentation: Abstracts for publications and documentation*. Geneva, Switzerland: Author.

Krippendorff, K. (2004). *Content analysis: An introduction to its methodology* (2nd ed.). Thousand Oaks, CA: Sage.

Lancaster, F. W. (2003). *Indexing and abstracting in theory and practice* (3rd ed.). Champaign: University of Illinois, Graduate School of Library and Information Science.

Landauer, T. K., Foltz, P. W., & Laham, D. (1998). Introduction to latent semantic analysis. *Discourse Processes, 25*, 259–284. Retrieved September 27, 2009, from lsa.colorado.edu/papers/dp1.LSAintro.pdf.

Levy, D. M. (1995). Cataloging in the digital order. *Proceedings of Digital Libraries 95.* Retrieved November 11, 2010, from www.csdl.tamu.edu/DL95/papers/levy/levy.html.

Luhn, H. P. (1960). Keyword-in-context index for technical literature. *American Documentation, 11*(4), 288–295.

McWhorter, J. H. (2001). *The power of Babel: A natural history of language.* New York: Henry Holt.

Nicholas, D., Huntington, P., & Jamali, H. R. (2007). The use, users, and role of abstracts in the digital scholarly environment. *Journal of Academic Librarianship, 33*(4), 446–453.

Ou, S., Khoo, C. S. G., & Goh, D. H. (2008). Design and development of a concept-based multi-document summarization system for research abstracts. *Journal of Information Science, 34*(3), 308–326.

Rush, J. E., Salvador, R., & Zamora, A. (1964). Automatic abstracting and indexing: Production of indicative abstracts by application of contextual inference and syntactic criteria. *American Documentation, 22*(4), 260–274.

Šauperl, A., Klasinc, J., & Lužar, S. (2008). Components of abstracts: Logical structure of scholarly abstracts in pharmacology, sociology, and linguistics and literature. *Journal of the American Society for Information Science and Technology, 59*(9), 1420–1432.

Schmandt-Besserat, D. (1992). *Before writing.* Austin: University of Texas Press.

Stevens, A. M. (2002). *Finding, reading, and using the law.* Albany, NY: Delmar.

CHAPTER 5

Organization of Information

5.1. What Is Organization of Information?

Information professionals facilitate access to a collection of information by organizing it. Sometimes the physical, information-bearing objects themselves are organized, as with the books in a library. In other cases information professionals provide an access structure that can present the collection in various ways to meet different user needs, such as with a library catalog that can be searched by keyword, author, or title. *Organization* in this sense entails the arrangement or apparent arrangement of representations of information in a way that groups together, or *collocates*, similar items.

Information is often organized to enhance *subject access*—providing users access to documents (books, articles, pictures) according to what they are *about* (their subjects) in contrast to access by nonsubject characteristics such as author or size. Organizational structures such as classification schemes, indexes, and catalogs often use basic human abilities for memory and thought to support the presentation of information. Librarians and bibliographers use the term *bibliographic control* for the many activities involved in representing (for retrieval and use) the items held in a library or archive or listed in an index or database.

In consideration of memory, Miller's (1956) "The Magical Number Seven Plus or Minus Two: Some Limits on Our Capacity for Processing Information" presents a basic understanding from cognitive psychology: Humans can generally handle from five to nine items in short-term (or "working") memory. When we need to remember more items, we may "chunk" or group them to reduce the number. For example, people often remember a telephone number or an identification number in groups of numerals.

Cognitive science also provides insight into how humans *categorize* things: how we group like items into categories and how we distinguish unlike items. Categorization traces back to Plato and Aristotle, who held that objects could be grouped by the similarities of their properties. This approach is the basis for taxonomies such as Linneaus's hierarchical arrangement of plants and animals on the basis of physical characteristics (which has recently been both supplemented and challenged by DNA and embryology). Computer scientists have attempted to emulate this process with "conceptual clustering," having a computer group together like items and provide labels for the groups or categories. Another explanation for human categorization is Rosch's (1973) and

Lakoff's (1987) prototype theory. It holds that membership in a category can be graded, with some "better" members than others. Thus, for most people, the concept of "bird" is better exemplified by a robin than by a penguin; a robin is a better prototype.

From cognitive science we understand that people have apparently innate abilities to remember some limited number of items and that we distinguish among items, grouping like things together. However, the basis for distinctions and perceived similarities depends on culture. Lakoff's (1987) book is titled *Women, Fire, and Dangerous Things* because these items are grouped together in the Australian language Dyirbal. "We all spend large parts of our day doing classification work," according to Bowker and Star (2000, pp. 1–2), "and we make up and use a range of ad hoc classifications as we do." Their examples include distinguishing between dirty and clean dishes, separating important email from "e-junk" (spam), and coping with the "muddled folk classification" on one's desktop (p. 2). To classify is human; information professionals can use this tendency to improve access to information.

5.2. Natural Language and Controlled Vocabularies

Conversations, written documents, television programs, blogs—words surround us, with new ones being coined all the time. These words and their mutating definitions are *natural language*, words and signs people develop and use for everyday communication. English is but one example of the more than 400 languages in use today (Library of Congress, 2007). Natural languages often have many different ways to express a single idea or to express slightly different shades of meaning. For example, *the morning star* and *the evening star* both refer to the planet Venus, but the two phrases convey different meanings. *Venus* denotes the planet; the two phrases evoke poetic connotations.

Information professionals cope with the complexities and subtleties of natural language essentially by "straightjacketing" language: allowing the use of only some of the words that exist and specifying what these words mean when employed to provide access to information. The result is *controlled vocabulary*, a subset of natural language with less nuance and more precision. The Yellow Pages section of the telephone directory provides an example: Looking for "computer furniture," one finds the instruction to "see office furniture and equipment."

Authority Control

People's names and the titles of works (especially music) often appear in various forms: an author may use a nickname in one place and the full name in another, add a middle initial, or change his or her last name (e.g., when married or divorced); and sometimes two or more authors may have the same name. To reduce confusion and increase the chances of finding the item needed, information professionals are responsible for choosing unambiguous forms for names and titles that might be confused. For example, the author Mark Twain was named Samuel Langhorn Clemens by his parents; he also published under the name Quintus Curtius Snodgrass. The Library of Congress established the authorized form of his name as "Twain, Mark, 1835–1910" (the dates of birth and death provide additional clarification).

Information professionals develop and maintain *syndetic* (from the Greek words for *bind together*) *structures* to identify the preferred term and help the user find that term or to suggest additional descriptors. For names and titles of works, the approach is straightforward: The *see* reference leads the user from the nonstandard form (*Quintus Curtius Snodgrass*) to the preferred term (*Twain, Mark, 1835–1910*). The possible alternatives are more numerous in the case of subject terms, which are handled through thesauri and lists of subject headings.

Thesauri and Subject Headings

Information professionals have developed controlled vocabularies, presented in thesauri and subject heading lists, to provide consistent subject indexing across documents and among multiple indexers. A thesaurus is a controlled vocabulary for a specified subject area, such as the *Thesaurus of Psychological Index Terms* from the American Psychological Association. Terms in a thesaurus are called *descriptors*. A subject heading list includes terms, called *subject headings*, for all subject areas; an example is the *Library of Congress Subject Headings*.

Terms for a controlled vocabulary can be derived from various sources. Often the words used in the documents in the collection provide an initial list; this is called *literary warrant*. Another approach, *user warrant*, takes as its basis the language of the intended users of the information in the collection. For example, the research literature in psychology might use the word *adolescents*, whereas information seekers might say *teenagers*.

A controlled vocabulary should reduce the complexities of language; it seeks to control use of synonyms (different terms for the same thing, as with the *morning* and *evening star*), homographs (one term with multiple meanings, such as *bass* for a fish, a voice, or a musical instrument), antonyms (terms with opposite meanings, such as *income* and *expense*), and differences between generic and specific terms. The examples in Figure 5.1 are selected from the *Thesaurus of Psychological Index Terms* (2007).

To *index* a collection, the information professional selects the descriptors or subject headings from the controlled vocabulary that best represent (see Chapter 4) the content of each item. The number of descriptors or subject headings expected or required, the "depth of indexing," depends on the nature and intended use of the collection (as well as the resources of the organization paying for the work).

Information professionals oversee the addition and deletion of terms in the controlled vocabulary. Because the list does not absorb new terms from natural language without this support, indexers can often bring new terms or usages to the attention of those responsible for updating a controlled vocabulary. Monitoring terms used to search the collection also provides guidance for those who control the controlled vocabulary.

5.3. Classification

Classification involves using alphabetical, numeric, or alphanumeric systems to represent information and often to allow for sequential linear arrangement of physical documents. The codes used in classification systems typically have no inherent meaning, although sporadic attempts have been made to design codes that include mnemonics (easy to remember by

---

- synonyms: the USE and USED FOR references
  Shyness USE Timidity
  Timidity USED FOR Shyness

- homographs: add clarification with parenthetical terms or brief definition
  Seals (Animal)
  Ethics: For ethics in social or cultural situations, consider MORALITY.

- antonyms (opposites) and other non-specific relationships: list Related Terms listing potentially useful descriptors
  Physical Disorders
      RELATED TERMS
        Learning Disorders
        Malingering

- generic versus specific: list Broader and Narrower Terms
  Personality Traits
      BROADER TERMS
        Personality
      NARROWER TERMS
        Adaptability (Personality)
        Egotism
        Sociability

Figure 5.1. Examples from the *Thesaurus of Psychological Index Terms (2007)*

reminding us of something else—e.g., all books on Music in a class "M"). Classification schemes have always faced a conflict, however, because of their dual role of indicating the content of the documents as well as providing an ordinal (or ordering) system for their arrangement. Some problems for classification schemes are the following: documents that deal with more than one topic, or with the same topic in different times or geographic zones; documents of different media and different sizes (such as quartos and elephant folios); the growth of knowledge in unexpected directions and combinations; and increased specificity of topics, leading to longer codes. Classification schemes were originally designed to be as brief as possible so that the classification identifier could fit on the spine of a book and could be easily remembered.

Historical Roots of Classification

Aristotle is often mentioned as the first person to develop a classification system. His *scala naturae* (literally *natural ladder* but also called the *great chain of being*) presents a solidly hierarchical structure—with general groupings being subdivided to describe more specific ones and each item having only one location on the ladder, as in the following examples:

- Animals can be divided into wild or domesticated.

- Domesticated animals can be divided into useful (horses) or docile (sheep).

Aristotle divided knowledge into three classes: theoretical, productive, and prudential arts and sciences. Theoretical knowledge was divided into "first philosophy" (or metaphysics—unchanging and independent), mathematics (unchanging but dependent), and natural philosophy (changing but independent).

Efforts during the 16th century to develop a classification for all knowledge, both theoretical and practical, came to fruition in Francis Bacon's (1605) *Advancement of Learning*. Bacon divided knowledge into a *trivium*: history (the product of human memory), *poesie* (poetry, or a product of imagination), and "natural" philosophy (generated by reason, using experiential methods). For centuries Bacon's three-part classification provided the basis for a college education at English universities.

Improvements in travel and communication in the late 19th and early 20th centuries greatly increased the creation of and access to information. One consequence of this information explosion was the need for more elaborate methods of classification. Melvil Dewey started work on the Dewey Decimal Classification (DDC) in 1873 and published the first edition in 1876. Charles Ammi Cutter began work on the Cutter Expansive Classification in

1880; in 1897 it became the basis for Herbert Putnam's Library of Congress Classification (LCC).

The DDC is used in most school and public libraries in the U.S. and has been adapted for libraries throughout the world. The DDC divides all knowledge into 10 main classes, numbered zero through nine. Each class is divided into 10 divisions, and each of these into 10 sections; this produces 100 divisions and 1,000 sections, each identified by a three-digit number (000 to 999). Further subdivisions are made with decimal notations (Figure 5.2).

---

700 The arts; fine and decorative arts
    780 Music
        787 Stringed instruments
          787.87 Guitars
            787.8707 Guitars - study and teaching

Figure 5.2   The Dewey Decimal Classification's use of decimal numbers for subdivision

By using decimal numbers, topics can be subdivided as needed. Another advantage of this classification scheme is its ability to display hierarchical relationships among topics.

The LCC is used in most research libraries in the U.S., as well as other libraries around the world. Its 21 basic classes are identified by a single letter; each class contains more specific subclasses. For example, Class H Social Sciences has subclasses such as HA Statistics, HB Economic Theory and Demography, and HC Economic History and Conditions. Each of these is further divided using numerals; Figure 5.3 demonstrates this using the music example.

M - Music
    MT - Instruction and study
        MT 539-654 - Plucked instruments
          MT 588 - Guitar (self instruction)

Figure 5.3   The Library of Congress Classification's use of letters and numbers for subdivision

Both the DDC and the LCC are *enumerative classifications*: their structures attempt to provide classifications for all possible topics. This can introduce problems when knowledge grows beyond the limits of the classification structure. The DDC's handling of religion is a good example: the 200s numbers (200–299) are for religion; 200–209 are for religion in general, 210s for natural theology, and 220–289 for Christian religions. This leaves 290–299 for "other and comparative religions," which may have reflected U.S. library holdings in Dewey's day but causes problems (such as very long numbers) for modern library collections.

The Universal Decimal Classification (UDC) was adapted from the DDC. The original work by Belgians Paul Otlet and Henri La Fontaine began in 1895 and was published from 1904 to 1907. Since then, it has been revised and developed under the guidance of the International Federation for Documentation and more recently the UDC Consortium (www.udcc.org). In addition to the Dewey-like hierarchical classification, the UDC uses auxiliary signs to indicate various special aspects of a subject and relationships between subjects. This ability to create and link concepts gives the UDC a faceted element (see next section); for example, maps for mining can be represented as 622:912—the codes for "mining" and "maps" joined by a colon. It is used worldwide, often in special libraries.

Faceted Classification

Enumerative classifications encounter three major types of problems:

1. Enumerative classifications do not easily accommodate nonhierarchical relationships. In the LCC, for example, puzzles are considered a subdivision of "Parties. Party games and stunts" rather than a related or associated aspect of such games.

2. Enumerative classifications require repetition of subdivisions. For example, the DDC uses the same section numerals for literature in various languages, as Figure 5.4 demonstrates. The repetition has mnemonic value (it becomes easier to remember because the pattern recurs), but the numbers for poetry, drama, fiction, essays, speeches, and so on must be repeated for each division, which increases the size of the classification scheme.

3. Enumerative classifications try to encompass all knowledge, which makes difficult the insertion of new ideas or the novel combination of existing ideas. Dewey's limited space for religions other than Christianity is one example. Interdisciplinary research often draws on and combines work from various fields: Dilevko and Dali (2004) found that research on tourism cites sources classified in more than 50 LCC subclasses, from Anthropogeography to Industrial Management.

Faceted classification aims to overcome these problems. Initial analysis identifies aspects or *facets* of a topic, and indexers describe each document in relation to the facets. The information seeker then combines the information needed in each facet in order to construct a description of the documents to

Poetry	Drama
811 American poetry in English	812 American drama
821 English poetry	822 English drama
831 German poetry	832 German drama
841 French poetry	842 French drama

Figure 5.4   Repetition in Dewey Decimal Classification subdivisions

be retrieved. S. R. Ranganathan (1967) developed the initial ideas of faceted classification; he argued that all subjects can be divided into five categories—Personality, Matter, Energy, Space, and Time. The U.K. Classification Research Group extended Ranganathan's system to 13 categories for the analysis and organization of terms: thing, kind, part, property, material, process, operation, patient, product, byproduct, agent, space, and time. The Bliss Bibliographic Classification is a faceted classification system that uses the Classification Research Group's theories. A document is classified by determining which categories are represented, identifying the notation for each of these categories, and assembling the notations to build a *classmark.* The examples in Figure 5.5 are from the Bliss Classification Association website (www.blissclassification.org.uk/bcclass.shtml). The combined classmark, QLV EXP L, is read in this way: The classifier has chosen "social welfare - old people" as the primary concept, so QLV appears first. The "Q" is dropped from the second concept, "library provision," so it appears as EPX. The third concept, "residential care," drops the "QE."

Faceted classification has found a new surge of interest among information architects, who view facets as a good way to provide access to complex information. Early information architects Rosenfeld and Morville (2008) noted that faceted classification provides an "enduring foundation" (p. 224)

An item on residential care for the elderly is placed first in the "Patient" category and then in a "Operation" sub-category. In the Social Welfare class (Q) is the classmark. Representing this compound class is QL V EL:

    Q Social welfare
    QEL Residential care
    QL V Old people

Adding more detail is straightforward. For example, library provision for the elderly in residential care combines:

    Q Social welfare
    QEL Residential care
    QEP X Library provision
    QL V Old people

The classmark QL V EPX L represents the subject exactly.

Figure 5.5   Building a Bliss Classification classmark

on which interface designers using the inherent power and flexibility of faceting can design and test alternative interfaces. For example, the FLA-MENCO (FLexible information Access using MEtadata in Novel Combinations) search interface supports searching in a database of fine arts images with facets such as media, location, objects, and shapes and colors.

5.4. Metadata

Metadata is classically defined as "data about data" or "information about information" (although *metadata* might be construed as plural, it is used as a singular collective noun). Metadata can be described somewhat less succinctly as structured data that describes an information resource. Metadata can be used for resource description and discovery, the management of information resources, and their long-term preservation (Day, 2001). The term originated in the context of electronic documents and has become increasingly more important with the advent of the World Wide Web and the explosion of digital information. Metadata makes digital information more easily describable and findable.

Different types of metadata can be distinguished, although the differences may be blurry in practice. The following types are common:

- Descriptive metadata is the broadest and most common. It describes a resource, or a collection of resources, and the content of the resource(s). It allows us to understand, retrieve, and access these resources with some level of precision.

- Administrative metadata is intended to aid the proper use of a resource. For example, unique identifiers specify the item being described, and record tracking keeps information on who changed what, and when.

- Legal metadata specifies legal rights and obligations (such as copyright) pertaining to the resource.

- Technological metadata specifies aspects such as file format.

- Structural metadata contains information about the structure of a resource. Resources can be complex, in that they themselves consist of several resources (for instance, a trilogy). Structural metadata specifies the constituents of such a resource.

- Preservation metadata aids the long-term accessibility of a resource. It records the preservation actions that have been applied to a resource over time. It also records information about a resource so that it can be precisely identified, and about the requirements that must be met in order to use a resource. Preservation metadata stores technical details about a resource's file format, structure, and use, the history of all actions performed on a resource, provenance history, and rights information relevant to preservation activities.

For example, consider a DVD set containing Season One of the television series *The X Files*. Metadata about the entire set might include "box set of three DVDs" (structural), "released January 31, 2006," or "Run time: 1124 minutes" (descriptive). To describe the first DVD in the set, we could say it was recorded in NTSC format with an aspect ratio of 1.33:1 (technological). Metadata about the content of the box set could include "starring David Duchovny and Gillian Anderson," "a science fiction show about investigating paranormal events" (descriptive), as well as "Copyright 20th Century Fox" (legal).

Form and Syntax

Metadata does not have one particular syntax or physical form. Depending on the application, it can be stored as XML (eXtensible Markup Language), RDF (Resource Description Framework), a MARC (MAchine Readable Cataloging) record, in a relational database, or in some other form.

The relation between metadata and the resource it describes can also vary, depending on the application. Metadata can be

- Part of the resource. A HyperText Markup Language (HTML) document can contain metadata about its title and keywords within the <title> ... </title> block.

- Linked to the resource. On the *Semantic Web* (an enhancement of the World Wide Web to include the meanings [semantics] of data), a metadata record may directly link to the resource it describes.

- Separate from the resource. The records in a library catalog are not directly linked to the items they are about.

Metadata Schemas

Different kinds of information objects require different kinds of metadata: A scientific article has little in common with a video game. Numerous metadata schemas have been developed, each providing specifications that are geared to specific applications and that describe what kinds of metadata can or should be provided. A metadata schema should define the following:

- What fields or elements are available: The Dublin Core metadata schema, for instance, defines such elements as title, creator, and format.

- What the precise meaning and intended use of these fields are: The broad meaning of a field can often be guessed from its name, but what the Dublin Core element *type* should include, for example, is not immediately obvious from its name.

- Which fields are optional and which are required: A Dublin Core user community creates an application profile and specifies which elements are required.

Usage

On the internet, specific metadata schemas are commonly defined in XML-related formats such as Document Type Definition (DTD) or XML Schema. One of the most popular and simplest schemas is Dublin Core, which defines 15 elements for describing an online resource. Dublin Core metadata is included in a webpage's XML or HTML markup.

Library metadata is used for accessing, recording, and archiving items in the collection. By viewing the record, typically stored in MARC format, we can learn about the item's title, author(s), physical size, call number, subject (through LC Subject Headings), and so on. Digital libraries also use administrative, technical, and legal metadata (which could include management information such as file format or copyright) and structural metadata—which ties together disparate items into a collection.

Museums and archives use the Encoded Archival Description (EAD) metadata schema to encode archival finding aids using an XML DTD. EAD's standardization makes it possible for users to search several archival collections at the same time.

Digital archives use preservation metadata to support the long-term preservation of digital objects. The PREMIS (PREservation Metadata: Implementation Strategies) Data Dictionary for Preservation Metadata defines the information needed to preserve digital objects for long periods of time. The Metadata Encoding and Transmission Standard packages preservation metadata into a standard XML container and supports the exchange of digital objects among institutions.

Metadata has a multitude of uses in information technology and business. For example, business intelligence applications allow businesses to examine the various dimensions of information about their sales trends and market competition in order to improve performance. This metadata can be stored and manipulated in spreadsheets, relational databases, or online analytical processing databases.

Metadata schemas exist for describing specific types of files. Adobe's Extensible Metadata Platform is one example of a structured metadata schema for describing digital images. This metadata can be embedded into image file formats such as TIFF, EXIF, and RAW.

Geospatial metadata is used to describe geographic objects. The U.S. Federal Geographic Data Committee has created the Content Standard for Digital Geospatial Metadata, which defines the facets to be used when describing geographic information. The standard is commonly used in geographic information systems applications.

Current and Future Use of Metadata

Functional Requirements for Bibliographic Records

For centuries, librarians have developed and revised the rules for describing (cataloging) books and other library holdings. In 1997, the International Federation of Library Associations and Institutions (IFLA; 1997) presented new requirements for such catalog records. IFLA's analysis for the Functional Requirements for Bibliographic Records (FRBR) used an entity-relationship approach, the same approach used for relational database systems (see Chapter 7). FRBR identifies three types of entities:

1. Group 1: Products of intellectual or artistic endeavor: work, expression, manifestation, and item

2. Group 2: Those responsible for the intellectual or artistic content, the physical production and dissemination, or the custodianship of the products in Group 1: person and corporate body

3. Group 3: The subjects of intellectual or artistic endeavor: concepts, objects, events, places

FRBR also describes the relationships among these entities:

- A *work* (a distinct intellectual or artistic creation) is realized through an *expression*. A *manifestation* (the physical embodiment of an *expression* of a *work*) and an *item* (a single exemplar of a *manifestation*) relate to the work's physical form.

- The persons (individuals) and corporate bodies (organizations or groups of people) in Group 2 relate to items in Group 1 as creators, producers, or owners.

- A work may have as its subject a *concept* (an abstract notion or idea), an *object* (a material thing), an *event* (an action or occurrence), or a *place* (a location).

According to FRBR, people use bibliographic records to find, identify, select, and obtain information resources, as well as to navigate the bibliographic systems. Tillett (2004) noted that "FRBR promises to have a profound influence on future systems design. Vendors and bibliographic utilities ...

have already embraced the FRBR conceptual model in designing their future systems" (p. 7).

Tagging

The examples described here are all structured metadata, which means they have a set of rules and guidelines that must be followed. With the advent of Web 2.0, however, internet users can "tag" information objects in an unstructured manner, with no restrictions on the format of their descriptions. Individual tags collectively comprise a *folksonomy*, a user-created taxonomy of descriptive terms. Examples of popular websites using tags and folksonomies include Flickr for photograph sharing, Delicious for social bookmarking, and the online retailer Amazon.com.

Here are some sources for further information:

- Dublin Core Metadata Initiative (dublincore.org)

- EAD: Encoded Archival Description Version 2002 Official Site (www.loc.gov/ead)

- W3C Semantic Web Activity (www.w3.org/2001/sw)

- XML Tutorial (www.w3schools.com/xml/default.asp)

5.5. Information Architecture

Information architecture (IA) is a multidisciplinary area of practice and research that encompasses many aspects of web design. It is especially focused on the organizational structure and information representation that allow people to easily find the information they need online. IA professionals seek to develop web applications that are useful and relevant in the user's context and directed toward users' individual or organizational needs. Rosenfeld and Morville (2008, p. 4) identify four aspects of IA:

1. The structural design of shared information environments

2. The combination of organization, labeling, search, and navigation systems within websites in intranets

3. The art and science of shaping information products and experiences to support usability and findability

4. An emerging discipline and community of practice focused on bringing principles of design and architecture to the digital landscape

IA incorporates knowledge from many fields, such as graphic design, cognitive psychology, computer science, and business; much of the academic theory underlying IA has roots in information science, especially in the area of information-seeking behavior and information needs. For example, Bates's (1989) berrypicking model describes how users iteratively refine their information needs as they query an information retrieval system; this model is highly influential in IA principles. Belkin's (1980) model demonstrates that anomalous states of knowledge make it difficult for users to explain their information needs; information architects hold that a system should provide representation of the user's problem rather than requiring the user to define the problem or question in the system's terms. IA practice encompasses many skills.

Information architects typically focus on one or two areas of specialization, such as

- Navigation: What should users click on or type in, in order to get to where they want to be on the website? Where are users "located" on the site and how do they know where they are located?

- Organization: What are the hierarchies and relationships in which information is placed on the site?

- Findability: How easy is it for users to locate what they need on the site?

- Search: If it is desirable to incorporate a search engine on the site, then what should be searched, how should it be searched, and how should results be displayed? According to common information science theories, people will use a search mechanism when they have a definite idea of what they need to find.

- Browsability: Can users find what they need easily by clicking on various links within the site? According to common information science theories, people tend to browse when they are not completely sure about what they need to find.

- Representation: What metadata is used for description of and access to documents on the site? Methods of representation could include controlled vocabularies, thesauri, ontologies, taxonomies, and folksonomies.

- Database design: Is the database that stores the information on the website developed in a manner that allows users to access it with an easy-to-use method?

It is essential to include user research in IA design work, rather than guessing what users might want or need. Including user research is called *user-centered design* or *participatory design*. Several research methods exist to gather data from potential site users, such as interviews, surveys, requests for feedback on website prototypes, or usability tests (see Chapter 9). IA developers are concerned primarily with whether users like and can successfully use the classifications, labels, and other descriptions that have been attributed to the site's content.

5.6. Archival Theory

Eastwood (1994, pp. 127–128) makes an articulate case for the nature and importance of archival theory:

> The first characteristic of archives—their impartiality—establishes the archival perspective on the relationship between facts and interpretation. ... Because archival documents are created as a means to express action and as a product of that action, ... we may put our faith in [an archive's] faithfulness to the facts and acts of it.
>
> The second characteristic of archives ... authenticity is contingent on the facts of creation, maintenance, and custody. Archives are authentic only when they are created with the need to act through them in mind and when they are preserved and maintained as faithful witness of fact and act by the creator and its legitimate successors.
>
> The third and fourth characteristics, naturalness and interrelatedness, both concern the manner in which the documents in an archives accumulate in the course of the transaction of affairs according to the needs of the matters at hand. They are natural, in the sense that they are not collected for some purpose outside the administrative needs generating them, and not put together according to some scheme to serve other than those needs, as are the objects in a museum or the documents in a library collection. The documents in any given archives then have their relationships established by the course of the conduct of affairs and according to its needs. ... archival theory dwells on the vital link between functional activity and document, and on the structure of administrative documentation.
>
> The final characteristic is uniqueness. Each document has a unique place in the structure of an archives. ... Being there signifies its relationship to activity and to the other documents accumulated in the course of that activity.

References

Bates, M. (1989). *The design of browsing and berrypicking techniques for the online search interface.* Retrieved November 11, 2010, from www.gseis.ucla.edu/faculty/bates/berry picking.html.

Belkin, N. J. (1980). Anomalous states of knowledge as a basis for information retrieval. *Canadian Journal of Information Science, 5,* 133–143.

Bowker, G. C. & Star, S. L. (2000). *Sorting things out: Classification and its consequences.* Cambridge, MA: MIT Press.

Day, M. (2001). Metadata in a nutshell. *Information Europe, 6(2),* 11. Retrieved November 11, 2011, from www.ukoln.ac.uk/metadata/publications/nutshell.

Dilevko, J., & Dali, K. (2004). Improving collection development and reference services for interdisciplinary fields through analysis of citation patterns: An example using tourism studies. *College & Research Libraries, 65(3),* 216–241.

Eastwood, T. (1994). What is archival theory and why is it important? *Archivaria, 37,* 122–130.

International Federation of Library Associations and Institutions. (1997). *Functional requirements for bibliographic records.* Retrieved November 11, 2010, from www.ifla.org/files/cataloguing/frbr/frbr_2008.pdf.

Lakoff, G. (1987). *Women, fire, and dangerous things: What categories reveal about the mind.* Chicago: University of Chicago Press.

Library of Congress. (2007). *MARC code list for languages: Introduction.* Washington, DC: Library of Congress Network Development and MARC Standards Office. Retrieved November 11, 2010, from www.loc.gov/marc/languages/introduction.pdf.

Miller, G. A. (1956). The magical number seven plus or minus two: Some limits on our capacity for processing information. *Psychological Review, 63(2),* 81–97.

Ranganathan, S. R. (1967). *Prolegomena to library classification.* New York: Asia Publishing House.

Rosch, E. H. (1973). Natural categories. *Cognitive Psychology, 4(3),* 328–350.

Rosenfeld, L., & Morville, P. (2008). *Information architecture for the World Wide Web* (3rd ed.). Sebastopol, CA: O'Reilly.

Thesaurus of psychological index terms (2007). (11th ed.; L. G. Tuleya, ed.) Washington, DC : American Psychological Association.

Tillett, B. (2004). *What is FRBR: A conceptual model for the bibliographic universe.* Washington, DC: Library of Congress. Retrieved November 11, 2010, from www.loc.gov/cds/downloads/FRBR.PDF.

CHAPTER 6

Computers and Networks

6.1. Hardware and Software Basics

A computer is a machine that receives, stores, and manipulates data and can be programmed to provide output in a useful format. Historically, a computer was a device for calculations, either a manual device such as an abacus or a mechanistic device such as mechanical calculator. In the mid-20th century, computer design began to separate the automated calculation functions from the programming. Digital computers perform calculations and manipulate data using binary representation of data (in 1s and 0s), which can be communicated electronically.

Today's digital computers, whether the mainframe that supports data mining at an insurance company or the personal device that lets you keep up with the news, include a physical component—the *hardware*—and instructions, or *software*. Any computer's capabilities depend on the nature and capacity of these elements.

Analog and Digital Communication

Computer communication systems transfer data between two points. These systems work in one of two distinct ways: analog and digital. Analog systems use an infinitely variable representation of the data, and digital systems translate the data into numbers—usually binary numbers (Walters, 2001).

Analog communication implies continuity because the signals are continuous waves that change in proportion to the data represented. Telephones began as analog communication systems, conveying data through sound waves. Analog systems tend to be slow, bulky, and inefficient for data transmission. As a signal travels, it breaks down and grows weaker. Noise in the network decreases the network's ability to regenerate and amplify the signal as it moves from the source to the receiver (recall the Shannon-Weaver model of communication from Chapter 2, developed while Shannon worked for the telephone company).

Digital communication transmits voice and data encoded as 1s and 0s. Digital transmission is fast and efficient, and a digital signal is relatively simple to clean and amplify because each piece of the data is either a 1 or a 0. As we are bombarded by data from all directions at increasing speeds, it is natural to move toward digital transmission as a standard for communication systems.

Hardware Basics

Hardware is the foundation to computing. Its four primary functions are

1. Processing: executing mathematical and logical instructions in order to transform data inputs into data outputs.

2. Storage: retaining program instructions and data for temporary, short-term, or long-term use.

3. Internal communication: moving data and instructions among internal and peripheral hardware components of the computer system.

4. External communication: interacting with people or things outside the system, including (human) systems administrators, users, and other computer systems.

The computer's components work together to accomplish these functions.

Processing

The *motherboard* is a printed circuit board with chips, connectors, and a power supply on it. Key components of a computer system come together, exchange data, and process information; the motherboard functions as the hub of all data exchange in a computer system.

The *central processing unit* (CPU), also called the *chip*, is described as the brain of a computer. The CPU performs mathematical and logical operations and also manages and moves information (instructions and data) as directed by the user or software. CPU speeds are measured by the number of completed instruction cycles per second; speeds can range from 600 megahertz (MHz; million cycles per second) to more than 4 gigahertz (GHz; billion cycles per second).

The *basic input/output system* (BIOS) chip contains the boot *firmware*, which controls the computer until the operating system loads. Firmware is software written on a read-only chip; the BIOS is powered by a small battery, so it functions even when the computer is without external electric power. The BIOS also contains information about the devices attached to the system, including the drives, external buses, video card, sound card, keyboard, mouse, and printer. The BIOS stores system configuration information as well as the date and time on the CMOS (Complementary Metal Oxide Semiconductor), a nonvolatile memory chip.

Storage: Retaining Program Instructions and Data

Random access memory (RAM) refers to a class of silicon chips that provide storage space for a computer to read and write data. This data is accessed by the CPU. DRAM (Dynamic Random Access Memory) is the most common type of memory chip. RAM and DRAM are volatile, allowing data to be stored only while the computer is running. Modern computers use various types of RAM: Single data rate (SDR) RAM was used in most computers prior to 2002. Most computers now use double data rate (DDR) RAM. New advances in technology have produced DDR2 and DDR3 RAM, which allow for faster transfer rates.

Computer memory chips provide *read-only memory* (ROM), storage that cannot be overwritten and is used for information that should not change. ROM is often used to store system boot-up information. Today, many systems use flash memory, which is faster than ROM and can be rewritten.

Hard disks, also called *hard drives*, consist of one or more magnetic plates sealed in a box as a data storage device in a computer. This box prevents air from entering and protects the plates from dust and other debris. A hard disk contains a read-write mechanism that retrieves and records data on the plates.

Removable data storage devices include floppy disks, compact discs (CDs)—including CD-ROM (read-only memory) and CD-RW (rewritable)—and tape units, DVD-ROM discs, and flash drives. Removable storage can be used to play music and video, back up data from other devices, store files and photos, and archive large data sets.

Internal Communication: Moving Data and Instructions Among Computer Components

A *bus* is a set of parallel communication lines that transmit data between two or more devices. A computer system contains multiple bus lines, including a *system* or *memory bus*, which connects the CPU with the main memory and peripheral devices; an *address bus*, which transmits bits of a memory address and the information about which device is communicating; a *data bus*, which carries the actual data being processed; and a *control bus*, which carries commands, responses, and status signals to and from devices and the CPU.

Device controllers monitor bus signals to peripheral devices, translate signals into commands, and allow multiple peripheral devices to share a bus port. Basically, device controllers direct and control the physical actions of storage and peripheral devices.

A *buffer* is a portion of the computer's memory set aside to hold data being transferred from one device to another. It reduces the time the CPU waits for data stored on much slower external devices; however, data stored in the buffer must be "saved" to more permanent storage before the computer is turned off.

Cache is a portion of RAM set aside to hold data that can be accessed quickly, increasing system performance. This data is also usually held in another storage device; however, the use of cache improves the speed of read-write operations. The computer's CPU uses the cache to reduce the average time to access memory. The cache is a smaller, faster memory that stores copies of the data from the most recent processes.

External Communication: Interacting With the World Outside the Computer

The computer's basic functions can be extended by many *input/output (I/O) devices*. These are often called *peripherals* because they are outside the primarily internal functions performed by the components on the motherboard. Some of these devices are essential for human interaction with the computer. Important peripheral devices include the following (Barrett & King, 2005):

- The *video display monitor* is a display screen that presents human-readable output from a computer.

- The computer *keyboard* is the primary text input device; it uses essentially the same configuration as a typewriter, with additional function keys.

- The *mouse* is an input device that permits users to point at selections on the screen. As the user moves the mouse across a flat surface, the system reads its location and provides a cursor, corresponding to the mouse's position. Touchpads and joysticks perform the same pointing and selection functions.

- Audio devices work with a *sound card* or a *multimedia controller* plugged into or embedded in the motherboard. This card converts digital signals to analog form and plays them through speakers, a headset, or a musical instrument digital interface synthesizer plugged into the computer.

- Optical devices include *digital cameras*, *optical scanners*, and *bar code scanners*. Optical input devices convert special-purpose symbols or images to binary data.

- The *printer* is an output device that accepts text and graphic data from a computer and reproduces it as ink on paper, labels, envelopes, or other media.

Software Basics

The instructions or programs for a computer are its software. These instructions control what the hardware does and when (in what sequence); the speed depends on the computer's internal clock, which is a hardware component and may be limited by its memory or storage capacity. It is customary to divide software into three types: system software, programming software, and application software.

System Software

System software includes two elements:

- The *operating system* (OS) is the link between the hardware and the software; the basic element of the OS is the *kernel*, which coordinates demands for CPU, memory, and I/O devices. Unix, Apple OS, and Windows are examples of OSs.

- *Device drivers* are also part of the system software; they provide instructions for how the computer communicates with a specific peripheral device such as a printer or mouse.

Programming Software

Programming software supports people writing computer programs. It comprises three types:

- *Compilers* translate from *source code*, written in human-like languages such as C++ or Pascal, to the machine-executable version of the instructions, called *object code*. Compiled instructions generally execute much faster than those from interpreted programs.

- *Interpreters* translate and execute source code essentially step-by-step; interpreted languages are considered useful for instruction or infrequent use. Perl, Python, and Java are examples.

- *Text editors*—such as Apple's TextEdit, vi and Emacs in Unix, and Windows's Notepad—are considered utilities that run in concert with the OS. They assist programmers by supporting the creation and editing of plain-text files.

Application Software

Application software allows people to use computer hardware for sophisticated applications without having to learn or write the very specialized instructions that would be required at the OS or programming levels. Word processing, database management, graphics, and web browsing are examples.

6.2. Networking Principles

Early computers were stand-alone devices but by the early 1960s were often connected in networks, either local area networks (LANs) or wide area networks (WANs). A LAN typically connects computers within an institute or small group, either by hardwiring (a physical connection of the machines) or through special networking software such as Microsoft workgroup networking. LANs are secured and controlled by the network software. A WAN covers a broader area and generally links the members through using transmission control protocol/internet protocol (TCP/IP). The internet and World Wide Web are examples of WANs.

Computer networks divide data into standard-sized *packets*, each of which is sent over the most efficient path through the network; the packets are reassembled to re-create the original file at the destination. In terms of connections, a network may be wired or wireless. Wired networks are commonly used when a building's cable system makes it easy to connect computers and servers. Wireless networks are popular in situations where physical connections are more difficult to make or where mobility is important.

The word internet was coined in 1962; a year later researchers at the U.S. Department of Defense Advanced Research Projects Agency (ARPA) began looking at ways to connect the various computer systems the agency was funding, and the ARPANET, a precursor of the internet, was formed (Computer History Museum, 2006).

Network Components

A computer network is composed of hardware and software that enable multiple users and computer systems to share data, software, and hardware resources. These resources can include printers, databases, multimedia, files, and webpages. Computer networks support communication such as email, instant messaging, collaborative applications, and newsgroups. Figure 6.1 shows the setup for a library LAN (Berkowitz, 2007).

The components of a network are

- A *bridge*, which connects network segments that use the same protocol. Bridges help maintain optimal network traffic by monitoring activity on each side, reading the destination information of a data packet, and determining the appropriate network destination. A bridge can also segment a large network into smaller, more efficient networks.

- A *hub*, a multi-port hardware device that provides network connection points for multiple computer systems or peripherals.

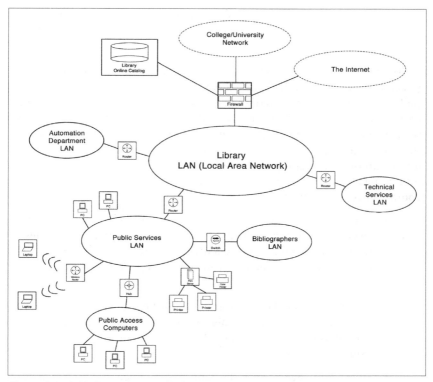

Figure 6.1 LAN for an academic library

An *active hub* repeats and rebroadcasts data packets on a network; a *passive hub* splits the signals sent through it.

- A *switch*, which combines the functions of a bridge and a hub (and is therefore more expensive than a hub). Switches connect computers on a LAN, examine the destination address information of each packet, and send the packet to the specified port on the switch rather than to all ports (unlike a hub). This provides an efficient use of LAN bandwidth and additional network security (DUX Computer Digest, 2010).

- A *router*, which examines data packet destination addresses and forwards the packet to the appropriate network segment. Routers can connect different physical networks.

- A *segment*, or a section of cable connecting nodes in a network.

- A *node*, which is an end point in a network, such as a workstation, printer, file server, switch, or hub between networks using different protocols.

Network *architecture* describes how the nodes are related. In a *client-server network*, one node is the server, providing resources to the other nodes; *peer-to-peer networks* have no server, but nodes share resources from each other. The *topology* describes the physical interconnections of the network elements (nodes and links). Common topologies include *bus, line, ring, tree, mesh,* and *star*. A network *protocol* specifies how information is transferred among the components of the network. The Open Systems Interconnection (OSI) reference model defines seven layers at which network components can connect:

- The application layer (Layer 7) interacts with the human user; this layer identifies the partner(s) in the communication, establishes resource availability, and synchronizes communication. Examples include hypertext transfer protocol (HTTP) and file transfer protocol.

- The presentation layer (Layer 6) establishes context between application layer entities; this layer is also responsible for encryption. Examples include Multipurpose Internet Mail Extensions (MIME).

- The session layer (Layer 5) establishes, manages, and terminates connections between local and remote computers. Network BIOS (NetBIOS) is an example.

- The transport layer (Layer 4) makes sure that data is delivered without errors and in the proper sequence. TCP is an example.

- The network layer (Layer 3) supports functional and procedural requirements for transferring variable-length data; it maintains quality of service for the transport layer. IP is an example. The familiar TCP/IP is thus a combination of functions at the transport and network layers.

- The data link layer (Layer 2) handles the procedural and functional means for data transfer between network components; it may detect and sometimes correct errors that occur at the physical layer. Address resolution protocol is an example.

- The physical layer (Layer 1) covers physical and electrical details of how two devices connect. For example, what cables and plugs will each device need? Ethernet and Recommended Standard 232 are examples of physical layer protocols.

The OSI reference model is an abstraction that helps account for the various kinds of communication needed to make a computer network function. Different protocols work at one or more layers of the model. Each network component functions on all seven layers, with each layer relying on those below it and communicating with its "opposite number" from the component with which it is interacting. In this way a personal computer can use the HTTP (application layer) protocol to communicate with a search engine's computer even if each uses entirely different protocols for the lower six layers.

Networking Standards

Many highly detailed standards are required for the components of computer networks to communicate effectively. The examples listed with the OSI reference model provide only a small sense of the nature of the standards needed. The Computer and Communication website (www.cmpcmm.com/cc/standards.html) provides an impressive list of networking-related standards.

To be effective, standards should be as easy as possible to implement and should apply in as many cases as possible. Various organizations exist to develop, maintain, modify, and in some cases enforce networking standards. Some are international (such as the International Organization for Standardization, which maintains the OSI reference model), and others focus on specific countries or regions. Underwriters Laboratories, for example, develops standards for electrical and electronic equipment in North America. Other important organizations that are involved in standards for networking:

- The American National Standards Institute (www.ansi.org) is a U.S.-based nonprofit organization that develops and promulgates standards for all aspects of business.

- The International Electrotechnical Commission (www.iec.ch) is a Swiss-based, global organization that creates and publishes international standards for electronic, electrical, and related technologies. It also addresses related terminology and symbols, compatibility issues, and environmental safety.

- The International Telecommunication Union-Telecommunication Standardization Sector (www.itu.int/ITU-T), formerly the Comité Consultatif Internationale de Téléphonique et Télégraphique, is the United Nations agency for information and communication technology issues. It coordinates global use of the radio spectrum, promotes cooperation in assigning satellite orbits, and works to improve telecommunication infrastructure in the developing world.

- The Internet Society (www.isoc.org) is a nonprofit organization composed of individual and organizational members interested in internet-related standards, education, and policy. Its subgroups are the Internet Corporation for Assigned Names and Numbers, which oversees names and addresses for the internet, including IP address space allocation, and the Internet Engineering Task Force, which is responsible for proposing, developing, and maintaining internet standards documents.

- The Institute of Electrical and Electronics Engineers (www.ieee.org) is a nonprofit, technical professional association, with members from more than 150 countries. Although based in the U.S., the association acts as a technical authority on computer engineering and telecommunications topics; it produces and maintains a large body of networking-related specifications and standards.

- The National Information Standards Organization (www.niso.org) is a nonprofit association accredited by the American National Standards Institute. It develops and maintains technical standards that apply traditional and new technologies to information-related needs, including retrieval, repurposing, storage, metadata, and preservation.

- The World Wide Web Consortium (www.w3c.org) emerged with the development of the World Wide Web at CERN (Centre Européen pour la Recherche Nucleaire) in Switzerland. Its early work formed the basis for the web hypertext markup language and the protocol and service environment known as HTTP. The group is also responsible for the cascading style sheets and extensible markup language standards.

Information professionals should be aware of both current and proposed standards in their areas of responsibility. The development and maintenance of standards affects the field generally, and many information professionals have opportunities to serve on standards-making committees and to comment on proposed standards. Standards are evolving documents and continue to be revised as technologies and other conditions warrant.

The Internet

The internet is a network of computer networks. It connects computers around the world using a standard, the Internet Protocol Suite (TCP/IP, working at OSI reference model layers 4, transport, and 3, network). The World

Wide Web, a collection of interlinked hypertext documents, is the best-known internet application. Although people often use *the web* and *the internet* to mean the same thing, the web is but one internet application. The internet also transmits email and streaming video, allows remote access to computers, supports distributed collaboration and file sharing, and delivers voice over internet protocol communications.

The IP address underlies the network. The IP address is a unique, numerical identifier and address for each computer in the network. Version 4 of the Internet Protocol (IPv4) uses a 32-bit address, which allows more than four billion unique addresses—a large number, but rapidly approaching exhaustion. Internet Protocol version 6 (IPv6), which uses 128 bits for the address, increases the number of possible addresses enormously; it is gradually replacing IPv4 addresses. For example, an IPv4 address might be *208.77.188.166*; the same address in IPv6 would be: *2001:db8:0:1234:0:567:1:1*.

Static IP addresses are assigned to a specific computer by a systems administrator. *Dynamic* IP addresses allow multiple devices to share a limited number of addresses.

Computers may connect to the internet using landline broadband (over coaxial cable, fiber optic cable, or copper wires), dial-up telephone lines, Wi-Fi (wireless), satellite, and 3G-technology cell phones. Internet cafes, libraries, and other public places provide internet access points called *hotspots*, where free internet access is available. Hotspots are being extended to larger areas and entire cities.

Cloud Computing

Second-generation computers (1956–1963; the first to use solid-state technology) provided the stereotype of the mainframe computer: a large, central machine to which programmers submitted their stacks of punched cards with program instructions. The third generation (1964–1971; with integrated circuits) concentrated even more processing power and speed in the central computer. Telecommunication networks of the day allowed remote users to interact with the mainframe; they used "dumb terminals" (for data entry and display, but with no processing capacity). The fourth generation (beginning in 1971; using microprocessors) has supported gradual migration of computer processing power from the central mainframe to smaller computers: minicomputers, personal (micro-) computers, and now a variety of handheld devices. This dispersion of computing power is sometimes called *distributed computing*; today's embedded microprocessors make possible *ubiquitous computing* (or *ubicomp*, also called *pervasive computing*), in which computing power is present in everyday objects (for example, a cell phone's "awareness" of its geographic location).

Early versions of cloud computing began around 2001; the concept gained traction with Amazon, Google, and IBM involvement beginning in 2005. Google's proposed Chrome OS is intended to support cloud computing, allowing any personal or hand-held computer to go through the web to use software and store data on Google's computers. Cloud computing almost looks like a return to the centralized, mainframe model; users access applications and storage as needed over the internet (which is often depicted as a cloud in network diagrams; Cleveland, 2010).

Cloud computing companies provide and manage data storage and software applications such as word processing, web-based email, database management, and inventory control. The user pays for the amount of service used, avoiding the expenses of purchasing and maintaining the hardware and software and having access from anywhere the internet is available. Critics complain that the user's applications and data are "hostage" to the organization hosting the cloud and that lack of choice about applications software limits the creativity of people who would design new applications (Zittrain, 2009). However, many individuals and organizations appreciate the convenience of ubiquitous access and the ability to treat computing power as a utility rather than a capital investment.

6.3. Computer Security

Security measures are essential to maintain the computer system's functionality and the data it houses. Physical and technical security are important, but users' awareness and mindful use of computing networks is essential.

Challenges to Computer Security

Computer hackers continue to develop new ways to attack and infiltrate computer systems:

- *Back doors* are easy ways for programmers to gain access to test and debug (correct mistakes in) computer programs. Back doors may remain after a program becomes operational, or a virus (software code intended to damage a computer or the information it stores) may create its own back door to allow a remote computer access to gather information such as passwords or account numbers.

- *Password cracking* (or guessing) is another common threat. In *brute force password cracking*, the hacker may try each word in a dictionary as a password. More sophisticated hackers use online password files, birth dates, or names of family members or pets to attempt to gain access.

- *Session hijacking* occurs when a client has authenticated its connection with a server and a hijacker then generates a signal to the client implying that it has been disconnected. The hijacker can take the place of the original client and make full use of the server. Session hijacking can occur in insecure web sessions if timeouts are not set correctly.

- *Buffer overflow attacks* send so much data to the computer's memory buffer that it overflows and crashes the system. The computer becomes unstable, and the intruder (or malicious code) can take control.

- *Spoofing* (or *phishing*) involves modifying a message's source address to make it appear to come from a different address. This can be used, for example, to trick an email recipient into sending identification or passwords to an untrustworthy correspondent. *Website spoofing* or *website phishing* involves creating a fraudulent website that looks legitimate, such as with misspelled URLs or use of subdomains. Users of the site reveal their passcodes, which the phishers can use to gain access to the legitimate site.

Security Basics

The first line of defense against these challenges is a user base that is educated and aware of security issues. Precautions need not be onerous. Users should lock or log off a computer when it is not in use. Passwords and passcodes are also important security devices; they should not be shared (except, as the saying goes, "with someone with whom you would share a toothbrush") and should be changed frequently. Easily remembered words (such as a name, identification number, or even the word *password*) are easy to guess, but a long string of arbitrary characters is difficult to remember and forces people to keep a written copy near the computer—not a very secure approach. Computer systems are designed to provide security in various ways. Encryption, firewalls, and virtual private networks are examples.

Encryption

One way to secure data from use by unintended recipients is to *encrypt* the data: to transform it so that it cannot be read unless the reader has the decoding key, or *cipher*. Encryption is especially important if confidential data will be transmitted over unprotected communications systems such as the internet.

Substitution and *transposition* are the simplest forms of encryption. In substitution, in use since the time of Julius Caesar, each letter in a message is replaced by a different letter. Caesar chose the letter three letters further along in the alphabet, so D = G, I = L, N = Q, E = H, and the word *dine* is encoded as *glqh*. With a transposition cipher, the message can be written left to right in lines of five characters, and then rewritten for transmission reading each column top to bottom.

Computers make much more sophisticated encryption methods possible. The *RSA algorithm* is the most commonly used encryption and authentication algorithm. Named for its inventors— Rivest, Shamir, and Adleman—it is often used to provide security in web browsers and as the basis for digital signatures used to authenticate entities on the internet. RSA involves a public key and a private key. The public key is available to anyone and is used to encrypt messages. Only the private key is able to decrypt messages that have been encrypted this way. The keys are generated using two large, randomly selected prime numbers. The message recipient performs the calculations and makes the public key available. Because only the recipient knows the private key, and because of the amount of work required to compute the private key, it is extremely difficult for anyone else to decode the message.

Firewalls

A network firewall is hardware or software that separates a computer(s) from a network (often the internet). Network-level firewalls typically operate at the OSI reference model layer 3 (the network layer); they check the protocol and destination of packets intended for the network and deny access by dropping (deleting) packets that do not meet specified criteria. Although network-level filtering is a good first line of defense, more sophisticated measures, at higher OSI layers, may also be adopted. Application-level firewalls can use a proxy server to send and receive packets, hiding the user's internet address and allowing time to assess the content and protocols being used, as well as the address of the remote source.

Virtual Private Networks

Virtual private networks (VPNs) use encryption and *tunneling* to provide secure data transmission; data packets for the private network are encapsulated and sent over the public network—usually the internet. A remote user connects with the computer system, logs in, and requests a tunnel for a VPN. The central computer authenticates the user and creates the other end of the tunnel. The tunnel works at layer 2 (data link) or layer 3 (network) of the OSI reference model. Messages are encrypted when sent by the user or the central computer, then decrypted when received by the other party. VPNs require considerable overhead to encrypt, package, unpackage, and decrypt each message. However, they provide considerable security and greatly improve accessibility of central resources without the cost of leased telecommunication lines (McDonald, 2010).

6.4. Conclusion

Understanding how computers work requires knowledge of the physical structures and capabilities of the hardware, as well as how these capabilities are organized and controlled through software. Effective computer management also requires the ability to understand and support users' activities while at the same time anticipating potential threats to the system. Computing and communication technologies continue to evolve, which means that the system manager must also find ways to keep up with advances that improve the capability, reliability, and accessibility of these important tools for information management.

References

Barrett, D., & King, T. (2005). *Computer networking illuminated.* Sudbury, MA: Jones and Bartlett.

Berkowitz, H. C. (2007). Representative academic library LAN with external access. Retrieved November 11, 2010, from upload.wikimedia.org/wikipedia/commons/2/27/NETWORK-Library-LAN.png.

Cleveland, D. (2010). Cloud computing. Wikinvest. Retrieved November 11, 2010, from www.wikinvest.com/concept/Cloud_Computing.

Computer History Museum. (2006). Exhibits: Internet history. Retrieved April 20, 2010, from www.computerhistory.org/internet_history.

DUX Computer Digest. (2010). What is the difference between an Ethernet hub and switch? Retrieved November 11, 2010, from www.duxcw.com/faq/network/hubsw.htm.

McDonald, C. (2010). Virtual private networks: An overview. *Intranet Journal.* Retrieved November 11, 2010, from www.intranetjournal.com/foundation/vpn-1.shtml.

Walters, E. G. (2001). *The essential guide to computing: The story of information technology.* Upper Saddle River, NJ: Prentice Hall.

Zittrain, W. (2009, July 19). Lost in the cloud. *New York Times.* Retrieved April 20, 2010, from www.nytimes.com/2009/07/20/opinion/20zittrain.html.

CHAPTER 7

Structured Information Systems

7.1. Introduction

Consider the two concepts *information* and *system* separately. As noted in Chapter 1, information can be anything that might inform somebody of something. A system can be understood as a group of independent but inter-related elements constituting a unified whole. To consider something a system is to consider it in a particular way that emphasizes the interrelations of the elements, working together to fulfill an overall purpose. An information system is thus not a system processing *information* but rather a system intended to inform somebody about something: an informing system.

Information systems are usually computer-based, although this is not essential. For example, the scientific communication system, which is based on conferences, journals, and libraries, may be understood as an information system, whether it employs printed or digital media.

More commonly, an information system is "a computer hardware and software system designed to accept, store, manipulate, and analyze data and to report results, usually on a regular, ongoing basis. An [information system] usually consists of a data input subsystem, a data storage and retrieval subsystem, a data analysis and manipulation subsystem, and a reporting subsystem" (Reitz, 2007).

Think back to your first cell phone directory, list of web links, collection of digital music, or email address book. How did you collect and organize the contents? Most such systems begin with a few easily recalled entries. As the number grows, the system can become unwieldy, and it becomes necessary to invest time to reorganize haphazard collections of information so that needed items can be found and used in a more efficient way.

In a *structured* information system, information is analyzed and organized into component parts, which in turn may have components, which are also organized. These are data-oriented systems, designed to facilitate data storage and retrieval.

Structured data is the "stuff" of most contemporary computer-based information systems, but it is important to realize the other, equally important aspect of information science: the social and cultural network in which all information systems are embedded. The technology that powers every information system is structured and designed with specific users in mind, and these users are the ultimate judges of the success or failure of the system.

This chapter examines how the elements that make up information systems—the design, structure, technical aspects—come together in an interactive, fundamentally social space to give users access to information that will serve their diverse information needs. Chapter 8, on information system applications, builds on these concepts and examines how they have been adapted to support capture, storage, and retrieval of more complex types of data. Chapter 9 considers users' perspectives on information systems.

We begin by investigating how careful analysis of information needs and resources lays the groundwork for a functional and maintainable information system. This initial design is the basis for the next step, conceptual modeling of the system components. We then consider the *relational data model*, the basis for almost all modern database systems.

7.2. Systems Analysis

This definition, adapted from the *Web Dictionary of Cybernetics and Systems* (Systems Analysis, 2002), provides a sense of the value and challenge in undertaking systems analysis:

> Systems analysis is an explicit, formal inquiry conducted to help someone (the decision maker) identify a course of action. Systems analysis is used when the issues involved are complex and the likely outcome(s) of possible courses of action are uncertain. Systems analysis usually has some combination of the following: identification (and re-identification) of objectives, constraints, and alternative courses of action; examination of the probable consequences of the alternatives in terms of costs, benefits, and risks; presentation of the results in a comparative framework so that the decision maker can make an informed choice from among the alternatives.

The goal of systems analysis is to develop, before the actual programming begins, a reasonably complete preliminary understanding of how, why, and by whom the system will be used. At this stage in the process, analysts are best served by asking stakeholders as many different kinds of questions as possible in order to obtain information about the potential requirements of the system. Possible questions can range from the pragmatic to the theoretical, such as the following:

- How much time is available to develop the system?

- What is the development budget?

- On what hardware and operating systems will the system be deployed?

- Who is going to use the system?

- What are the target users' information needs?

- In what environment will the system be used?

- How, how often, and by whom will the system be maintained?

In addition to asking these kinds of questions, analysts have emphasized the value of ethnography in systems analysis "to develop a thorough understanding of current work practices as a basis for the design of computer support. A major point in ethnographically inspired approaches is that work is a socially organized activity where the actual behavior differs from how it is described by those who do it" (Simonsen, 1997, p. 82).

To perform an ethnographic systems analysis, analysts both observe and actually work with target users, informing the design through their first-hand experience. Such participatory design approaches are becoming more popular as analysts, systems designers, and programmers realize the value that user experience can have on developing more effective, more usable systems.

Even after the information system has been designed and implemented, it is advisable to perform regular follow-up analyses to ensure that the system is performing as designed and effectively meeting the users' needs. This approach improves the understanding of how and why users adopt information systems. This kind of information is invaluable from a development standpoint because, ultimately, the users, not the designers, decide how successful an information system is.

Much of the early work on information system design was based on the *system development life cycle*, a designer-centered, top-down approach. This and other design approaches are the topic of the next section.

7.3. Design

Traditional approaches to design, such as the system development life cycle, tend to follow a *waterfall model*, with results from one step forming the basis for the next. The steps in this process define a rigid, linear sequence of events that, if successful, result in the completion of the information system.

Critics of the waterfall model contend that system design should be like a spiral, with feedback from each step informing design and improvement throughout the process. Newer versions are explicitly *iterative*, meaning that the system is never truly finished, but rather that each completed model is always awaiting evaluation and redesign.

The traditional system development life cycle consists of seven basic steps:

1. A *feasibility study* creates the preliminary plan for the system.

2. *Requirements analysis* involves determining the needs or conditions to be met by the system. At this stage, the analyst must consider the system from various perspectives, being aware that the requirements of the various stakeholders may differ or even conflict.

3. System design uses the findings from the requirements analysis to produce *specifications (documentation)* for the way the software should perform. If the information system will be integrated with other automated systems, the software design may be a flow chart or text describing a planned sequence of events. If it is intended for human interaction, the system designers may adopt a user-centered approach and test various options with intended users through a storyboard mock-up.

4. *Implementation* is the creation of the program, database, or other software components to realize the design.

5. *Testing* ensures that the system as implemented performs as designed. This is the first step in providing quality assurance for the stakeholders.

6. *Acceptance and deployment* put the system into operation.

7. *Maintenance* involves changes to the system to correct errors, update it to meet new needs, and improve its performance.

Even when deeply involved in a particular step in the design process, designers should keep the big picture in mind, realizing that all information systems are designed for specific user groups with particular information needs. From a design standpoint, this means that both the technical systems and the information itself must be structured to enable efficient and effective information access. One way that designers try to ensure that the systems they design meet these needs effectively is through *conceptual modeling*.

7.4. Conceptual Modeling

The requirements analysis and design steps require great skill, both in working with people to solicit and understand the requirements of the information system and in formulating a plan for a system to meet those needs. The practice of conceptual modeling facilitates these processes. "Models are ideas about the world—how it might be organized and how it might work. Models describe relationships: parts that make up wholes; structures that bind them; and how parts behave in relation to one another" (Dubberly, 2009, p. 54). A *conceptual data model* names the items of significance for the information system and characteristics (*attributes*) of and associations (*relationships*) among those items.

The most widely accepted standard for modeling systems is the Unified Modeling Language (UML), "a non-proprietary, third generation modeling language. The UML is an open method used to specify, visualize, construct, and document the artifacts of an object-oriented software-intensive system under development. The UML represents a compilation of 'best engineering practices' which have proven successful in modeling large, complex systems" (Unified modeling language, 2010).

Designers employ various models to develop effective database systems:

- *User interface models* establish how users will see and interact with the data. The Unified Modeling Language for Interactive Applications integrates user modeling facilities into UML. It can be used to represent the user interface (Stephens, 2009).

- *Semantic object models* represent entities, their attributes, and their relationships. Figure 7.1 is a semantic model of how students, professors, and courses (three different entities) are connected. The student entity has attributes such as name and student ID. The student and professor entities are both related to the course entity. Semantic object models function at a fairly high level. Although they represent the basic classes and their possible relationships

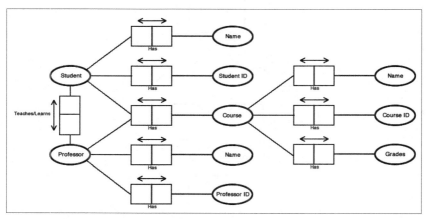

Figure 7.1 Semantic model of academic activities

well, semantic object models do not depict all the possible details of an information system (Stephens, 2009).

- *Entity-relationship models* also depict the relationships between distinct data objects, classifying them as entities, attributes, or identifiers. Specific semantic symbols within the diagram allow entity-relationship models to represent specific aspects of the relationship between entities, such as cardinality and inheritance (Stephens, 2009, pp. 106–113). Figure 7.2 shows an entity-relationship model of the academic world in which students (entity) take (relationship) courses (entity) and earn (relationship) grades (entity).

- *Relational models* provide a clear, straightforward presentation of the elements in a database in the form of a table. This model is useful for understanding the system and for facilitating communication among those who design, implement, and maintain it. Both semantic object models and entity-relationship models can be converted to relational models by creating tables to represent the entities and attributes, and then determining the relationships among data elements. Relational models are discussed in more detail in the next two sections.

It is established practice to represent these models as diagrams that detail the characteristics and/or potential uses of the information system being designed.

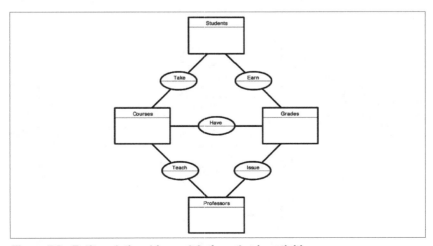

Figure 7.2 Entity-relationship model of academic activities

7.5. Databases

A database is a collection of data that is stored to facilitate addition, updates, deletion, and access. A database is often implemented using specific software called a database management system.

Database Functionality

CRUD is the mnemonic acronym that stands for the four fundamental operations any database should support: Users should be able to create, read, update, and delete information contained in the database (Stephens, 2009). To accomplish these tasks, the system must support *retrieval*: users should be able to locate efficiently every piece of data contained in the database.

Databases must be accurate and consistent. Therefore, the system emphasizes the validity of the content: whenever a record is created, updated, or deleted, the database checks or verifies that the information is of the correct type, represents permissible values, and is in an acceptable state.

In addition, good databases should provide easy error correction, efficient operation, extensibility as data and number of users increase, and security. If many users will need access to the same data from multiple locations, data sharing might also be important.

Data Models

"A data model is a framework for describing the structure of databases. A schema is the structure of a particular database" (Sciore, 2009, p. 7). Of the many data models that have been developed, four are in common use today:

- *Flat files* contain text only, although text may include characters (such as commas or tabs) that can provide some structure to data. eXtensible Markup Language (XML) files are an example.

- *Spreadsheets* also store data in tabular form and allow for data manipulation, but do not allow for complex relationships among data elements.

- *Relational databases* store data in tabular form (in rows and columns) and allow users to search for (retrieve) data on the basis of certain criteria (queries) (Stephens, 2009).

- *Object-oriented databases* (OODBs) support object-oriented programming, in which functions and procedures for an entity are bundled together and handled as a discrete object. In an OODB, data is stored as objects. Retrieval is relatively easy because it is not necessary to join tables (as required in relational databases) and because object identifiers provide direct access. OODBs facilitate multimedia applications because the methods to handle data in any format are *inherited* by each object and accessible when the object is retrieved (Object-oriented database, 2010).

7.6. Relational Databases

The relational model of data management was introduced in 1970 (Codd, 1970). It used the abstract notion of the table to represent how data is stored, and it separated data storage from retrieval. Invention of *structured query language* (SQL) later that decade and improvements in retrieval speed have helped the relational model dominate the market today and influence ideas of future developments in database management (Anthes, 2010).

The Relational Data Model

In a relational database, the data is organized into two-dimensional *tables*. Tables contain *records*, which have one or more *fields*, and each field has a specific *type* and a specific *value*. Fields can also contain *null values*—values that (for any number of reasons) do not exist or are unknown (Sciore, 2009).

Records are presented as rows (sometimes called *tuples*) in the table. The fields (or *attributes*) are presented as vertical columns. Each row contains the data for one instance of the items in the table; each column represents a certain characteristic of the data. For example, Table 7.1 contains information about university students and the classes they have taken. The first row names the attributes, student name and course name, and each of the other rows holds that information for one student.

Keys and Normalization

Keys are extremely important for relational databases. Keys are the attributes used to identify a record. Think of a key as a record's social security number—the unique number that identifies only one record and does not change.

Table 7.1 can show how keys are important. What happens if there are two sections of the same class? What if two different students have the same name? In the relational data model, each row is identified by a *primary key* that uniquely identifies that row in the relation. Often this is accomplished by creating a unique ID number for each item (see Tables 7.2 and 7.3). As Table 7.4 shows, assigning a unique ID number to both students and courses clarifies the original data.

Now we can see that there are actually two different students with the name Stacy Wilson and that the records for Intro to Finance are for two different semesters. Having a key for each item is also essential for *normalization*, the

Table 7.1   Students and courses

Student Name	Course Name
Stacy Wilson	Macroeconomics
Stacy Wilson	Intro to Finance
Hans Goldberg	Intro to Finance
Mary Rhee	Calculus
Mary Rhee	Finite Math

process of removing redundant information from a database.

Information in a database is often split into multiple tables to help with the organization of resources, prevent individual tables from becoming too large, improve processing efficiency, and ensure the security of records. For example, the data regarding students' grades might be recorded as in Table 7.5. Only the essential data appears in Table 7.5, making it more efficient and more secure.

Now we begin to see how records in a relational database are "related" to each other—if records in one table contain primary keys for records in another table, these "connected" fields in the first table can serve as *foreign keys* leading us to the corresponding data in the second table. This allows the database to retrieve data from more than one table in response to a query.

Consider Table 7.6, containing information about the professors who taught the courses. We can use this with our other tables to retrieve information from the relational database.

Retrieval: Relational Algebra

Codd's (1970) introduction of the relational data model included relational algebra, a logical, procedural language for retrieving data from related tables. Relational algebra has seven operations, including *join*, which specifies how to combine related information stored in different tables.

We will use Tables 7.2, 7.3, 7.5, and 7.6 to see how to get complete academic records for each student, including which courses were taken from which professor and what grades the students earned. We begin the *join* by finding the primary and foreign keys (identifying attributes) that connect each table to the next.

What attributes do the tables have in common? Table 7.2 and Table 7.5 both contain the attribute "Student ID." Table 7.3 and Table 7.5 both contain

Table 7.2   Students identified by ID numbers

Student ID	Student Name
S22359784	Stacy Wilson
S33987125	Stacy Wilson
S22495411	Hans Goldberg
S22366012	Mary Rhee
S22366012	Mary Rhee

Table 7.3   Courses identified by ID numbers

Course ID	Course Name
E239Sp10	Macroeconomics
B194Fa09	Intro to Finance
B194Sp10	Intro to Finance
M165Fa09	Calculus
M294Sp10	Finite Math

Table 7.4   Revised version of Table 7.1

Student ID	Student Name	Course ID	Course Name
S22359784	Stacy Wilson	E239Sp10	Macroeconomics
S33987125	Stacy Wilson	B194Fa09	Intro to Finance
S22495411	Hans Goldberg	B194Sp10	Intro to Finance
S22366012	Mary Rhee	M165Fa09	Calculus
S22366012	Mary Rhee	M294Sp10	Finite Math

the attribute "Course ID." Table 7.5 and Table 7.6 also both contain the attribute "Course ID." Figure 7.3 shows how a *join* on all the tables would work. Table 7.7 shows the complete listing of students, courses, professors, and grades assembled from the relationships in all these tables.

Table 7.5 Students' grades in courses

Student ID	Course ID	Grade
S22359784	E239Sp10	A
S33987125	B194Fa09	B
S22495411	B194Sp10	B+
S22366012	M165Fa09	B
S22366012	M294Sp10	C

Table 7.6 Professors and courses taught

Professor ID	Professor Name	Course ID
P16592412	Dr. James Smyth	E239Sp10
P27851908	Dr. Ole Martez	B194Fa09
P65934281	Dr. MaLeesa Johnson	B194Sp10
P30024367	Dr. Zoran Sanovic	M165Fa09
P30024367	Dr. Zoran Sanovic	M294Sp10

Beyond Relational Databases

The relational approach has provided exceptionally effective and reliable support for data management for decades. However, the model reflects the mainframe computer focus of the 1970s, with data storage and access handled on a central computer that supplies information as needed to clients (programs that provide access to and update the database). These industrial-strength databases emphasize data security and take great care to prevent errors that might occur if, for example, two people attempted to update a contact's email address at the same time.

Today, ubiquitous computing is pushing computer science to develop more modular and more easily reconfigurable database models. Seltzer (2008) notes that applications such as web searching, XML management, and mobile device caching require new thinking about the interactions between a database and its clients; even huge data storage applications such as *data*

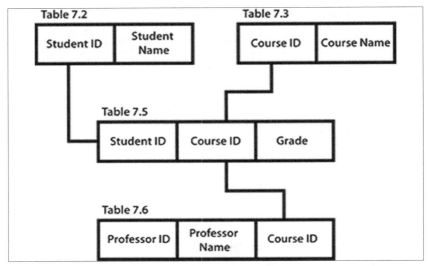

Figure 7.3 **Relational join to create student transcripts**

Table 7.7 **Student transcript information**

Student ID	Student Name	Course ID	Course Name	Grade	Professor ID	Professor Name
S22359784	Stacy Wilson	E239Sp10	Macroeconomics	A	P16592412	Dr. James Smyth
S33987125	Stacy Wilson	B194Fa09	Intro to Finance	B	P27851908	Dr. Ole Martez
S22495411	Hans Goldberg	B194Sp10	Intro to Finance	B+	P65934281	Dr. MaLeesa Johnson
S22366012	Mary Rhee	M165Fa09	Calculus	B	P30024367	Dr. Zoran Sanovic
S22366012	Mary Rhee	M294Sp10	Finite Math	C	P30024367	Dr. Zoran Sanovic

warehousing and *data mining* (e.g., of retail customer transactions) are "read-mostly," so that the high overhead cost of preventing simultaneous updates may not be necessary. New approaches to database management must be flexible and configurable; for example, the designer might choose to emphasize quick access to updated information in some cases and to support graceful recovery from interruptions in others.

References

Anthes, G. (2010). Happy birthday, RDBMS! *Communications of the ACM, 53*(5), 16–17.

Codd, E. F. (1970). A relational model of data for large shared data banks. *Communications of the ACM, 13*(6), 377–387.

Dubberly, H. (2009). Models of models. *Interactions, 16*(3), 54–60.

Object-oriented database. (2010). *Free online dictionary of computing.* Retrieved November 11, 2010, from foldoc.org/object-oriented+database.

Reitz, J. M. (2007). *Online dictionary for library and information science.* Santa Barbara, CA: Libraries Unlimited. Retrieved November 11, 2010, from lu.com/odlis.

Sciore, E. (2009). *Database design and implementation.* Hoboken, NJ: Wiley.

Seltzer, M. (2008). Beyond relational databases. *Communications of the ACM, 51*(7), 52–58.

Simonsen, J. (1997). Using ethnography in contextual design. *Communications of the ACM, 40*(7), 82–88.

Stephens, R. (2009). *Beginning database design solutions.* Indianapolis: Wiley.

Systems analysis. (2002). *Web dictionary of cybernetics and systems.* Retrieved May 10, 2011, from cleamc11.vub.ac.be/ASC/SYSTEM_ANALY.html.

Unified modeling language. (2010). *Free online dictionary of computing.* Retrieved November 11, 2010, from foldoc.org/UML.

CHAPTER 8

Information System Applications

8.1. Information Retrieval

Information professionals use the word *retrieval* in a particular sense: accessing information stored by a computer. When they speak of *information retrieval*, most people mean retrieval of a document (webpages, records, etc.) in which information is stored. These documents may or may not be indexed or classified to facilitate their retrieval. Search requests are formulated in terms of the vocabulary used by the system being interrogated. The search is executed by matching the search statement, or *query*, with items in the database being searched. The results (*hits* or *retrieval set*) are the subset of the database that matches the query. The result of a good search should not be too large to allow rational examination of the output, nor should it be so small as to exclude documents containing relevant information. Achieving the desired results by formulating an optimal search strategy is often as much art as science and, as with much else in life, requires practice.

Finding information on the web is an everyday example of information retrieval. Most people use a search engine such as Google and cheerfully insert terms without much thought to the processes that underlie the search procedure. Only those who look at Advanced Search see what might be called the standard model of information retrieval. On that page the Google user is invited to enter "all these words," "this exact wording or phrase," "one or more of these words," and "don't show pages that have any of the [following] unwanted words." This is how Google incorporates the Boolean operators AND, OR, and NOT to optimize the retrieval of webpages.

Employing Boolean search logic is useful but not always sufficient. Retrieval effectiveness can be improved by taking advantage of the database's structure (see Chapter 7) and vocabulary control (Chapter 5). Synonyms and near-synonyms (words or symbols that are identical or very similar) and homographs (words or symbols having more than one meaning) can lead to false retrieval. Such issues may be dealt with in advance—with a structured database—or else handled at search time. Many web search engines, such as Google, store information on links among websites to enhance the relevance of items retrieved.

Term Truncation and Proximity Searching

When creating a query, searchers can take advantage of the redundancy of natural language. Several words derive from the same roots, making it useful to search for portions of a word. For example, one might have a broad interest in libraries, librarians, and librarianship. In this case, searching for a pattern match on the character string *Librar* would locate all these terms. A special character called a *wild card*, often an asterisk or a slash mark, indicates where the pattern match should stop. Thus, a searcher could enter *Librar** or *Librar/* as part of the query statement. This would tend to broaden the search and retrieve many more documents. Note that *Lib/* would be an unsatisfactory choice, because it would match such terms as *liberty, libation,* and *libel.* In other words, *Lib/* would be too broad.

Although it is more common to truncate on the end of a term, it is sometimes useful to be able to truncate at the beginning. For example, a searcher who wanted information about antibiotics might request all items on -*mycin*. Systems permitting this left-hand truncation employ special symbols at the front of the term; they may also allow simultaneous left- and right-hand truncation.

Some systems support searches with proximity operators, which specify that words must appear as a phrase or within a user-specified distance of each other. For example, a search for information on digital libraries might be the words: *digital librar**, using the asterisk for truncation. The search can be made more precise by specifying that the words must occur, say, within three words of each other: *digital (3W) librar**, which would retrieve a document titled *Libraries in the Digital Age.* To be even more precise, the searcher could use quotation marks to require that the phrase *"digital librar*"* occur in the document retrieved.

Set Theory and Boolean Logic

It is useful to think of the web, the collections held by information centers and libraries, or any given database as a set of items (webpages, documents, records). This allows one to apply elements of set theory and Boolean algebra to formulate an optimal search strategy. The basic theory involves the coordination of data elements within the records in the database.

Strictly speaking, a *set* is any collection of items that satisfies the following three conditions: 1) each item must have an attribute or attributes that allow one to answer yes or no with respect to the question of whether the item is a member of the set; 2) each item must be distinct and should not appear more than once; and 3) the order of the items in the set should be inconsequential. This is also the case with *combinations* and *permutations* (Davis & Rush, 1979).

Set membership may be specified in either of two ways: by the *roster method*, which involves simply listing the elements contained in the set

P = {60°, 65°, 70°, 75°}

or by the *descriptive method*

P = {x | x is a temperature of the day}

which should be read as: "P is a set of elements x such that x is a temperature of the day."

The descriptive method can even be used for *infinite sets*, such as "P is a set of elements x of the universal set, such that x is a positive integer." The *universal set*, by definition, is a set containing all the elements relevant to a given situation. The *null set*, in contrast, is a set with no elements in it; it is empty. Infinite sets have interesting properties, but they are usually ignored in applied information science because no database is infinite, although many, such as the web, are enormous.

The order of elements in a set does not matter, a characteristic that also distinguishes combinations from permutations. The number of possible subsets in a set of n elements is 2^n; the number of combinations of n items is $2^n - 1$.

For a set with only three elements, the number of subsets is 2^3, or 8. Why 8 instead of 7? Because the null set is also a subset! In preparing queries for information retrieval, it is important to note that a relatively small number of elements can lead to a very large number of possible subsets (retrieval sets). A set with four terms has 16 possible subsets; with five terms, 32; and so on.

The Boolean operators are essentially self-explanatory. AND logic means exactly what it says: All terms must be present for a hit to result. NOT, of course, means that a document is unwanted if a given term appears. OR means that at least one of the terms must be present. Usually, *inclusive* OR is meant for information retrieval, although some systems also permit *exclusive* OR, meaning either one term or the other but not both.

Weighted-Term Extensions of Boolean Search Logic

Weighted-term search logic is similar to Boolean search logic and shares its theoretical basis in set theory. However, weighted term searching is more flexible because the searcher assigns each term in the query a number proportional to the value that the searcher places on that term for that particular search.

Typically, the searcher first selects a threshold value or cutoff weight. This value is an arbitrary integer within the limits of the system; it remains constant throughout the search. Weights relative to this threshold value are assigned to each term in the query. If the weight assigned to a term is equal to or greater than the threshold value, documents indexed under that term will be retrieved. If the weight assigned to the term is less than the threshold value, the documents indexed under the term will not be retrieved unless the term appears in combination with other terms and the sum of the terms' weights is equal to or greater than the threshold value.

Negative threshold values have their uses, too. To retrieve documents indexed under term A or term B but not both, a negative threshold value is selected, and the weights of terms A and B can be set equal to it. If either of the desired terms appears by itself, then the document will be retrieved because the value of the term will equal the threshold value. However, if both terms appear, the document will not be retrieved because their combined weight will be less than the threshold value. This is the weighted-term equivalent of the Boolean exclusive OR.

The sum of the weights of the search terms in a document can be thought of as a kind of document weight. Sorting the retrieval set by document weights makes it possible to display the items retrieved in decreasing order of their probable relevance. Thus, if several hundred documents are likely to satisfy a given search request, the searcher will see the most promising documents first, rather than a random sample.

Ranking Boolean Search Results

A *powers-of-two* algorithm can automatically assign weights to query terms as they are entered. If n terms are entered, the first entered term is given a 2^n weight, the second a $2^{(n-1)}$ weight, and so forth, until the last receives a 2^1 weight (2). Terms to be negated are given a negative weight equal to the sum of the positive weights, and terms of possible interest receive a weight of 1 (2^0). The threshold is set at 2, and an accumulator for each document sums the weights of occurrences of query terms to generate a retrieval status value; this value is then used to sort the documents into decreasing order of probable relevance. The searcher can change the weighting scheme, and thus the output ranking, by changing the order in which the terms are entered (Davis & McKim, 1999).

Statistical Approaches to Information Retrieval

The computer is obviously a key component in computer-based information retrieval; this suggests that some automated processing of the database or the items that match a query might enhance the system's performance. One approach to using computation to improve retrieval is called the *bag of words*. Each term (word or word stem) in a database is identified, and the number of times a term occurs in each document is counted. Each document then has a *term frequency*, the number of times that term occurs in that document. Because terms will probably occur more often in long documents than in short ones, we normalize by dividing the number of times a term occurs by the sum of occurrences of all terms in the document. The term frequency for a document is thus

$$tf_{i,j} = n_{i,j} \div \Sigma_k n_{k,j}$$

where $n_{i,j}$ is the number of times the term occurs in document d_j, which is divided by the sum of the occurrences of all terms in the document.

The *inverse document frequency* measures the general importance of the term in the database. We divide the number of all documents by the number of documents containing the term and taking the logarithm of that quotient:

$$idf_i = \log (|D| \div |\{d: t_i \times d\}|$$

Here

|D| is the total number of documents in the database
|{d: $t_i \times$ d}| is the number of documents where the term t_i
appears

Thus, the calculation becomes

$$(tf\text{-}idf)_{i,j} = tf_{i,j} \times idf_i$$

With the use of tf × idf, a query can retrieve documents ranked not by whether a term occurs but by how much weight that term has in each document. Enhancements and extensions to tf × idf include calculating frequencies for multiword terms, identifying synonyms in the database, and using feedback from the searcher to improve search results.

Helpful Hints and Guidelines for Searchers

Experienced searchers apply several rules of thumb for revising search strategies. In the simplest case, if a search retrieves undesired results, the searcher can choose a more appropriate database, use different terms, or develop a more sophisticated query statement. If the search produces too little output, it is possible that the searcher has used too much logical AND or NOT, because both of these operators tend to restrict the search. Similarly, if too many items are retrieved, there may have been too much use of logical OR or excessive use of term truncation, both of which tend to broaden a search. The searcher can counteract these problems by cutting back on the use of the offending type of operator or by introducing an operator having the opposite effect. Before changing the terms in the query, examine how the existing terms have been coordinated.

Retrieving nothing (the null set) does not necessarily indicate a bad search. For example, an inventor wishing to establish the novelty of a new device would be delighted to find that there are no patents for similar devices. Similarly, doctoral students would be glad to learn that no dissertations have been written on their chosen topics. Achieving search results that are 100 percent relevant should suggest that something may have been missed because the search strategy was too narrow.

Research on Information Retrieval

Information retrieval research in the 1950s and 1960s focused on creating performance measures. Cyril Cleverdon (Cleverdon & Keen, 1966) developed the concepts of *recall* and *precision* for studies of retrieval effectiveness conducted at the Cranfield Institute in the U.K. Precision is the number of relevant documents retrieved by a search, divided by the total number of documents retrieved by that search. Recall is the number of relevant documents retrieved by a search divided by the total number of relevant documents in the database. Computing precision is straightforward, and searchers often consider how many nonrelevant documents can be tolerated in a given search. Recall is more complicated—how does one know about relevant documents not retrieved? Recall may be estimated by comparing the results of one strategy with all relevant documents retrieved by several strategies. Both of these measures beg the question of how the relevance of documents is determined.

The Cranfield studies and similar early work essentially assumed that relevance was an objective attribute: It existed in the documents examined. This mechanistic approach was soon found to be less than satisfactory, because two people, looking at the same search request and document, would sometimes have different assessments of the document's relevance to the request. Even before the Cranfield experiments, Vickery (1959) promoted the distinction between *user relevance* and *subject relevance*. *Pertinence* and *utility* were also used by a number of authors to emphasize that relevance judgments will vary with the individual judge, and over time (Saracevic, 2007).

Froehlich (1994, p. 124) identified six themes from the history of research on relevance:

1. The inability to define *relevance*: Although we seem to have an intuitive sense of what it means for a document to be relevant to a search request or an information need, researchers have not been able to agree on a definition for the term.

2. The inadequacy of *topicality* as the basis of relevance judgments: Topicality is sometimes termed *aboutness*. It means that the item in question is on the subject of the search request. A major problem is that topicality varies from one information seeker (or judge of relevance) to another.

3. The diversity of nontopical, user-centered criteria that affect relevance judgments: Situational relevance (Wilson, 1973) captures the notion that the user's prior knowledge, beliefs about the reliability of the source, and ease of access to the document (among other things) affect the relevance judgment.

4. The dynamic and fluid character of information-seeking behavior: One individual's assessment of the relevance of a particular document will change over time; searching for and finding information induces changes in understanding.

5. The need for appropriate methodologies: The importance of understanding users' judgments means more naturalistic research methods are needed so that researchers can observe and investigate how decisions are made.

6. The need for more complex, robust models for system design and evaluation: Cognitive science provides a useful basis, but the activities involved in relevance assessment are complex (see Chapter 3, section on information seeking).

Much of the research and development for web search engines such as Google is proprietary. However, one can infer that a blend of techniques has been employed, including assessing the number and quality of links to a given website or page (Brin & Page, 1998). Using such links is similar to tracking citations in the print literature to establish connections among journal articles (see Chapter 11, sections on bibliometrics and webometrics).

Current academic research on information retrieval is best exemplified by the Text REtrieval Conference (TREC; trec.nist.gov), sponsored by the U.S. National Institute of Standards and Technology (NIST) and the U.S. Department of Defense. TREC prepares large data sets in specific areas of focus, called *tracks*. The tracks represent real-world retrieval problems in areas such as blogs, web searching, and chemical information retrieval. Participants prepare their information retrieval systems to use the NIST data and answer questions NIST selects. The results from each information retrieval system are compared and discussed to provide a basis for improving retrieval technologies and techniques.

8.2. Digital Libraries

The idea of the *digital library* grabbed attention in science and technology circles in the 1990s. From 1994 to 1998, three U.S. government agencies—the National Science Foundation, the Defense Advanced Research Projects Agency, and the National Aeronautics and Space Administration—funded six projects in the first phase of the Digital Libraries Initiative at a cost of $30 million. Lynch (2005) traces the history of the idea of the digital library back to H. G. Wells and Paul Otlet; Lynch describes the term as an "oxymoronic phrase [that] has attracted dreamers and engineers, visionaries and entrepreneurs, a diversity of social scientists, lawyers, scientists and technicians. And even, ironically, librarians" (paragraph 1).

Lynch's observation captures the point that librarians had already been eyeing the increasing capabilities of information and communication technologies and working on ways these capabilities could be harnessed to support library functions. In 1999, the three founding institutions were joined for the second phase of the Digital Libraries Initiative by the National Library of Medicine, the Library of Congress, and the National Endowment for the Humanities, with participation from the National Archives and the Smithsonian Institution to provide $55 million to extend and develop innovative digital library technologies and applications.

This governmental initiative had counterparts in other countries (e.g., U.K. Electronic Libraries Programme and the European Network of Excellence on Digital Libraries, known as DELOS) and encouraged scientists, engineers, and librarians to examine problems together. Initial research considered how to store and retrieve large, complex data collections (text, sound, images, spoken word, video) and how to develop and maintain a *cyberinfrastructure* to support access. Through participation in digital library projects, higher education, cultural memory institutions, government agencies, and the commercial sector have discovered that they can contribute to the development of systems and services such as digital asset management, digital collection creation and management, and institutional repositories.

A digital library is a library in which collections are stored in digital formats and are accessible by computers via networks such as the internet. Born-digital collections are composed entirely of resources designed and produced electronically. Digital libraries may also be created by digitizing paper-based information resources. Today most libraries are hybrids, providing access to both physical and digital collections. Some publishers have created integrated collections of their electronic publications. Although these have some of the capabilities of a digital library, sometimes even the name, they do not include the diversity of sources usually expected in a digital library.

In the traditional print era, libraries purchased physical copies of docu-ments and loaned them to users free of charge. Copies were needed in local libraries, and each library selected, described, and organized its own collec-tion. In the digital environment, however, any electronic document is just one click away, and there is no need for local copies of documents. Some writers predict that libraries will be used less because producers or publish-ers of electronic documents will deliver them directly to users.

Current publishing and distribution arrangements assign libraries admin-istrative functions such as handling subscription fees and rights manage-ment for electronic journals, online databases, and other digital content (these topics are addressed in the next section, Electronic Resources Management). Libraries are also taking on some publishing responsibilities as they digitize and make available their own specialized collections, work with scholars to create repositories of published and unpublished work, and collaborate with university presses to maintain and disseminate publications (see Chapter 11 for more detail).

8.3. Electronic Resources Management

Electronic resources management (ERM) was born of the practical need to adapt and integrate acquisition processes for electronic resources into the online world. Libraries have addressed the complex physical, licensing, and technical realities of ERM in various ways. Electronic resources include elec-tronic journals, ebooks, databases, and internally produced digital resources, which are the basis for institutional repositories. Institutional repositories are online archives that collect, preserve, and provide unrestricted access to the publications of institutional research. ERM involves the following essen-tial functions:

- Selection

- Trial setup

- Selection approval

- Licensing

- Ordering

- Billing

- Cataloging

- Access activation

- Maintenance of ERM administrative tools

- Remote access monitoring

- Usage data collection

- Troubleshooting

- Renewal and cancellation

These functions form the ERM life cycle, from selection, through access activation and monitoring, to renewal or cancellation. The life cycle can be seen as a progression, with functions close to each other performed by a single administrator or electronic resources librarian. All of these ERM functions can be part of an electronic resources librarian's job description; overlap between the clusters of functions performed by electronic resource librarians is common.

Electronic resources may be acquired as one-time purchases, through a subscription, or as a combination of subscription and one-time purchase (for example, recent volumes of an electronic journal acquired as a subscription, and archive or backfile volumes acquired as a one-time purchase).

Some ebooks appear as monographs—one-time publications, complete as issued. Databases and electronic journals are generally handled as continuing publications, with no planned date to cease publication. The model for other resources is unclear: An online encyclopedia is monographic when handled as a one-time purchase but has continuing access when purchased on the subscription model (e.g., print and online purchase with online access maintained only if the institution continues to purchase the annual print update). Book series (e.g., Springer's *Lecture Notes in Computer Science*) can be monographic, when each constituent book has a separate access point, or a continuing publication, when made available as a series.

ERM is both an extension of traditional monographic and serials acquisitions processes and a new area for library management. New responsibilities include negotiating licensing agreements, supporting electronic access, and monitoring usage.

Licensing

Farb (2006) quotes the director of the University of Wisconsin–Madison library as saying, "Libraries are agreeing to licenses that provide no guarantee of continued access to the content if the subscription ends. What this means, of course, is that universities are only renting this information." When libraries purchase printed material, they own the items purchased. With electronic information sources, however, the library typically leases access for a specified period; even if a database is supplied to the institution and mounted on its computer, the content usually belongs to the database provider and must be returned when the contract expires. When the database resides on the provider's computer and library users have only the right of access, the library has even less control over the information. As Farb observes, such arrangements have major implications for libraries' traditional responsibilities for preserving information.

Libraries and publishers are exploring ways to preserve born-digital scholarly publications. Portico (www.portico.org) and LOCKSS (Lots of Copies Keeps Stuff Safe; www.lockss.org) make arrangements to store archival copies of electronic publications, assuring that they will be available for future scholars.

Both librarians and publishers are investing considerably more time in negotiating and maintaining license agreements than they did in the print era. Libraries may be bound by state law or institutional practice to require special wording or exceptions to publishers' standard contracts. Hahn (2007) describes the Shared Electronic Resource Understanding project as an alternative to licensing. It "expresses commonly shared understandings of the content provider, the subscribing institution and authorized users; the nature of the content; use of materials and inappropriate uses; privacy and confidentiality; online performance and service provision; and archiving and perpetual access" (Hahn, 2007, paragraph 1).

Supporting Electronic Access

Information professionals often assist people in finding appropriate resources; providing this service may be challenging when communication with the information seeker is conducted, for example, through email or online chat. From the ERM perspective, however, support includes the following aspects:

- Ensuring that users are aware of the available resources (listings of resources in the library's online catalog or on webpages)

- Identifying any restrictions on use (e.g., being in the library building or having a campus ID may be required)

- Arranging automatic verification of authorized users with vendor

- Providing links from the library's listings to the resources

- Resolving problems when links fail

- Coordinating access when a resource is available through multiple sources, such as different dates of online coverage for a journal available from different vendors

Monitoring Usage

Many license agreements limit the number of simultaneous users or the amount of material that may be downloaded (copied to the user's computer). Farb (2006) notes that the established U.S. limit on copyright through the fair use exemption is absent in many standard license agreements. These agreements may also interfere with "the right of every individual to both seek and receive information from all points of view without restriction," as the American Library Association (2009) defines *intellectual freedom*. Information professionals may feel awkward about being placed in the position of overseeing who uses resources, how much, and for what purposes. Although monitoring is typically done automatically, the information professional will be called on to resolve cases in which the vendor alleges that someone has misused a resource.

Aggregated usage statistics showing, for example, how many sessions were conducted with various vendors in the past year can help electronic resources managers decide whether licenses for more (or fewer) simultaneous users should be purchased, which agreements to renew or cancel, and which resources to promote, among other things.

As libraries transition from a mainly print to an online environment, new methods, tools, and access options continue to be developed. ERM is approached differently from one institution to another. A single electronic resources librarian or a group coordinated by such a librarian is common; libraries allocate ERM responsibilities in various ways, and some functions may be handled by other departments. In the library's organizational structure, the electronic resources librarian may be part of the public services or acquisitions department; in some cases ERM is handled collaboratively by various library departments, with no designated electronic resources librarian.

8.4. Information Visualization

Humans develop visual information systems from infancy; images and gestures form a basis for communication that is often our preferred mode of interaction, even in adulthood. Information visualization emphasizes this proclivity, converting nonspatial data to effective visual presentation. It has been used to help searchers make sense of information retrieved, to see patterns in data, and to support collaboration and communication. Research in this area focuses on how best to display such complex relationships.

20th-Century Visual Theoreticians

Information visualization research in the 20th century owes much to John Tukey (1977), who introduced the box plot as a way to show statistical information graphically; Rudolf Arnheim (2004), who noted the primacy of perception and images, not words, as the basis for thought; and Erwin Panofsky (1972), who developed the field of *iconography*—the identification, description, and interpretation of images.

In 1967, French cartographer and geographer Jacques Bertin (1983) described how graphic tools present a set of signs and a rule-based language that allow one to transcribe existing complex relations of difference among qualitative and quantitative data. Edward Tufte's (1983, 1990) important books on information visualization also encouraged the use of visual paradigms to augment understanding of complex relationships by synthesizing both statistics and aesthetic dimensions. For Bertin and Tufte, the power of visual perception and graphic presentation has a double function, serving both as a tool for discovery and as a way to augment cognition. Their ideas influenced a generation of information system designers.

Computing and Information Visualization

Interest in wider pragmatic possibilities of information visualization began to explode with the micro-computing revolution. The declining costs of computing produced workstations with robust processing capabilities, which encouraged experts from various perspectives to think across disciplines. University researchers took advantage of the new technology to create information visualization products, interfaces, and services.

Bringing a heterodox visual design agenda to the engineering-dominated halls of the Massachusetts Institute of Technology, visual designer and researcher Muriel Cooper synthesized visual design concepts with computer and information design (Abrams, 1994). The experiments and legacy of Cooper's Visual Language Workshop provided credibility to the fledgling discipline. Essentially, Cooper began mapping principles of modern graphic design to the display of digital information. Her work was informed by Tufte (1983, 1990), Bertin (1983), Arnheim (2004), Gombrich (1995), and more eclectic sources such as Bauhaus architectural modernists and early film theoreticians. The theoretical conceptualizations became grist for new digital possibilities such as information landscapes, cartographic fly-throughs, and the use of three-dimensionality to structure complex information systems.

Cooper's and her students' work introduced many in the next generation of innovators to the possibilities for computers and the potential use of graphics to build information systems and enhance information conceptualization through visualization, aesthetics, and interactivity. The command-line interface of the day (see Figure 8.1) was challenged by such now-commonplace

```
$ ed bash_profile
S45
10
if [ "$TERM" = "ncr7901" ]; then

        Source ~/ncr

fi

if [ $(uname) = "SunOS" ]; then

        # Use GCC for the 'cc' command

        Export PATH=$HOME/gcc-bin:$PATH

fi
```

Figure 8.1   Example of a command-line interface: editing a shell script on a Unix system, using the "ed" editor (commons.wikimedia.org/wiki/File:Unix-ed-shellscript.png)

displays as typographic landscapes, interactive visual media, and cartographic, "zoomable" maps. For example, doctoral student David Small (2002) developed innovative methods to visualize the human genome with a fly-through chromosome.

Ben Shneiderman's (2003) Human-Computer Interaction Laboratory at the University of Maryland–College Park is also known for its strong focus on visual models and information visualization strategies for enhancing human usability. This group pioneered progressive and interactive interface designs for digital libraries, including dynamic database queries, starfield displays for information recognition (see Figure 8.2), and treemaps to visualize and interactively explore large data sets.

As information visualization research and products flourished on university campuses, innovation was also being encouraged at Bell Labs, Xerox Palo Alto Research Center (PARC), and a nascent computer manufacturer called Apple. Bringing together a disparate group of thinkers in the early 1970s, PARC built upon the U.S. military's innovative early research on visualization at the Defense Advanced Research Projects Agency. Early projects proved prescient. For example, the Aspen Movie Map (Massachusetts Institute of Technology Architecture Machine Group, 1981) presented an interactive digital video tour of Aspen, Colorado, a system widely realized in commercial products such as Google Maps some 30 years later (see Figure 8.3). The movie map's touch screen possibilities have yet to be realized on wider commercial levels.

Better known is the 1979 PARC invention of the graphical user interface (GUI) using icons, windows, and frames (see Figure 8.4). These ideas were popularized by Apple's Macintosh computer and later duplicated in the

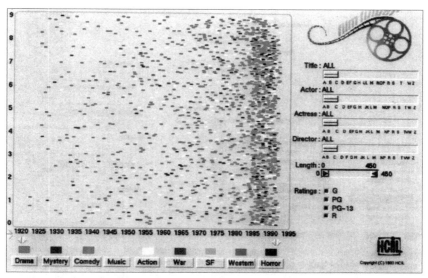

Figure 8.2   Starfield Display (1994), later commercialized as Spotfire (Courtesy
of the University of Maryland Human-Computer Interaction Lab,
www.cs.umd.edu/hcil/spotfire)

Microsoft Windows operating system (Card, Mackinlay, & Shneiderman, 1999).

Many visualization research experiments became standard in subsequent computer developments, but several remain unique and unrealized on commercial levels. Much of the territory remains fertile for further exploration.

Information Visualization Flowers

The late 1990s and the turn of the new millennium heralded a renaissance in dissemination and productivity for information visualization. Two major trends converged during this period: the rapid adoption of research by information visualization's pioneers and the work's democratization by a new generation of practitioners who had access to wider-bandwidth networks.

John Maeda built on Cooper's legacy at the Massachusetts Institute of Technology, establishing the Aesthetics and Computation Group. This was emblematic of a late 1990s trend of classically trained computer and information scientists' work with aesthetic paradigms. Maeda's teaching and research influenced directions of information design as a tool for expression, combining skilled computer programming with openness to aesthetics and information design. This work helped champion the interactive motion

Figure 8.3 A screenshot of the Aspen Movie Map

graphics that are commonplace on the internet today. Maeda's Design by Numbers project was a global initiative to teach visual artists about computer programming through a freely available, custom software system. Paola Antonelli, curator of the Department of Architecture and Design at New York's Museum of Modern Art, wrote the foreword to Maeda's (2001) book, noting information visualization's lofty ambitions—to synthesize previously segregated disciplines of aesthetics and technology, right and left brain, through the fulcrum of information visualization.

Blurring of lines between programming and art, design and information, spread with the proliferation of networked computer applications and possibilities for further synthesis of graphic manipulation and computer programming. This could be seen through the rise of new hybrid applications such as Macromedia (now Adobe) Flash programming and graphical environment. Flash presented a networked application environment in which previously segregated and traditionally left-brain programming logic could be combined with right-brain visual tools. As a graphic design and web animation program, Flash offered artists a new tool for online design. Its increasingly robust object-oriented programming environment provided interactive programming and information visualization possibilities previously restricted to high-end research institutions with heavyweight programming capacity. Flash combined two previously out-of-reach capabilities in a

Figure 8.4   Early graphical interface (Xerox Star, circa 1979). Note the use of
icons, folders for directories and multiple windows; these
information visualization metaphors are now ubiquitous on
computing platforms. (Used with permission of PARC,
www.parc.com)

single, economical, and commercially available program with back-end
database connectivity. This advance extended the range of information visualization, interface, and application design to a larger design and programming community.

Designers incorporated information architecture and interactive navigation as well. Flash implementations such as tag clouds exemplify how large,
complex databases, such as library catalogs, can be displayed visually to
encourage exploration (see Figure 8.5).

For example, we can think of finding a book through the metaphor of an
aerial landing. From an entire overview of the *knowledgescape*, or universe of
knowledge, one navigates and zooms down a taxonomic chain. Starting in
the knowledge cloud, the universe of knowledge is seen globally. One then
navigates to a particular continent, say Natural Sciences, then down the taxonomic chain to Zoology. One lands in a specific cluster of subject headings
or book items to find detailed resources about Butterflies.

Information Visualization Research

The pioneers of information visualization were an eclectic and irascible bunch who published and dipped into academic conferences in a variety of scholarly associations, societies, and heterodox institute journals (Korfhage, 1997). They demonstrated remarkable breadth of interdisciplinary research.

Because of the high cost of computing and limited access to computer networks, many early research and development efforts petered out. Ironically, this nadir occurred just as effective information visualization was becoming possible on lower-priced, commercial, networked computers. Much early research was later commercialized in specific information visualization software. A good example is Google's Image Search, which used metadata to conduct image retrieval in 2002. These systems built on research that had earlier explored captioning, keywords, and descriptors as access points for image retrieval. Many challenges remain, notably the question of how to represent and retrieve information in video formats.

Information visualization research communities in the academic sphere are multidisciplinary and synthetic. Focused groups in professional associations include the American Society for Information Science and Technology's Special Interest Group on Information Visualization, Images, and Sound and the Association for Computing Machinery's Special Interest Group on Graphics and Interactive Techniques.

Today researchers explore a spectrum of historical and emerging topics: multimedia visualization, three-dimensional mapping, social image tagging, digital visual copyright, video retrieval, sense-making through information

Figure 8.5   Display of the words in this chapter, created by Wordle (www.wordle. net). Font size indicates frequency of use.

visualization, visual indexing, new image browsing, image classification, and potential semiotics of color and sound.

To talk about information visualization is to speak of the future synergies and developments for interacting with the human perceptual apparatus. Most paradigms being commercialized today were paper ideas of researchers 50 years ago. These were realized as specialized projects by a few elite institutions in the 1980s. These applications permeate our world today. Developments in information visualization continue to expand in scope and impact. Online games are being transformed into more serious information-centered endeavors. *Star Trek*'s "holodeck" may not be far off. As processing power increases and the cost of computing decreases, the potential for mapping virtual worlds for information-centered applications has yet to be fully imagined.

References

Abrams, J. (1994). Muriel Cooper's visible wisdom. *AIGA, The Professional Association for Design*. Retrieved November 11, 2010, from www.aiga.org/medalist-murielcooper.

Adams, R. M., Stancampiano, B., McKenna, M., & Small, D. (2002, October). Case study: A virtual environment for genomic data visualization. Paper presented at the 13th IEEE Visualization Conference, Boston, MA.

American Library Association. (2009). *Intellectual freedom and censorship Q & A*. Retrieved November 11, 2010, from www.ala.org/ala/aboutala/offices/oif/basics/ifcensorship qanda.cfm.

Arnheim, R. (2004). *Visual thinking*. Berkeley: University of California Press.

Bertin, J. (1983). *Semiology of graphics* (W. J. Berg, Trans.). Madison: University of Wisconsin Press.

Brin, S., & Page, L. (1998). The anatomy of a large-scale hypertextual Web search engine. *Seventh International World-Wide Web Conference*. Retrieved November 11, 2010, from ilpubs.stanford.edu:8090/361.

Card, S. K., Mackinlay, J. D., & Shneiderman, B. (1999). *Readings in information visualization: Using vision to think*. San Francisco: Morgan Kaufman.

Cleverdon, C., & Keen, M. (1966). *Factors determining the performance of indexing systems: Test results*. Cranfield, UK: Aslib Cranfield Research Project.

Davis, C. H., & McKim, G. W. (1999). Systematic weighting and ranking: Cutting the Gordian knot. *Journal of the American Society for Information Science, 50*(7), 626–628.

Davis, C. H., & Rush, J. E. (1979). *Guide to information science*. Westport, CT: Greenwood.

Farb, S. (2006). Libraries, licensing, and the challenge of stewardship. *FirstMonday, 11*(7). Retrieved November 11, 2010, from firstmonday.org/htbin/cgiwrap/bin/ojs/index.php/ fm/article/view/1364/1283.

Froehlich, T. J. (1994). Relevance reconsidered: Towards an agenda for the 21st century: Introduction to special topic issue on relevance research. *Journal of the American Society for Information Science, 45*(3), 124–134.

Gombrich, E. (1995). *The story of art* (16th ed.). New York: Phaidon.

Hahn, K. L. (2007). SERU (Shared Electronic Resource Understanding): Opening up new possibilities for electronic resource transactions. *D-Lib Magazine, 13*(11/12). Retrieved November 11, 2010, from dlib.org/dlib/november07/hahn/11hahn.html.

Korfhage, R. (1997). *Bibliography on first phase information visualization.* Retrieved November 11, 2010, from www.asis.org/SIG/SIGVIS/hostedMaterial/bibliography.pdf.

Lynch, C. (2005). Where do we go from here? The next decade for digital libraries. *D-Lib Magazine, 11*(7/8). Retrieved November 11, 2010, from www.dlib.org/dlib/july05/lynch/07lynch.html.

Maeda, J. (2001). *Design by numbers.* Boston: MIT Press.

Massachusetts Institute of Technology Architecture Machine Group. (1981). Interactive movie map. Retrieved July 25, 2009, from www.naimark.net/projects/aspen/aspen_v1.html.

Panofsky, E. (1972). *Studies in iconology: Humanistic themes in the art of the Renaissance.* New York: Harper & Row.

Saracevic, T. (2007). Relevance: A review of the literature and a framework for thinking on the notion in information science. Part II: nature and manifestations of relevance. *Journal of the American Society for Information Science and Technology, 58*(3), 1915–1933.

Shneiderman, B. (2003). *Craft of information visualization: Readings and reflections.* New York: Morgan Kaufmann.

Tufte, E. (1983). *The visual display of quantitative information* (2nd ed.). Cheshire, CT: Graphics Press.

Tufte, E. R. (1990). *Envisioning information.* Cheshire, CT: Graphics Press.

Tukey, J. W. (1977). Exploratory data analysis. Reading, MA: Addison-Wesley.

Vickery, B. C. (1959). Subject analysis for information retrieval. *Proceedings of the International Conference on Scientific Information* (Vol. 2, pp. 855–866). Washington, DC: National Academy of Sciences. Retrieved November 11, 2010, from www.nap.edu/openbook.php?isbn=NI000518&page=855.

Wilson, P. (1973). Situational relevance. *Information Storage & Retrieval, 9*(8), 457–471.

CHAPTER 9

Evaluation of Information Systems

9.1. Methods of Evaluation

Information systems represent large investments of time and money, and their adoption (or not) has consequences for the individuals who work with the system and others who rely on the work of those individuals. For a variety of reasons, it is important to assess how well information systems perform. Evaluation of information systems can have a number of goals or purposes. An evaluation might seek to

- Increase understanding of human behavior, including human-computer interaction (HCI) and human-computer-human interaction

- Discover how tasks and work processes are mediated by technology and how these processes influence the adoption and adaptation of technology

- Influence the design of technology

- Influence technology investment and purchase decisions

- Support product marketing efforts

Sometimes an evaluation will have multiple goals. For example, Sonnenwald, Whitton, and Maglaughlin (2003) sought to provide insights regarding the efficacy of technology supporting scientific collaboration, increase understanding of collaborative scientific work processes mediated by technology, and inform the design of collaboration technology. Three basic types of evaluations have emerged: *self-studies*, *laboratory studies*, and *field studies* (e.g., Andriessen, 1996; Pinelle & Gutwin, 2000; Twidale, Randall, & Bentley, 1994).

Self-Studies

In a self-study, designers and developers inspect a system to evaluate whether it satisfies system requirements, best practice standards, or both. Techniques include walkthrough inspections, system simulations, and heuristic evaluation. Walkthrough, or peer-review, inspections focus on identifying problems in software code and discussing solutions to those problems (Weigers, 2001). The inspections are typically performed by peers—colleagues of the people who developed the software. In a system simulation, input from users (or other systems or both) is simulated and used to evaluate a system. For example, in the Text Retrieval Conference (Voorhees & Buckland, 2007) and the Cross-Language Evaluation Forum (Peters, 2002), queries from users are simulated and submitted to information retrieval systems. When processing the queries, all systems search the same databases. The search results are captured and compared in order to evaluate the systems' performance. Self-studies provide relatively quick feedback while incurring minimal costs. However, designer and developer bias may interfere with the evaluation: Designers and developers may overlook or misinterpret findings because they have a personal interest in, and knowledge of, the system. Furthermore, no self-study can address whether the system will be adopted and used. Laboratory studies address some of these concerns by including controlled experiments and quasi-experiments that involve participants (other than the designers and developers) using the system to solve representative tasks.

Laboratory Studies

Laboratory studies can help generate insights into a system's usability and effectiveness (e.g., Wixon & Wilson, 1997), participants' attitudes toward the system (e.g., Sonnenwald et al., 2003), or potential system impact on task or work processes and performance (e.g., Söderholm et al., 2008). Thus, these studies can support both summative evaluation, providing feedback on a current design, and formative evaluation, providing feedback on possible improvements for future versions of a system. The latter is particularly useful in an iterative design-evaluation approach. Evaluation data collected in laboratory studies may include

- Logs of computer transactions

- Task performance measures such as the amount of time to complete a task

- Pre- and post-test questionnaires that gather user expectations and impressions

- Think-aloud protocols, in which the user describes his or her thoughts while performing the task

- Audio and video recordings of user-computer interactions

- Pre- and post-interviews to gather user expectations and impressions

The laboratory study approach provides several advantages. First, the evaluation can take place before all the necessary infrastructure and system components are developed and deployed. This is useful when the system to be evaluated requires technical infrastructure, such as high-speed, robust, and secure internet connections, that may not yet be available in the target context of use. In fact, the system may not even exist; sometimes it is beneficial to evaluate the potential of a system before it is developed because of the development costs.

A second advantage of laboratory studies is that the results are available more quickly than are the results of field study evaluations. Considerable time can pass between the design and development of technology and its deployment and adoption (or rejection). A lab experiment does not depend on these cycles of deployment and adoption, which allows the evaluation to provide more timely feedback to designers, developers, and other stakeholders.

A primary disadvantage of the laboratory study is its inherent artificiality. This can be reduced by selecting experimental tasks that replicate actual tasks and work situations relevant for the target user population and context of use. How closely the experiment mirrors real-world conditions is referred to as *ecological validity*. Ecological validity can be measured by asking study participants, in a questionnaire administered immediately after they have participated in a session, how realistic the experiment was and how absorbed they were during the session. Other challenges in designing laboratory studies include selecting a study population that is a representative sample of intended users and selecting valid and reliable measures.

Field Studies

A field study is a semi-structured period of observation of users in their natural environment. Participants are observed using the system in the context of their everyday lives or work. Examples of field studies include work by Xie (2008) and Walsh, Kucker, Maloney, and Gabbay (2000). These studies investigate patterns of adoption and adaptation as well as nonadoption of systems, the relationships among technologies, and task and work processes and outcomes. Evaluation data collected in field studies may include

- Unstructured interviews: The interviewer begins with some open-ended questions, but the conversation develops in response to the interviewee's responses.

- Semi-structured interviews: The interviewer has a framework of topics to be explored and may use both structured and open-ended questions.

- Focus groups: Small groups of users (often 6 to 12 people) respond to questions and interact with each other to discuss their use of the system.

- Diaries: Individuals record their experiences and reactions to the system; these may be written on paper, kept electronically, or audio-recorded.

- Observations: Observers record gestures, comments, and other actions; users may be observed directly, observers may be behind a one-way mirror, or users may be video-recorded for later analysis.

- Questionnaires: Detailed questions are prepared in advance; responses may be collected through one-on-one interviews or by paper or computer survey instruments.

- Computer logs: Typically, computer logs record the exact time and content of each user entry and system response; for web use, logs can show each website visited.

- Work artifacts: These include training manuals, "cheat sheets," and work performance measures such as the time required for a qualified user to perform a certain task.

- Process measures, including sociometric data: Who supervises whom; who talks with, emails, or texts whom.

Like laboratory studies, field studies can be conducted before a system is created in order to develop system requirements (e.g., Sonnenwald et al., 2001). But when conducted as part of an evaluation, field studies are usually summative in nature, describing a system's impact on processes and outcomes after it has been introduced into a setting. Because they are performed on a system in normal use, field studies remove speculation or prediction concerning the system's use and impact.

Challenges involved in conducting field studies include gaining access to settings and participants, as well as having sufficient time and resources to conduct and analyze interviews and observations, especially when user skills and attitudes change over time. Evaluating collaboration technology is especially difficult because users are geographically dispersed. Another challenge is that the results of a field study may not have any impact on the design of a system; the study's results may be too late to be incorporated into the system but can provide insights for future systems.

Usability Perspective

In summary, the design of an evaluation should take into account the type of information system to be evaluated, the purposes of the evaluation, the context in which the system will be used, the specific tasks or work processes it will support, and the resources (including time, money, and expertise) available to conduct the evaluation. There will always be trade-offs and compromises when designing an evaluation. Each evaluation approach has strengths and weaknesses; the challenge is to determine which approach, or combination of approaches, is best considering the purposes, context, and resources available for the evaluation.

9.2. Human-Computer Interaction

Human-computer interaction (HCI) is "concerned with the design, evaluation and implementation of interactive computing systems for human use and with the study of major phenomena surrounding them" (Association for Computing Machinery, 1996, "Definition of HCI," p. 5). It draws on research from human factors—the psychological, social, physical, biological, and safety characteristics of a user and the system (Adams, 2009b); *cognitive psychology*—the study of how people acquire, process, and store information, as well as parts of computer science concerned with systems and visualization; and *ergonomics*—making products and tasks comfortable and efficient for the user (Adams, 2009a). The Association for Computing Machinery (1996, "Field of HCI," p. 8) noted that "the growth of discretionary computing and the mass personal computer and workstation computer markets have meant that sales of computers are more directly tied to the quality of their interfaces than in the past." This introduction 1) considers how HCI has been studied and the lessons learned; 2) examines the notion and assessment of usability; and 3) concludes with a brief subsection on recent developments in HCI, focusing on how computers can support human-to-human communication.

Lessons From HCI

Not long ago, the "I" in HCI stood for *interface*; research aimed to study a user at a desktop computer and optimize interaction at the interface between the two. The human side of HCI focused on understanding human information processing and use of language for communication and for interaction with the computer. The discussion of language use and understanding in Chapter 4 provides perspective on the reasons that designers of computer systems worked hard to develop systems with even rudimentary abilities to interact with humans using natural language. Getting "inside the user's head" is a challenging assignment; cognitive psychology laid the basis for much early work in HCI. Card, Moran, and Newell's (1983) book, *The Psychology of Human-Computer Interaction*, set the stage for 20 years of empirical research.

Ju's (2007) research comparing geography majors with computer science majors in their use of an online geographic information system is a good example. Ju recorded completion time, task completeness, and mouse movements for each student. She found that subject expertise did not affect how long students took to complete the tasks or their success; however, expertise did affect how the students interacted with the system. Following established practice from psychology, the researcher hypothesized how subject expertise might affect the time required and success with the assigned tasks; the research was then conducted in a controlled setting (a lab), each student was tested individually, and statistical measures (analysis of variance) and analysis techniques (goals, operators, methods, and selection rules) were used to compare student performance.

Fitting the system to the user is the focus of ergonomics, another research area that gained prominence as HCI developed in the 1980s. The International Ergonomics Association (2009) has identified three areas of interest:

- Physical: anatomical, physiological, and biomechanical capabilities and limitations of people using the system

- Cognitive: mental processes, such as perception, memory, reasoning, and motor response of system users

- Organizational: organizational structures, policies, and processes of sociotechnical systems

Venda and Venda (1995) analyzed ergonomics studies to develop the *law of mutual adaptation*, which postulates that system users will perform best when the computer system's capabilities match the cognitive skill structures and behavior strategies of the human user. Efficiency gains are subject to diminishing returns because, as a user develops more advanced cognitive skill structures, he or she can find additional strategies to perform the same task. Through its interface, a "mutually adaptive" system can support these new skills and strategies, thus increasing the user's efficiency in performing the task (Carey, 1997, p. 5).

Studies of users (or people similar to intended users) and experience in adapting systems to fit people (instead of the other way around) encouraged system designers to

- Focus on user(s) and task(s) early in system design: Who will use the system, how often will they use it, and what tasks will they do most often? (A data entry system to be used by experts 8 hours a day should support quick access to common tasks. The infrequent user posing an occasional query to the same system will need more support from the interface; speed of access can be sacrificed for a more "chatty" interaction.)

- Use empirical measures to test the interface: Quantitative usability measures such as the time to complete the task(s) and the number of errors made during the task(s) allow comparison of various interfaces.

- Adopt an iterative design approach: 1) Design the interface, 2) test the interface, and 3) analyze the results. Repeat this process.

A good design can make an interface easier to learn and faster to use, can reduce errors, and can increase the users' sense of satisfaction. Wickens, Lee, Liu, and Gordon Becker (2004) derived 13 design principles, which they grouped according to a focus on perception, mental models, attention, or memory:

Perceptual principles:

1. Make displays legible (or audible). A display's legibility is critical and necessary for designing a usable display. If the characters or objects being displayed cannot be discernible, then the operator cannot effectively make use of them.

2. Avoid absolute judgment limits. Do not ask the user to determine the level of a variable on the basis of a single sensory variable (e.g., color, size, loudness). These sensory variables can contain many possible levels.

3. Design for top-down processing. Signals are likely perceived and interpreted in accordance with what is expected based on a user's past experience. If a signal is presented contrary to the user's expectation, more physical evidence of that signal may need to be presented to ensure that it is understood correctly.

4. Make use of redundancy gain. If a signal is presented more than once, it is more likely that it will be understood correctly. This can be done by presenting the signal in alternative physical forms (e.g., color and shape, voice and print) because redundancy does not imply repetition. A traffic light is a good example of redundancy, in that color and position are redundant.

5. Use elements that can be easily discriminated from each other, because similarity causes confusion. Signals that appear to be similar will likely be confused. The high ratio of similar features to different features causes signals to be perceived as similar. For example, A423B9 is more similar to A423B8 than 92 is to 93. Unnecessary similar features should be removed, and dissimilar features should be highlighted.

Mental model principles:

6. Principle of pictorial realism. A display should look like the variable that it represents (e.g., high temperature on a thermometer should be shown as a higher vertical level). If there are multiple elements, they can be configured in a manner that looks as they would in the represented environment.

7. Principle of the moving part. Moving elements should move in a pattern and direction compatible with the user's mental model of how the things they represent actually move. For example, the moving element on an altimeter should move upward with increasing altitude.

Principles based on attention:

8. Minimize information access cost. When the user's attention is directed from one location to another to access necessary information, there is an associated cost in time or effort. A display design should minimize this cost by allowing for frequently accessed sources to be located at the nearest possible positions. However, adequate legibility should not be sacrificed to reduce this cost.

9. Use proximity to connect related information. Divided attention between two information sources may be necessary for the completion of one task. These sources must be mentally integrated and are defined to have close *mental proximity*. Information access costs should be low, which can be achieved in many ways (e.g., close proximity or linkage by common colors, patterns, or shapes). However, close display proximity can be harmful if it causes too much clutter.

10. Use multiple senses. A user can more easily process information across different resources. For example, visual and auditory information can be presented simultaneously rather than presenting only visual or only auditory information.

Memory principles:

11. Replace memory with visual information: knowledge in the world. A user should not need to retain important information solely in working memory or to retrieve it from long-term memory. A menu, checklist, or another display can aid users by easing their use of their memory. However, the use of memory may sometimes benefit the user rather than the need for reference to some type of knowledge in the world (e.g., an expert computer operator would

use direct commands from memory rather than referring to a manual). The use of knowledge in a user's head and knowledge in the world must be balanced for an effective design.

12. Provide predictive aids. Proactive actions are usually more effective than reactions. A display should attempt to eliminate resource-demanding cognitive tasks and replace them with simpler perceptual tasks in order to reduce the use of the user's mental resources. Doing so will allow the user not only to focus on current conditions but also to think about possible future conditions. An example of a predictive aid is a road sign displaying the distance from a certain destination.

13. Provide consistency. Old habits from other displays will easily transfer to support processing of new displays if the displays are designed in a consistent manner. A user's long-term memory will trigger actions that the user expects to be appropriate. A design must accept this fact and use consistency among different displays.

Usability

It is important to understand usability in order to enhance the functionality and the acceptance of information systems. The International Organization for Standardization (1994) holds that usability is "the extent to which a product can be used by specified users to achieve specified goals with effectiveness, efficiency, and satisfaction in a specified context of use" (p. 10).

Jakob Nielsen (1993), a well-known usability expert, identified five attributes of usability:

- Learnability

- Efficiency

- Memorability

- Handling of errors

- Satisfaction

Jeng (2006) added usefulness, ease of use, ease of operation, pleasure in use, ease of navigation, intuitiveness, ability to engage the user, flexibility, effectiveness, and memorability.

Usability is a property of the total system, including interface design, functional design, data and metadata, and computer systems and networks. All these components must work together smoothly to create a system that is both effective and easy-to-use. When examining usability issues, it is also essential to bring in technical, cognitive, and social perspectives; usability is not an isolated quality but a feature diffused throughout the ecology of technology. Four components are essential: the user, the task, the tool used, and the environment in which people work—which influences how they use artifacts (Jeng, 2006; see also Bennett, 1972, 1979; Eason, 1981; Shackel, 1991).

Usability Evaluation Techniques

Focus groups, questionnaires, think-aloud protocols, computer log analysis, and field studies are often employed in usability evaluation. The following techniques have been developed specifically for usability testing:

- *Card sort* is one of the simplest yet most useful techniques. It requires few resources, needs little time to complete, and often provides useful insights: Subjects are given cards, each labeled with a content item or function; they group the cards in the way that makes sense to them. Card sort can be used to test the structure or organization of a digital library, an information system, or a website. It is most effective when participants have never seen the site or when the site is undergoing a major redesign.

- *Category membership expectation* is designed to test participants' understanding of categories and their labels. Participants are asked to describe what they would expect to find under particular category names. Like the card sort, this is a good method for looking at vocabulary. The major drawback is that it can be exhausting for the participants if there are a large number of categories (Campbell, 2001).

- *Heuristic evaluation*, sometimes called *usability audit* or *heuristic expert review*, is widely used. It yields reasonable benefits for low cost. Typically three to five evaluators use a list of recognized usability principles (called *heuristics* or *rules of thumb*) to analyze the interface. Heuristic evaluation is often most effective when done at the beginning of a project and then repeated at later stages of development (Hom, 2000). The evaluators generally can detect most of the usability problems; however, the reports tend to focus on microfeatures of an interface rather than the global picture.

- *Cognitive walkthrough* also involves expert evaluators. They design specific task scenarios, define the user's goals and purpose for each task, and break the tasks into relatively small pieces. The evaluator plays the part of the user working with the site, noting problems, paths, and barriers (Lewis & Wharton, 1997). Because it does not involve actual users, it can be conducted any time and as frequently as desired, for instance to clean up a website. Cognitive walkthrough is more limited in scope than heuristic evaluation, but it provides a clear structure for conducting the analysis once user profiles and tasks have been defined. Both heuristic evaluation and cognitive walkthrough address surface features of usability well but do not identify deeper issues, such as how users formulate good queries, evaluate results, and interact with the information.

- *Claims analysis* is less structured than cognitive walkthrough. It is more difficult to learn, but it supports the analyst in thinking about usability issues more deeply. Claims analysis provokes thinking about why things are the way they are and how they could be different. In this method, the usability engineer identifies significant features in a design and generates hypotheses about what consequences these features might have for users engaged in activities.

- *Concept-based analysis of surface and structural misfits* (CASSM) considers design in terms of concepts: the user's concepts, those implemented within the system, and those represented at the interface. The analysis focuses on the quality of fit between the user and system concepts (Blandford, Keith, Connell, & Edwards, 2004; Connell, Green, & Blandford, 2003). CASSM does not deal with usability issues at the levels of detail of heuristic evaluation, cognitive walkthrough, or claims analysis. It is a more broad-brush approach; it is also more difficult to learn than heuristic evaluation or cognitive walkthrough. Both claims analysis and CASSM probe deeper issues; claims analysis is more demanding of the analyst and delivers a wider range of insights.

- *Paper prototyping* involves representative users performing realistic tasks by interacting with a paper version of the interface that is manipulated by a person "playing computer." The simulated computer offers a new screen display (sheet of paper) for each choice the user makes (Snyder, 2003).

Next Steps for HCI

Computer and communication technologies play a much greater role in everyday life now than they did a quarter century ago. Sellen, Rogers, Harper, and Rodden (2009) took stock of these changes and discussed their implications for future developments in HCI. They have identified five transformations in our relationships with computers:

1. The end of interface stability as computers are embedded in home appliances, cars, and clothing as well as public spaces such as malls and airports

2. The growth of technodependency as more sophisticated, autonomous computers are given tasks related to such things as shopping, travel, and medical care

3. The growth in hyperconnectivity as digital communication devices take our time and attention

4. The end of the ephemeral with the growth of each person's "digital footprint," consisting of information about where we are and what we purchase that would formerly have been discarded

5. The growth of creative engagement as digital tools (e.g., Web 2.0) allow for play, self-expression, and new ways of seeing the world

Sellen and colleagues (2009) would redefine HCI. Humans are not just users of computers; as consumers, creators, and producers, they value aesthetic and emotional aspects of their interactions with technology. Computers today are digital technologies embedded in our world; computers also rely on this embedded infrastructure, so the "C" in HCI must expand to comprehend network connections as well. Finally, the interaction may be within a person's body, between bodies, between a body and an object (not just by typing or mousing), or among many bodies and objects—for example, in a public space. Sellen and colleagues concluded that "the conception of technology use as a conscious act becomes difficult to sustain" and "HCI must take into account the truly human element, conceptualizing 'users' as embodied individuals who have desires and concerns and who function within a social, economic, and political ecology" (p. 66).

References

Association for Computing Machinery Special Interest Group on Computer-Human Interaction Curriculum Development Group (1996). Curricula for Human-Computer Interaction. Retrieved May 10, 2011, from old.sigchi.org/cdg.

Adams, C. (2009a). Ergonomics. *About.com*. Retrieved November 11, 2010, from ergonomics.about.com/od/glossary/g/defergonomics.htm.

Adams, C. (2009b). Human factors. *About.com*. Retrieved November 11, 2010, from ergonomics.about.com/od/glossary/g/defhumanfactors.htm.

Andriessen, J. H. E. (1996). The why, how and what to evaluate of interaction technology: A review and proposed integration. In P. J. Thomas (Ed.), *CSCW requirements and evaluation* (pp. 107–124). London: Springer Verlag.

Bennett, J. L. (1972). The user interface in interactive systems. *Annual Review of Information Science and Technology, 7,* 159–196.

Bennett, J. L. (1979). The commercial impact of usability in interactive systems. In B. Shackel (Ed.), *Man-computer communication, infotech state-of-the-art* (Vol. 2, pp. 1–17). Maidenhead, UK: Infotech International.

Blandford, A., Keith, S., Connell, I., & Edwards, H. (2004, June). Analytical usability evaluation for digital libraries: A case study. *Proceedings of the ACM/IEEE Joint Conference on Digital Libraries,* Tucson, AZ. DOI:10.1109/JCDL.2004.1336093.

Campbell, N. (2001). *Usability assessment of library-related web sites: Methods and case studies.* Chicago: Library Information Technology Association, American Library Association.

Card, S. K., Moran, T. P., & Newell, A. (1983). *The psychology of human-computer interaction.* Hillsdale, NJ: Erlbaum.

Carey, J. M. (Ed.). (1997). *Human factors in information systems: Relationship between user interface design and human performance.* Norwood, NJ: Intellect Books.

Connell, I., Green, T., & Blandford, A. (2003). Ontological sketch models: Highlighting user-system misfits. In E. O'Neill, P. Palanque, & P. Johnson (Eds.), *People and computers XVII: Designing for society: Proceedings of HCI 2003* (pp. 163–178). London: Springer.

Eason, K. D. (1981). A task-tool analysis of manager-computer interaction. In B. Shackel (Ed.), *Man-computer interaction: Human factors aspects of computers and people* (pp. 289–307). Rockville, MD: Sijthoff and Noordhoff.

Hom, J. (2000). *Usability methods toolbox: Heuristic evaluation.* Retrieved November 11, 2010, from usability.jameshom.com/heuristic.htm.

International Ergonomics Association. (2009). *What is ergonomics?* Retrieved July 31, 2009, from www.iea.cc/01_what/What%20is%20Ergonomics.html.

International Organization for Standardization. (1994). *Ergonomic requirements for office work with visual display terminals. Part 11: Guidance on usability* (ISO DIS 9241-11). London: International Organization for Standardization.

Jeng, J. (2006). *Usability of the digital library: An evaluation model.* Unpublished doctoral dissertation, Rutgers University, New Brunswick, NJ.

Ju, B. (2007). Does domain knowledge matter: Mapping users' expertise to their information interactions. *Journal of the American Society for Information Science and Technology, 58*(13), 2007–2020.

Lewis, C., & Wharton, C. (1997). Cognitive walkthroughs. In M. G. Helander, T. K. Landauer, & P. V. Prabhu (Eds.), *Handbook of human-computer interaction* (pp. 717–732). New York: Elsevier Science.

Nielsen, J. (1993). *Usability engineering.* Cambridge, MA: Academic Press.

Peters, C. (2002). Evaluating cross-language systems the CLEF way. *Cultivate Interactive, 6.* Retrieved November 10, 2010, from www.cultivate-int.org/issue6/clef.

Pinelle, D., & Gutwin, C. (2000). A review of groupware evaluations. *Proceedings of the IEEE International Workshops on Enabling Technologies: Infrastructure for Collaborative Enterprises 2000,* 86–91. DOI: 10.1109/ENABL.2000.883709.

Sellen, A., Rogers, Y., Harper, R., & Rodden, T. (2009). Reflecting human values in the digital age. *Communications of the ACM, 52*(3), 58–66.

Shackel, B. (1991). Usability: Context, framework, definition, design and evaluation. In B. Shackel & S. J. Richardson (Eds.), *Human factors for informatics usability* (pp. 21–37). New York: Cambridge University Press.

Snyder, C. (2003). *Paper prototyping: The fast and easy way to design and refine user interfaces.* Boston: Morgan Kaufmann.

Söderholm, H. M., Sonnenwald, D. H., Cairns, B., Manning, J. E., Welch, G., & Fuchs, H. (2008). Exploring the potential of video technologies for collaboration in emergency medical care. Part II: Task performance. *Journal of the American Society for Information Science and Technology, 59*(14), 2335–2349.

Sonnenwald, D. H., Bergquist, R., Maglaughlin, K. A., Kupstas-Soo, E., & Whitton, M. (2001). Designing to support collaborative scientific research across distances: The nanoManipulator example. In E. Churchill, D. Snowdon, & A. Munro (Eds.), *Collaborative virtual environments* (pp. 202–224). London: Springer Verlag.

Sonnenwald, D. H., Whitton, M. C., & Maglaughlin, K. L. (2003). Evaluating a scientific collaboratory: Results of a controlled experiment. *ACM Transactions on Computer Human Interaction, 10*(2), 150–176.

Twidale, M., Randall, D., & Bentley, R. (1994). Situated evaluation for cooperative systems. *Proceedings of the ACM Conference on Computer Supported Cooperative Work,* 441–452.

Venda, V. F., & Venda, Y. V. (1995). *Dynamics in ergonomics, psychology, and decisions: Introduction to ergodynamics.* Norwood, NJ: Ablex.

Voorhees, E. M., & Buckland, L. P. (Eds.). (2007). *The sixteenth Text Retrieval Conference* (NIST Special Publication 500-273). Retrieved November 11, 2010, from trec.nist.gov/pubs/trec16/t16_proceedings.html.

Walsh, J. P., Kucker, S., Maloney, N. G., & Gabbay, S. (2000). Connecting minds: Computer-mediated communication and scientific work. *Journal of the American Society for Information Science, 51*(14), 1295–1305.

Weigers, K. E. (2001). *Peer reviews in software: A practical guide.* New York: Addison-Wesley.

Wickens, C. D., Lee, J. D., Liu, Y., & Gordon Becker, S. E. (2004). *An introduction to human factors engineering* (2nd ed.). Upper Saddle River, NJ: Pearson Prentice Hall.

Wixon, D., & Wilson, C. (1997). Usability engineering framework for product design and evaluation. In M. G. Helander, T. K. Landauer, & P. V. Prabhu (Eds.), *Handbook of human-computer interaction* (pp. 653–688). New York: Elsevier Science.

Xie, H. I. (2008). Users' evaluation of digital libraries: Their uses, their criteria, and their assessment. *Information Processing & Management, 44*(3), 1346–1373.

CHAPTER 10

Information Management

10.1. Introduction

In the 1970s, the information science community explicitly enlarged its scope to consider not only information storage and retrieval but also the developments in information creation, management, and policy that were evident, especially with the development of more capable technologies. Information came to be seen as a resource—one with both costs and benefits for an organization. Macevičiūtė and Wilson (2002) have described four consequences:

1. The economics of information became an important topic for research.

2. As more attention was directed to the content of databases, the importance of text (not just numbers) was recognized, and more effort went toward improved handling of textual data.

3. The user-centered approach to systems emerged as a way to increase accessibility and use of information resources.

4. The need for national, local, and organizational information policies and strategies was recognized.

When the journal *Information Storage & Retrieval* changed its title to *Information Processing & Management*, its editor noted, "the information needs of research, management, and policy-making emerge as critical requirements, and effective access to information from many disciplines and from many parts of the world becomes imperative. Thus we must view information processing and management as an integral part of overall public policy-making, linked to social and economic affairs as well as to science and technology" (Fry, 1975, p. i). Library and information science educators also broadened their focus to prepare graduates for information management positions in the private sector (Wilson, 1989); some schools changed their names to include *information management* as well.

The term information management is ambiguous, but in information science settings, it often connotes an explicit management (often business) perspective. In 2000 Macevičiūtė and Wilson (2002) reviewed the content of six journals in information management; they identified 14 main subjects of the field:

- Application areas (banking, healthcare, and manufacturing being most prominent)
- Artificial intelligence
- Economics of information
- Education for information management
- Information management (predominantly aiding business strategy)
- Information networks (mainly internet related)
- Information professionals
- Information systems
- Information technology (predominantly economics, strategy, and organizational impact)
- Information use and users
- Knowledge management
- Organizations (culture, environment)
- Telecommunication industry
- Theory and research methods

The authors concluded that information management "has continued to thrive and much of what is now included is far removed even from modern information science, although information management draws upon ideas from both librarianship and information science. In one form or another it is likely to persist in the future, since information problems are likely to persist in organizations. The means for resolving the problems may change, but the need to understand those problems and develop solutions will remain" (Macevičiūtė & Wilson, 2002, Conclusion).

Wilson (2003) subsequently observed, "Whether information management is a passing fancy or a new way of considering the role of information in organizational performance must await the test of time; however, there can be little doubt that the concept has had a significant impact on the thinking of professionals working in a variety of fields. Managers of computer services have become information managers (and even directors of information management services); records managers, archivists, information scientists and special librarians have changed their titles and shifted their professional orientations" (p. 275).

10.2. Social Informatics

What Is Social Informatics?

Rob Kling (2003), one of the founders of the field, has provided this definition of *social informatics* (SI):

> the systematic, interdisciplinary study of the design, uses and consequences of information technologies (IT) that takes into account their interaction with institutional and cultural contexts. Thus, it is the study of the social aspects of computers, telecommunications, and related technologies, and examines issues such as the ways that IT shape organizational and social relations, or the ways in which social forces influence the use and design of IT. For example, SI researchers are interested in questions about the future consequences of IT developments. (p. 2656)

A shorter definition is "Social informatics is the systematic study of social aspects of computerization" (Kling, Rosenbaum, & Sawyer, 2005, p. 3).

As a field of study, SI draws on several disciplines, including information science, anthropology, software engineering, computer science, instructional systems, political science, and sociology. It is a new field, sometimes considered a subfield of socioeconomic research. Like human-computer interaction or gerontology, SI is characterized by the problems examined, not the theories or methods used (Kling et al., 2005, p. 6). Because the field is young, SI researchers come from various disciplinary backgrounds, and their publications are scattered among journals from many fields.

History of SI

Early, engineering-based approaches to understanding the interactions between humans and computers investigated new technologies, but a few researchers looked at social impacts, for example, privacy (Westin & Baker, 1972). Bell (1973) took a broad, informatics perspective on society and the impact of computers. At the University of California–Irvine, the URBIS Group's studies of how computers affected local government in the 1980s helped invent research that would look beyond the engineering perspective to analyze qualitative data about social background and behavior; Dutton (2005) claimed that Rob Kling coined the term *social* informatics while he worked with the URBIS Group.

Researchers and developers in Scandinavian countries, Great Britain, and northern Europe also wanted more than simplistic predictions or models of the likely social impacts of information tools. They sought to go beyond socially or technologically deterministic theories and look equally at social issues and technology. Their research began to focus on both the surrounding social context and the mechanical properties of information systems.

By the 1990s, researchers in various fields began to recognize the inaccuracy of many predictions about the social effects of specific information and communication technologies (ICTs); careful study revealed that the prognosticators often used oversimplified conceptual models of specific kinds of ICTs or of the nature of the relationship between technology and social change. For example, Suchman (1996) studied a plan by a group of attorneys to develop an expert system that would code documents in preparing civil litigation; she found that the human coders' work required more complex judgments than an expert system could handle and recommended that the coders be supported, rather than replaced, by the new system.

In 1996, researchers interested in "the interdisciplinary study of the design, uses, and consequences of ICTs that takes into account their interaction with institutional and cultural contexts" (Kling et al., 2005, p. 6) selected SI as the name for their field. It represented international studies with various information technology names, or simply informatics in Europe. Some of the terms and phrases replaced by SI are *new media, compunications, télématique* (French), *informatique* (French), *social impacts* (or analysis) *of computing*, and *computer-mediated communication studies*. Centers for SI have been established at Indiana University at Bloomington and at Napier University in Edinburgh, Scotland.

Knowing how to build information systems and engineer communications without understanding the work practices and social context of users can lead to waste and problems. Empirical evidence from more than 30 years of research supports this conclusion, but because these studies appear in such a variety of sources, many systems developers do not know they exist.

SI researchers study technology in the context of human organizations and institutions. Instead of asking deterministic questions such as how new technologies—such as wireless handsets and smartphones—will change people, SI asks about the impacts of individuals' use of technology on the social groups in which they participate. And, in the other direction, how do groups influence technological developments? Applying SI to business applications is challenged by a world full of academic silos and technology-driven markets.

SI Perspective on System Design and Development

Imagine investigating the relationships between university students and Facebook. How does one study the interaction and impact they have on each other? What needs preceded the technical tools or development of the social networks? Do new features come from the users or the inventors? Using SI as a framework, one might study how users influence the capabilities of a product, which could help developers of new versions and (new) members of the social networks. SI research aids system designers in understanding the following issues:

- How humans interact with an information system

- How policies in organizations and institutions affect behavior and work practices

- Which application or process resources support the sharing of information

Table 10.1 (adapted from Kling et al., 2005, p. 42) contrasts traditional, engineer-based perspectives with social design views of research and applications.

Note that *explicit knowledge* involves objective, technical, and reasoned knowledge, such as policies, procedures, data, and documents; *tacit knowledge*, however, is subjective and based on experience and personal cognition.

Researchers have used the SI perspective on system design and evaluation in a wide range of organizations and institutions. The following examples show how SI contributes to understanding of information dissemination in organizations, product development, and strategic and business intelligence (information about other organizations, often competitors).

Information Dissemination

Traditional approaches to track and illustrate the spread of information in an organization use data flow diagram techniques. Data flow diagrams provide models of business processes and the flow of data, such as the origins and sharing of a purchase order. By illustrating where information is sent and received, data flowcharts reveal the structure of an organization. Institutional policies and business processes are also reflected in diagrams or models of where data is stored and when it flows. Figure 10.1 shows the basic data flow diagram for someone who loans videos to friends (and keeps very complete records of the transactions).

In comparison, SI research has led to new views of information dissemination and social connections. *Social network analysis* has been one of the most influential research perspectives; it represents the relationships among social entities so that the patterns and their implications can be studied. Relationships can be built on economic, political, personally interactive, and affective connections. Figure 10.2 illustrates the social network and sharing of information—the interactions—among seven student nurses blogging about work and healthcare issues (Swain, 2006). Thicker lines indicate more sharing of information.

Table 10.1   Engineer and social design views of research and applications

Engineering or Designer Approach	Social Design View
Explicit views of work	*Tacit views of work*
Work can be documented, made visible.	Aspects of work are silent and shared.
Tasks are easy to articulate and transfer.	Work is understood without articulation.
Training makes work possible.	Learning makes work possible.
Tasks are at the core of work.	Knowledge is at the core of work.
Position is clear in a hierarchy.	Position is defined by informal political networks and contacts.
Procedures and techniques are the basis of action or doing work.	Conceptual understanding is the basis of action or doing work.
Methods and procedures are the guides to work.	Rules-of-thumb and judgment are the guides to work.
Intended goals	
Improve work efficiency.	Improve work practices.
Reduce human error.	Discover and solve problems.
Design assumptions	
User needs are identified by what is visible and documented; they can be rationalized into one set of needs.	User needs emerge from observing everyday work practices, which may conflict, and thus there are often real differences in needs.
Design is linear and can be documented at the end of system development.	System design is iterative and requires prototyping.
Individual work is to be supported through process clarity.	Collaboration and collaborative learning take place in a social context.
Efficiency is a desired outcome.	Skill development is a desired outcome.
Technological choices	
People can adapt to technologies chosen to support organizational values.	Configurations matter and interact with human work activities.
Convenience is provided by technology.	Flexibility requires social choices.

Social networks and information flow illustrations have been presented as product features in Bebo, Facebook, and MySpace. For example, social networks provide a user with views of who else relates to whom in the online exchange of information.

In the summer of 2008, Facebook introduced a redesign of its social networking site to 90 million viewers; thousands of users protested, using petitions and online groups to request maintaining the option to toggle between the old and new versions (Swartz, 2008). The company responded as users

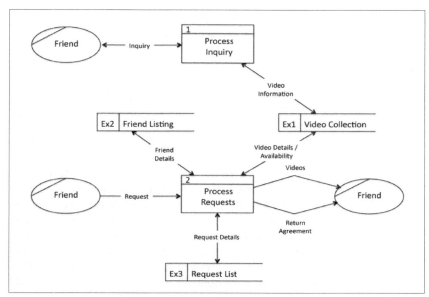

Figure 10.1 Data flow diagram comprised of three data stores (open rectangles Ex1, Ex2, and Ex3)—Video Collection, Friend Listing, and Request List—and two processes (rectangles 1 and 2)—Inquiry and Requests. When a Friend (an external agent, indicated by the oval bubble) inquires about a video, data flow from the Video Collection (Ex1) file to the Inquiry Process. When a Friend asks to borrow a video, data flow from Ex1, Ex2, and Ex3 to the Requests process, which provides the video and a return agreement to the Friend.

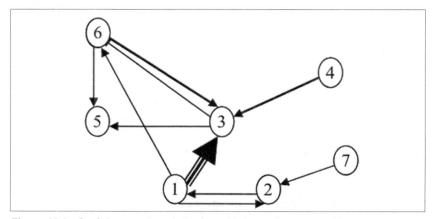

Figure 10.2 Social network and sharing of information among bloggers

gradually moved to a revised version with less clutter and continued features that allow a constantly updated analysis of friends' changes.

Product Development

SI has adopted techniques from anthropology and sociology. Careful observation of behavior helps SI researchers recognize nuances that other engineers and designers might miss.

For example, a 1990s study of the work practices in a telecommunications company provided a social perspective of information systems (Sachs, 1995). The researcher had been trained as an anthropologist; she looked at the social choices involved in the installation of telephone lines. The ICTs used by the technicians had been designed with assumptions about the number of employees required to respond to a service request. When efficiency consultants observed technicians talking among themselves and forming teams to go on calls, the behavior was seen as socializing and nonproductive. The consultants recommended reducing conversations and sending out the first available technician. The consultants built a "trouble ticket" system to schedule and track calls and responses. However, the expected increase in productivity and efficiency did not occur. The SI researcher noted that with the eliminated conversations, the technicians "compared notes … they figured out what [a problem] was and worked on it together" (Sachs, 1995, p. 39). In the absence of an SI perspective, valuable troubleshooting behavior had been overlooked. In addition, understanding the social context revealed that the technicians developed specializations; some were more efficient at responding to certain problems than were others. The trouble ticket strategy had assumed that standardized training made all technicians equal and that any one of them could respond to a service request.

Digitization of records in healthcare requires sophisticated data processing and management. Patterson, Cook, and Render (2002) report on a Veterans Administration hospital's efforts to digitize patient records. The project took a simple, direct view of the work done by nurses, and the records were designed to reflect these nurses' work habits. Because the system designers did not collect or take account of the collaboration that goes into creating patient records, the nurses had to spend more time, not less, in working around the new system that was intended to reduce workloads and improve efficiency.

Strategic and Business Intelligence

Historically, both hierarchical bureaucracy and access control have been dominant issues in intelligence gathering and analysis, ranging from competitive intelligence to national security. A top-down structure can strengthen control over the flow of information in an organization, but such communication constraints also hinder the sharing of data and ideas. Recent developments in social software have brought something of a transformation to the intelligence community. For example, Web 2.0 collaboration tools, such as blogs, wikis, RSS, and instant messaging, have become increasingly popular among various intelligence analysts (Thompson, 2006).

What mechanisms underlie the collaborative creation of intelligence? Could wikis and blogs indeed help intelligence professionals? To what extent do the collaborative tools support, enhance, or hinder intelligence practices? How do intelligence professionals perceive the value of social computing in their daily work? A Canadian study investigated how competitive intelligence professionals using social software can connect with like-minded colleagues, informants, and intelligence users. In *strategic intelligence* efforts, they work jointly to piece together clues and identify patterns in business trends and technology development (Jin, Bouthillier, Bowen, Boettger, Montgomery, Pillania, et al., 2007).

Why Study SI?

In 2005, it was estimated that only about 300 people worldwide were doing SI research. That research was going on in Australia, Europe, Israel, Japan, South Korea, and the U.S. Today, research is conducted in more countries, but it is hard to estimate how many researchers consider themselves social informaticians. Although publications from social-oriented informatics research are scattered across disciplines, three approaches are common:

1. Normative research: The application of empirical studies in the development of theories, practices, and policies for socio-technical interaction networks

2. Theoretical analysis: Analytical study that leads to the definition of methodologies and theories in institutional settings

3. Critical analysis: The use of nontraditional views to study technologies in order to influence the design and implementation of information systems

The findings of SI research are built on careful, contextually situated, and empirically grounded analysis; this contrasts with the typical promotions for new ICTs made by vendors, pundits, and uncritical analysts. Such optimism often leads to the design and implementation of ICTs that may occasionally work well and be valuable. Too often, however, projects are abandoned or unusable, thus incurring needless waste and inspiring misplaced hopes in the capabilities of ICTs to bring about positive changes in the workplace or home (see Kling et al., 2005).

Dutton (2005) pointed out that "the intellectual craftwork that underpins its multidisciplinary research is critical to the success of Social Informatics" (p. xiii); conducting SI research is not a cookbook operation. It requires scholars who have patience, a willingness to collaborate, the ability to observe people in social settings, the agility in analysis to see patterns and trends, and a willingness to transfer intellectual capital to others. Nevertheless, the need to combine technological design with qualitative research about users will grow as computers have impacts on users in changing social contexts and as users influence communications.

10.3. Knowledge Management

In a sense, knowledge management is the logical next step, after data (facts from observations) management and information (collection of facts with context) management. However, as discussed in Chapter 2, knowledge is generated by people, which makes it considerably more complex:

> Knowledge is a fluid mix of framed experience, values, contextual information, and expert insight that provides a framework for evaluating and incorporating new experiences and information. It originates and is applied in the minds of knowers. In organizations, it often becomes embedded not only in documents or repositories but also in organizational routines, processes, practices, and norms. (Davenport & Prusak, 1998, p. 5)

Blair (2002) described knowledge management in this way: "The management and support of expertise, then, unlike data and information management, … is primarily the management of individuals with specific abilities, rather than the management of repositories of data and information" (p. 1022). Experts in any area (from gaming to genetic analysis) have "tacit knowledge"—they know how to do things, but this knowledge is not (easily) expressed. The classic example is the Xerox photocopier technicians who were able to diagnose photocopier problems by the sounds and vibrations from the machines (Brown & Duguid, 2000). The knowledge of experts is often developed and shared in a "community of practice," where "a particular practice is common and coordinated … generic understandings are created and shared, and negotiation is conducted" (Davenport & Hall, 2002, p. 172). Establishing, maintaining, and facilitating communication between both experts (in their communities of practice) and novices is key to knowledge management. An organization seeking to manage its knowledge needs a "major commitment on the part of its members—the experts and novices must be willing to share what they know with others" (Blair, 2002, p. 1022).

Database management and information retrieval technologies support knowledge management. "Knowledge and expertise can be unpredictably varied, [and] the data and information that assist them can be unpredictably variable in their form or content. Data, text, images, schematics, video, audio, webpages, compound and multimedia documents can all be important ancillaries to knowledge management. Consequently, we must have widely available commercial technology that can physically manage this wide variety of informative media" (Blair, 2002, p. 1026).

Globalization and the shift toward a knowledge economy are key drivers of knowledge management. The increased emphasis on skilled-based activities and technological advances has made it possible for organizations to compete globally. Globalization presents opportunities for businesses from developed countries, at the cutting edge of research and technology, and it poses challenges and problems to developing nations that do not have sufficient knowledge infrastructure: Intellectual capital is what translates into wealth and sustainable development. Organizations as well as governments around the world have recognized the importance of intellectual capital and begun to pay attention to the knowledge infrastructure needed to enable them to compete. This includes the education system, information resources, technological resources, human capital in terms of skilled workers, and the respect for intellectual capital.

Knowledge Management Practices

Knowledge management is considered the new frontier of human resource management: In the current business environment, success is based increasingly on the ability to leverage organizational knowledge effectively and to anticipate and ride the waves of change through innovation.

Consulting firms originally developed and experimented with knowledge management to benefit their own organizations. They then reached out to extend these solutions to their clients; the main objectives were intellectual capital valorization, organizational processes' innovation, and sustenance of new organizational solutions. From this perspective, both intellectual capital and knowledge workers are considered as strategic resources; information and communication technology and organizational process optimization are thus factors enabling knowledge management.

To support corporate ICT investments for knowledge management, top management requires justifiable and reliable return on investment. Specific, quantitative, and mainly technically oriented indicators must be combined with more qualitative and management-oriented indicators to measure the return on investments of knowledge management solutions. Problems typical of traditional training solutions may be encountered in this measurement.

An integrated and holistic approach to knowledge management includes technical, organizational, and people-oriented aspects. An enterprise portal provides a single, secure access point that is the integration hub for

- Information and communications technology and database management systems

- Process workflows and maps of competence, which represent embedded and implicit organizational knowledge and its potential for innovation and efficiency improvements

- Professional social networks, such as communities of practice, emphasizing the people-oriented aspect of knowledge management

The *community of practice model*, an organization system based on knowledge rather than hierarchy, is a lean and flexible organization in which members consolidate, update, and distribute specific corporate knowledge based on the professional family to which they belong. In particular, a community of practice may constitute a change accelerator if it is both integrated and in synergy with the corporate organization.

Early implementations have required a strong behavioral change in combination with changes in organizational structure and management. Because human beings tend to be change-averse, change management has been considered a key factor in a successful implementation of knowledge management solutions. Constant commitment from top management and a cultural revolution in middle management have been required. Knowledge management ties knowledge to innovation (from an organizational perspective) and to creativity, entrepreneurship, and leadership (from a knowledge worker's point of view). This can foster both entrepreneurial creativity and the creation of *learning organizations.*

A learning organization has integrated and holistic knowledge management solutions, enabling it to create strategic differentiation in a given market. The key factor is its capability to combine business competence with process skills and collaborative styles. In such an adaptable organization, change will no longer be an event of massive proportions requiring change management; instead, change will be continuous and embedded in the processes for organizational decision-making. The goal is to create an intelligent and market-driven organization, capable of innovation, collaboration, efficiency, flexibility, adaptability, and strategic leadership through learning.

References

Bell, D. (1973). *The coming of post-industrial society: A venture in social forecasting*. New York: Basic Books.

Blair, D. C. (2002). Knowledge management: Hype, hope, or help? *Journal of the American Society for Information Science and Technology, 53*(12), 1019–1028.

Brown, J. S., & Duguid, P. (2000). *The social life of information.* Cambridge, MA: Harvard Business School Press.

Davenport, E., & Hall, H. (2002). Organizational knowledge and communities of practice. *Annual Review of Information Science and Technology, 36*(1), 171–227.

Davenport, T., & Prusak, L. (1998). *Working knowledge.* Boston: Harvard Business School Press.

Dutton, W. H. (2005). Foreword. In R. Kling, H. Rosenbaum, & S. Sawyer (Eds.), *Understanding and communicating social informatics: A framework for studying and teaching the human contexts of information and communication technologies* (pp. xi–xv). Medford, NJ: Information Today.

Fry, B. M. (1975). A change in title and scope to meet changing needs. *Information Processing & Management, 11*(1), i.

Jin, T., Bouthillier, F., Bowen, B., Boettger, S., Montgomery, M., Pillania, R., et al. (2007). Traditional and non-traditional knowledge management in research and practice. *Proceedings of the American Society for Information Science and Technology, 44,* 1–5. DOI: 10.1002/meet.1450440114.

Kling, R. (2003). Social informatics. *Encyclopedia of library and information science* (pp. 2656–2661). New York: Dekker.

Kling, R., Rosenbaum, H., & Sawyer, S. (2005). *Understanding and communicating social informatics: A framework for studying and teaching the human contexts of information and communication technologies.* Medford, NJ: Information Today.

Macevičiūtė, E., & Wilson, T. D. (2002). The development of the information management research area. *Information Research, 7*(3). Retrieved November 11, 2010, from informationr.net/ir/7-3/paper133.html.

Patterson, E. S., Cook, R. I., & Render, M. L. (2002). Improving patient safety by identifying side effects from introducing bar coding in medication administration. *Journal of the American Medical Informatics Association, 9*(5), 540-553. DOI:10.1197/jamia.M1061.

Sachs, P. (1995, September). Transforming work: Collaboration, learning, and design. *Communications of the ACM, 38*(9), 36–44. DOI:10.1145/223248.223258.

Suchman, L. (1996). Supporting articulation work. In R. Kling (Ed.), *Computerization and controversy: Value conflicts and social choices* (2nd ed., pp. 407–413). San Diego, CA: Academic Press.

Swain, D. (2006). Can blogging be used to improve medication error collection as part of health informatics knowledge management? In S. Hawamdeh (Ed.), *Creating collaborative advantage through knowledge and innovation* (pp. 301–314). Hackensack, NJ: World Scientific.

Swartz, J. (2008, September 22). Some Facebook users aren't fond of website's new face. *USA Today.* Retrieved November 11, 2010, from www.usatoday.com/tech/products/2008-09-21-facebook_N.htm.

Thompson, C. (2006, December 3). Open-source spying. *New York Times.* Retrieved November 11, 2010, from www.nytimes.com/2006/12/03/magazine/03intelligence.html.

Westin, A., & Baker, M. (1972). *Databanks in a free society: Computers, record-keeping, and privacy.* New York: Quadrangle Books.

Wilson T. D. (1989). Towards an information management curriculum. *Journal of Information Science, 15*(4–5), 203–209.

Wilson, T. D. (2003). Information management. In I. J. Feather & P. Sturges (Eds.), *International Encyclopedia of Information and Library Science* (2nd. ed., pp. 263–278). London: Routledge.

CHAPTER 11

Publication and Information Technologies

11.1. Information Generation

Individuals and organizations continually generate information and produce knowledge. The creative impulse underlying the "origination" of information, to use Borko's (1968, p. 3) term, is typically the province of psychology, although some information systems attempt to create conditions that will inspire innovation.

Only a fraction of all the information we generate is made public. In the print culture, publishers or publishing houses are the primary filters, deciding what should be accepted and disseminated to the public. Now that individuals may "publish" their work on the internet, the concept of publication is blurred. Nor is all information intended to become public; for example, corporations protect trade secrets, and the military restricts access for reasons of security. In the public sphere and the academic sector, however, dissemination of one's ideas and recognition for contributions is generally sought and admired.

Information Explosion

For decades researchers have noted the increasing rate of publication. Rider (1944) suggested that libraries would be unable to cope with the geometrical increase in the number of books published. Price (1975) demonstrated the geometric growth of scientific publications; both Rider's and Price's books are classics in the literature about the *information explosion*. Lyman and Varian (2003) reported that in 2002 the world produced about 5 exabytes of new information, stored on print, film, magnetic, and optical storage media (of which 92 percent was stored on magnetic media, mostly hard disks). This is almost 800 megabytes of recorded information per person (the equivalent of about 30 feet [9.1 meters] of books) in 1 year.

Although there is a dramatic increase in the number of publications, this alone is not evidence that the amount of information has increased; the rapid obsolescence of many recent publications and the exceptional staying power of works from decades or centuries ago demonstrate that merely publishing information does not guarantee its lasting utility (Spang-Hanssen, 2001).

Primary, Secondary, and Tertiary Information Sources

The UNISIST (1971) model of the flow of scientific and technical information identifies three types of organizations involved in the production and dissemination of information. Søndergaard, Andersen, and Hjørland (2003) updated the UNISIST list to include practices beyond science and technology domains and to reflect the changes in scientific and scholarly communication introduced by the internet. Combining these two sources provides a list of five types of information sources and services:

1. Primary sources such as editors and publishers are responsible for selection, publication, and distribution. Examples include conference papers, journal articles, monographs ("books"), eprint servers, email and discussion lists, social networking sites, and blogs. Source literature, which researchers use as data for the work they publish, would include data archives, product information and trade literature, and music.

2. Secondary sources, such as abstracting and indexing services, libraries, and information centers provide analysis, storage, and dissemination. Examples include subject bibliographies and bibliographical databases, abstract journals, indexes, citation indexes and databases, digital libraries, and search engines. Language control devices assist in the use of sources such as translation dictionaries, thesauri, and controlled vocabularies (see Chapter 4).

3. Tertiary sources, such as reviews, catalogs, and guides to the literature, provide evaluation, compression, and consolidation. Examples include handbooks, textbooks, and review articles.

4. Incidental information (about computers and software or about job opportunities, for example) is also important, even though it is not part of a domain's regular knowledge production. Examples include directories, conference calendars, and personal homepages.

5. Popularizations that export knowledge produced in a domain include magazines, mass market books (including general encyclopedias), mass media, and multimedia presentations.

The amount of information being recorded in all these areas continues to increase. The primary sources used in scholarly communication are of particular interest because they reflect the generation of new information and the production of knowledge.

11.2. Scholarly Communication

Many researchers and scholars currently developing the technologies and analyses that will underlie future developments work in universities, research centers, and industry. As discussed in Chapter 2, the introduction and vetting of new ideas through scholarly communication traces back at least to Francis Bacon at the beginning of the 17th century. The Association of College and Research Libraries (2009) defines scholarly communication as "the system through which research and other scholarly writings are created, evaluated for quality, disseminated to the scholarly community, and preserved for future use"; it is typically accomplished through "research papers, primary data and other evidence, creative activity and other products of research and scholarship" (paragraph 1).

Original scholarship thus appears in the primary information sources listed in the previous section; secondary and tertiary sources generally cumulate, evaluate, comment upon, recast for different audiences, and disseminate the information produced by researchers and scholars. This section looks at three components of the scholarly communication system that are being transformed by information and communication technologies: research in *collaboratories*, *peer review*, and *open access publishing*.

Collaboratories

Collaboration among scientists has increased dramatically in the past century; the equipment and support needed for research in areas ranging from astronomy to genetics has hastened the development of large-scale science (Weinberg, 1961; what Price, 1963, termed *big science*). The number of journal articles with more than one author continues to increase—authors sometimes number in the hundreds, and today authors are much more likely to acknowledge support from technical and support staff as well as funding agencies (Sonnenwald, 2007). Expectations of the scholarly community ("publish or perish") may encourage the elevation of what would have been an acknowledgment to a co-authorship status and the growth of "hyper-authorship" (Cronin, 2001, p. 558). Scientific collaborations extend beyond local institutions, with many having multidisciplinary perspectives and global scope. In addition to their scientific and technical skills, researchers need administrative abilities to coordinate their groups. They rely on technology to support the communication, provide access to scientific instruments, and record the information that is fundamental to modern science.

In 1989 William Wulf, at the National Science Foundation, coined the term *collaboratory* by combining the words collaboration and laboratory. He defined it as "a center without walls, in which users can perform their research without regard to geographical location—interacting with colleagues, accessing instrumentation, sharing data and computational resources, and accessing information in digital libraries" (Committee Toward a National Collaboratory, 1993, p. vii).

Some scientific instruments are expensive, such as telescopes and super colliders, and researchers compete for time to run experiments with this equipment. Working in collaboratories helps keep use of these instruments at full capacity: Staff local to the instrument develop and maintain skills with the equipment while researchers from other locations prepare experiments, oversee their implementation, and analyze the results (Finholt, 2002). Collaboratories support research in oceanography, biology, space physics, and environmental molecular science. Finholt (2002) concluded that

1. Use does not need to be constant in order to provide value.

2. Systems that are easily integrated into existing work environments are more readily adopted.

3. Some domains (such as data collection) are more naturally inclined toward collaboration than others (data collection vs. contemplation and idea formation).

4. Long-distance collaboration creates new experience for participants, including altered roles (e.g., operators who must be more responsive, students who guide faculty, senior investigators who must accommodate less experienced participants). (p. 95)

Collaboratories have been promoted as a way to improve scientific progress by reducing the limitations of space, time, and status. Inequalities are diminished when all participants interact over the internet. At least so far, however, status differences appear to be maintained. Humans, even scientists, can interact with only a limited number of people engaged in forwarding the field: the *invisible college* (Crane, 1972; Price, 1963); and although nonelite scientists may have electronic communication with the elite, few such interactions develop into collaborative relationships (Finholt, 2002). However, collaboratories also facilitate communication among scientists outside the elite groups, which Finholt suggested may expand participation and promote the development of new perspectives.

Peer Review

Publishers function as filters, deciding what information will be disseminated—they are a primary defense against being overwhelmed by the information explosion. In scholarly publishing, this filtering is often done by means of peer review: Researchers knowledgeable in the field read, comment on, and make recommendations regarding the acceptance of work submitted for publication. Peer review is used extensively in the sciences and social sciences.

The peer review process is usually "blind," in that the author does not know who the reviewers are. It may also be "double blind," so that the reviewer does not know the identity of the author(s) he or she is reviewing; however, experienced reviewers and authors may be able to guess the identity, even if they are not told. In some cases the author may suggest reviewers to the editor. Critics of peer review have raised concerns about its psychological limitations (for example, reviewers who move from criticism to abuse of the work at hand), conflicts of interest (for example, reviewers trying to suppress papers critical of their own research or of work in which they have a financial interest), and ethical problems (such as the reviewer suppressing or even stealing the author's ideas). The internet can support more transparent interactions that provide alternatives to the traditional procedures for peer review. The science journal *Nature* (2006) hosted a debate that featured various perspectives on the problems and possible new approaches.

Open Access

Open access (OA) is free online access, for any user, to the full text of scientific and scholarly material: free availability and unrestricted use. Suber (2007) describes OA as the "unrestricted reading, downloading, copying, sharing, storing, printing, searching, linking, and crawling of the full text of the work" (The legal basis of OA is the consent of the copyright holder …).

OA material is usually copyrighted so that the author can maintain the integrity of the work rather than limit its use. Many authors use a *Creative Commons* license (creativecommons.org/about/licenses), which allows the author to set the level of restrictions on use of the work. Levels range from *attribution*, where users may distribute, display, and perform the copyrighted work and derivative works based upon it, but only if they give proper credit to the author, to *attribution-noncommercial-no derivatives*, which allows copying and sharing of the work as long as the license holder receives credit and the work is not changed or used commercially.

OA thus challenges the established economic models of publishing, in which the publisher takes the risk, foots the bill, and reaps any economic reward. OA is not without production costs; however, because so much of the creation, preparation, and distribution are done online, these can be lower than the costs of print publication. Two models of OA have evolved for journal articles: *gold* and *green*.

An OA journal (the *gold route*) follows the usual practices for submission and peer review. Journal articles are published online and are freely available. Costs may be paid by some combination of the authors, an author's employer or funding agency, subsidies from universities or professional organizations, institutional subscriptions, and advertising. The Public Library of Science (www.plos.org/index.php) is a nonprofit organization of scientists and physicians that publishes seven OA journals; BioMed Central (www.biomedcentral.com) is the for-profit publisher of about 200 peer-reviewed journals.

With *green route* OA the author of a journal article "self archives" by placing a copy of the article in a repository—an online collection of digital information that provides open access and long-term preservation. Repositories may accept preprints (the version submitted for publication in a non-OA venue), postprints (the version as published), or both. Repositories may also include material not intended for publication, such as working papers, internal reports, instructional materials, and data files. Some repositories are discipline-specific; arXiv (arxiv.org), the repository for physics, mathematics, and computer science, is the best known. Many universities and research institutions have established institutional repositories (e.g., DSpace at the Massachusetts Institute of Technology, dspace.mit.edu), which are not limited by subject.

Authors of scholarly publications are interested in the impact of their work. This is commonly assessed by counting the number of times an article is cited by other articles: More citations mean greater impact (discussed later). Several researchers (e.g., Hajjem, Harnad, & Gingras, 2005, some of them strong advocates for OA publishing and therefore with a vested interest in the topic, have shown that journal articles available through OA are cited sooner and more often than other, similar articles. Because potential readers worldwide have easy access to OA publications, the increased rates of citation are certainly plausible, as well as intriguing.

11.3. Bibliometrics and Citation Analysis

Bibliometrics literally means "book measurement." Pritchard (1969) coined this term for "all studies which seek to quantify processes of written communication" and "the application of mathematics and statistical methods to books and other media of communication" (pp. 348–349). Previously, "statistical bibliography" (Hulme, 1923) had been used to describe the study of science and technology by counting documents. *Scientometrics* and *informetrics* are related. Scientometrics (from the Russian *naukometria*) is the study of the quantitative features and characteristics of science; although these characteristics may be nondocumentary, scientometricians are primarily concerned with quantitative studies of scientific document collections. Informetrics deals with the measurement of all aspects of information (Egghe & Rousseau, 1990); it is not limited to quantitative studies of written communication or to the study of the quantitative features and characteristics of science. Bibliometricians work with analyses of publications and of citations.

Publication and Citation Analysis

Publication analysis concerns the quantitative analysis of document collections; it includes, for example, publication counts of authors, journals, institutions, and countries. The study of scientific collaboration is also a form of publication analysis.

Citation analysis distinguishes between references and citations. Price (1970) proposed and adopted the convention that "if Paper R contains a bibliographic footnote using and describing Paper C, then R contains a reference to C, and C has a citation from R" (p. 7). Paper R is thus the citing document and Paper C the cited document (Diodato, 1994). Another way to view this is that a citation is the acknowledgment one bibliographic unit receives from another whereas a reference is the acknowledgment one unit gives to another (Narin, 1976).

Citation analysis has four main applications (Nicolaisen, 2007):

1. Qualitative and quantitative evaluation of scientists, publications, and scientific institutions

2. Modeling of the historical development of science and technology

3. Information search and retrieval

4. Knowledge organization based on bibliographic coupling and co-citation analysis

Bibliographic Coupling and Co-Citation Analysis

Documents are said to be *bibliographically coupled* if they share one or more bibliographic references. Kessler (1963) introduced the concept and argued for its usefulness as an indicator of subject relatedness. Soon thereafter Martyn (1964) criticized the notion, observing that the bibliographically coupled documents may cite different pieces of information in the cited document; moreover, the strength of association between two sets of bibliographically coupled documents may be unequal. These observations led Martyn to conclude that bibliographic coupling is merely an indication of the existence of the probability, value unknown, of relationship between two documents rather than a constant unit of similarity.

Marshakova (1973) and Small (1973) proposed that documents' relatedness could be measured by their co-citation frequency: how often they appear simultaneously in the reference list of other documents. Price (1965) suggested that networks of scientific papers that are linked, or "knitted" together by citations, reveal either a research front, which builds on very recent work, or taxonomic subjects, tied into "the eternal record of human knowledge" (p. 515). Several people have noted that citations are made for many reasons, not all of which indicate subject relatedness; for example, ceremonial citations might mention eminent people or colleagues whose work is only tangentially related to the paper (Cole & Cole, 1973). Various schemes have been suggested to clarify citer motivations, but Martyn's (1964) criticisms of bibliographic coupling also apply to co-citation analysis.

Regardless of the objections, bibliographic coupling and co-citation analysis have been adopted and used extensively. Visualization of research domains through bibliometric mapping (using the techniques of bibliographic coupling and co-citation analysis) has become one of the major specialties in bibliometrics.

The Bibliometric Laws

Three important "laws" (descriptions of natural events) underpin bibliometrics: Zipf's (1935) observation that speakers and writers use relatively few words most of the time; Bradford's (1948) work demonstrating that a small number of journals in a given field account for most of the core articles; and Lotka's (1926) discovery that relatively few authors generate most journal articles (Potter, 1988).

Zipf's law (1935, 1949) states that when the words in natural language speech or text are ranked by frequency of use, the frequency of any word is inversely proportional to its frequency rank. In English, the word *the* usually ranks first, followed by *of* and *and.* Analysis of the Brown Corpus of English language found that *the* accounted for 7 percent of all word uses, *of* got 3.5 percent, and *and,* about 2.8 percent. Mosteller and Wallace (1964) used Zipf's law to determine the authorship of 12 disputed *Federalist Papers* by comparing the frequency of the use of function words (*a, all,* and *also,* through *would* and *your*). Zipf's law has also been used to investigate how word frequency influences information retrieval (for example, Blair, 1990; Egghe, 1991; Fedorowicz, 1982; Ohly, 1982; Wyllys, 1981).

Bradford's *law of scattering* (Bradford, 1948, 1953) states that documents on a given subject are distributed (or scattered) across the journal literature according to a certain mathematical function. After ranking all journals by how many articles they contribute to the subject, the number of the journals that must be scanned to produce nearly equal numbers of articles is roughly in proportion to $1: n: n^2 \ldots$, where n is called the *Bradford multiplier.* In other words, a small core of journals has as many papers on a given subject as a much larger number of journals, n, which again has as many papers on the subject as n^2 journals.

Lotka's law (Lotka, 1926) states that the number of authors making n contributions is about $1/na$ of those making one contribution, where a is often nearly two. Thus, the number of authors each contributing n articles is proportional to $1/n2$. If 100 authors each produce one article, 25 authors produce two articles, 11 authors produce three articles, and so on.

The practical uses of the three bibliometric laws are limited. Bradford's law has been suggested as a measure for library collection management (Nisonger, 1998), for the organization of library services (Brookes, 1969), for solving practical problems related to information seeking and retrieval (White, 1981), and by Bradford (1948, 1953) himself to support a new way to organize bibliographical work and scientific documentation. Hjørland and Nicolaisen (2005) challenged the assumption that Bradford's law is neutral and objective, pointing out that how the researcher delimits the subject will influence the results.

11.4. Webometrics

Webometrics in information science is currently dominated by World Wide Web link analysis and strongly influenced by citation analysis, being typically applied to scientific data. This section discusses the use of link count metrics in the broad context of informetrics, assessing methodologies and their potential for general social science research. The closely related area of *web citation analysis* is also reviewed, as are search engine evaluation and metric-based research into blogs and social network sites.

In the early years of the web, several information scientists recognized the structural similarity between hyperlinks and citations, noticing that both are inter-document connections and pointers (Larson, 1996; Rodríguez i Gairín, 1997; Rousseau, 1997). This observation underpinned the creation of a new field—webometrics (Almind & Ingwersen, 1997)—defined as the application of quantitative techniques to the web, using methods drawn from informetrics (Björneborn & Ingwersen, 2004).

The power of the web could first be easily tapped for link analysis when commercial search engines released interfaces allowing link searches (Ingwersen, 1998; Rodríguez i Gairín, 1997). For example, in 1997 it became possible with AltaVista to submit extremely powerful queries, such as for the number of webpages in the world that linked to Swedish pages. This meant that with a few hours' work submitting search engine queries, the "impact" of sets of websites could be compared (assuming that links, similar to citations, measure the impact of published information). At the time, most citation analysis was conducted with the use of the citation databases produced by the Institute for Scientific Information, and the searcher or the searcher's institution paid for access. With link analysis, the web "database" is freely available, allowing access to a wider set of potential researchers. With the use of commercial search engines, the impact of many entities was compared, including journals, countries, universities or departments within a country, and library websites (An & Qiu, 2004; Harter & Ford, 2000; Ingwersen, 1998; Smith, 1999; Tang & Thelwall, 2008; Thomas & Willet, 2000). The early studies showed that care was needed to conduct appropriate link analyses because of many complicating factors such as duplicate webpages and sites, errors in search engine reporting, incomplete search engine coverage of the web, link replication within a site, and spurious or trivial reasons for link creation (Bar-Ilan, 2001; Björneborn & Ingwersen, 2001; Egghe, 2000; Harter & Ford, 2000; Smith, 1999; Snyder & Rosenbaum, 1999; van Raan, 2001). Nevertheless, link analysis has produced interesting and useful results and has been adopted by several non-information science fields, as shown below.

This review of webometrics focuses on recent results in the most developed area, link analysis, and covers web-based citation analysis more briefly. The main review is preceded by a brief methodological discussion and speculation about the range of types of information that this new informetric technique may be employed to help measure.

Web Data Sources

Large-scale web statistics can be obtained from commercial search engines, borrowed from web link databases, or obtained directly with a *link crawler* or *spider*—a computer program that moves methodically through the World Wide Web and extracts the links it encounters. When using these tools, the researcher should check to ensure that the results returned by the search engine are correct and in line with expectations (Mayr & Tosques, 2005).

Commercial search engines have problems of coverage (not crawling some sites, crawling others incompletely) and so are not optimal for link analysis, although their use is often unavoidable (Thelwall, 2004). The freely available collection of web link databases online at cybermetrics.wlv.ac.uk/database includes the university website link structures of five countries and tools to analyze the results in various ways. A free web crawler is available at socsci bot.wlv.ac.uk for those who need to gather their own data. This software can crawl sites of up to 15,000 pages but is not suitable for very large sites.

Link Analysis

Link Creation Motivations

A few studies have investigated why links are created. These studies mainly operate on a small scale and use either an information science–style classification approach or a more sociological, ethnographic method. Link creators have a variety of motivations (Bar-Ilan, 2004b, 2004c; Harries, Wilkinson, Price, Fairclough, & Thelwall, 2004; Wilkinson, Harries, Thelwall, & Price, 2003). Link patterns vary according to the level at which they are aggregated, with geographic and cognitive connections dominating at different subnational,

national, and international levels and at discipline and interdisciplinary aggregation levels (Heimeriks & Van den Besselaar, 2006). Similarly, there are some indications that link types vary with the depth (number of clicks from the home page) of links, at least for some academic-related organizations (Vasileiadou & Van den Besselaar, 2006). At the level of subjects, disciplinary differences in linking patterns have been noticed in large-scale studies (see later), and an attempt has been made to theorize these differences in order to understand them (Fry, 2006).

The variety in link types makes link classification studies difficult, but link creation motivations are an essential part of understanding the results of link analysis studies.

Interdepartmental Link Analysis

Most departmental link analyses have aimed to validate link counts as a measure of research impact. A common hypothesis is that the number of links to a department correlates with an established research measure, such as citation counts. Link counts are often normalized by dividing the number of links to a department by the number of pages or researchers in the target department, versions of Ingwersen's (1998) *web impact factor*. Typically also, links within a departmental site are excluded, assumed to be for internal navigational purposes.

Although early results were discouraging (Thomas & Willet, 2000), subsequent studies have demonstrated a correlation between research measures and link counts, supporting the use of links to track research (Li, Thelwall, Musgrove, & Wilkinson, 2003). Links should not be used as a significant part of research assessment in the way that citations sometimes are, however, because only a small percentage of links reflect research achievements directly (e.g., links to online articles acting like online citations). Most indications of research impact are indirect, such as those related to teaching or reflecting membership in a shared organization or research group (Harries et al., 2004; Wilkinson et al., 2003).

Departmental link analyses have demonstrated enormous differences in web publishing. Even aside from natural web users such as computer scientists, one study showed that in the U.S., physicists publish and interlink at least a thousand times more than historians do (Tang & Thelwall, 2003). Li, Thelwall, Wilkinson, and Musgrove's (2005a, 2005b) studies of disciplinary differences are the most detailed yet, covering similar hard science disciplines in similar countries (physics, chemistry, and biology in Australia, Canada, and the U.K.). They found that even similar disciplines use the web in very different ways, such as the extent to which they interlink. This finding is also consistent with some theories from social informatics (Kling & McKim, 2000), which assert that the use of communication technology does not lead to easy universal patterns: Small-scale practical needs can determine how technologies are adopted and adapted. Perhaps more surprising are Li's findings of international differences within the same field; for instance, biology links in Australia were significantly less international (60 percent) than those of the U.K. (74 percent) and Canada (80 percent). From a functionalist perspective, and given the international nature of science, broad similarities in web use might be expected. Nevertheless, the differences support organizational sociologies of science that emphasize the importance of multiple social factors in the practice of science (Fuchs, 1992). From a practical, informetric perspective, the lesson is that link counts are perhaps most valuable for identifying unexpected differences and, because link pages can be traced, identifying their cause. Thus, link analysis seems a natural partner to sociologies of science, as is citation analysis.

A good example is the use of link analysis, in conjunction with other sources of information about connections among researchers (such as European collaborative project membership), to investigate patterns of collaboration in Europe for a specific field (Heimeriks, Hörlesberger, & Van den Besselaar, 2003). This example demonstrates the value of link analysis as part of a multiple-method approach in scientometrics.

Social Network Analysis

Social network analysts are a second set of researchers who have identified links as interesting because they are similar to their normal object of study (Wasserman & Faust, 1994). These researchers study groups of individuals or organizations, focusing on the connections among the members. For example, Rogers and Kincaid (1981) analyzed information flows in a village by word of mouth, using networks of social acquaintances to explain the communication patterns found.

Park (2003) coined the phrase "hyperlink network analysis" for the use of social network analysis (SNA) techniques for networks formed by the links between webpages. Research questions in this area tend to focus on the network properties of sets of websites, using SNA measures. These measures assess properties such as the centrality of individual nodes (webpages or sites) within a network, using metrics such as *inlink counts, outlink counts*, and the frequency with which a *node* appears on the shortest chain of links between pairs of nodes—*betweenness centrality*. For example, Garrido and Halavais (2003) investigated websites supporting the Zapatista Mexican peasant revolutionary movement and found gender politics to play a surprisingly central role in the web network, second only to official Zapatista information sites. A criticism of SNA-style hyperlink analysis is its tendency to assume that hyperlinks are always communication devices, whereas in reality they play a variety of roles (Park & Thelwall, 2003).

Information science researchers have recognized the potential for SNA techniques to assess information networks (Otte & Rousseau, 2002).

Björneborn (2004) applied SNA metrics to U.K. academic websites at the domain level, finding interesting patterns of cross-disciplinary connections. This new area of research may yield insights into information structures and academic communication patterns, perhaps inspired by sociological and mathematical theories of networks (Granovetter, 1973; Watts & Strogatz, 1998).

Some computer scientists have also analyzed social networks using web links (Adamic & Adar, 2003). Their curiosity about social groups may be related both to the development of software for group activities such as online collaboration and to the potential of exploiting group knowledge in improving computer systems (e.g., *collaborative filtering*). Social analyses of the web seem to be a promising research direction for many different scientific fields.

The application of types of link analysis to specialist web environments also holds promise. A good example is *wikimetrics,* developed by Jakob Voss. Statistical analyses revealed the rapid growth of Wikipedia, not only in the total number of articles and pages, but also in the size of individual articles and the number of links per article (Voss, 2005). Others have also used large-scale analyses to study phenomena such as preferential attachment (Capocci et al., 2006). Wikis seem to be particularly good environments for small-world link analyses and studies about the connections between different pieces of information. Social networking sites such as Delicious, Digg, reddit, and Slashdot, which allow individuals to submit stories and others to rate these stories, are natural environments to study user behavior and connections between information and users.

The Social Sciences Link Analysis Methodology

Thelwall (2004) proposed a generic framework for link analysis in social science research:

1. Formulate an appropriate research question, taking into account existing knowledge of web structure.

2. Conduct a pilot study.

3. Identify webpages or sites that are appropriate to address a research question.

4. Collect link data from a commercial search engine or a personal crawler, taking appropriate safeguards to ensure that the results obtained are accurate.

5. Apply data cleansing techniques to the links, if possible, and select an appropriate counting method.

6. Partially validate the link count results through correlation tests.

7. Partially validate the interpretation of the results through a link classification exercise.

8. Report results with an interpretation consistent with the link classification exercise, including either a detailed description of the classification or examples to illustrate the categories.

9. Report the limitations of the study and parameters used in data collection and processing (steps 3 to 5 above). (p. 3)

This framework echoes many of the points made previously, but notice that there is a preliminary stage with a pilot study. This is important because the variety of uses made of the web (Burnett & Marshall, 2002) means that our intuitions about how web links ought to be used in a particular context can be wrong. The pilot study allows a research problem that will not yield an informative link analysis to be aborted before too much effort has been invested. Perhaps the most important message of the framework, however, is the centrality of link-type classification studies. If we have no idea why links are created, then we can make only the most abstract inferences from link counts.

Future Directions for Link Analysis

Information scientists currently have several promising directions for future link analysis research (four are discussed briefly, and a fifth, blog link analysis, is described in more detail):

- Reasons links are created, particularly in academic contexts. A few such investigations have been conducted, as discussed above, but more are needed in order to understand this fundamental question.

- Time series analyses. One problem endemic to web link analyses is that the web is continuously evolving, and any web study may be out of date by the time it is published. Hence it is important to know how all types of web link analysis results vary over time. A low rate of variation would lengthen the "shelf-life" of "webometric" findings.

- Application of SNA measures to information collections. Following Björneborn (2004), more research needs to assess insights from the web into the structure of information and online groupings such as invisible colleges (Caldas, 2003; Zuccala, 2006). One problem to be resolved—perhaps differently in every study—is that link creation is not endemic: The absence of a link between two websites or pages does not mean that they are unrelated.

- Support for wider social sciences research. The web is not exclusively an academic space; it can be used in wider social science research, both as an object in its own right (e.g., to study online communities) and as an easily accessible source of information about offline phenomena that happen to be reflected in the web.

Blog Link Analyses

Blogs are online diaries maintained by millions of web users (BBC, 2005; Nardi, Schiano, Gumbrecht, & Swartz, 2004). Their main attraction is their ease of use. An inexperienced web user can create and maintain an attractive blog without knowledge of the technical details of web publishing. Blogs are an enormous repository of information of varying quality. Many are information-centered, created by people wishing to provide frequently updated expert information on a given topic. Such blogs play the role of a specialist newsletter (Bar-Ilan, 2004a). An example is *The Shifted Librarian* (www.theshiftedlibrarian.com), which is full of facts related to libraries. Extensive linking occurs within and between blogs (Kumar, Novak, Raghavan, & Tomkins, 2004; Marlow, 2004). Many blogs allow visitors to post comments on a blog entry, and it is also easy for a blogger to post a follow-up comment on his or her own blog, linking to the original via its permanent URL. Another link feature is the *blogroll* list of links to other similar or recommended blogs.

Because link creation is so easy and natural within blogspace, it seems a particularly promising medium for link analysis. In fact, link counts are used to compile a daily list of the 100 most popular blogs (www.blogstreet. com/top100.html). Link counts could also be used in ways analogous to citation analysis: Blog links can connect individual posts (*documents*), and bloggers (*authors*) create many posts. There are also differences: the lack of quality control over blog posts; the fact that, unlike scientific publications, blog posts are probably rarely central to the author's job; and the lack of the natural topic organization that journals provide for articles. Nevertheless, the following seem to be likely applications of blog link counts:

- Lists of the most popular blogs (by analogy with most often-cited authors)

- Lists of the most popular individual blog posts (most often-cited articles)

- Relational analysis or network diagrams of the links between blogs (author co-citation or citation graphs)

- Relational analysis or network diagrams of the links between individual blog posts (article citation diagrams)

Beyond deciding what is possible for future blog link analyses, it is important to discuss what is likely to be useful and how link analysis can best be exploited. Clearly there is no pressing need for evaluational blog link analysis comparable to the need to use citations to evaluate scientists' productivity: it might be useful but will not significantly help to direct government research funding. The key findings will likely be most useful for social science research by providing information about the phenomenon of blogging and by providing data about the spread of individual topics (e.g., presidential debate topics could be of interest to political scientists) or, more generally, for the analysis of information diffusion in blogspace by finding spreading patterns that are common across many topics (Gill, 2004; Gruhl, Guha, Liben-Nowell, & Tomkins, 2004). Topic-centered blog link analysis will probably need to employ some kind of text analysis to identify topic-relevant blogs or blog posts and will probably need to be semi-automated with software to gather and filter blog data.

Web-Based Citation Analysis

Although early attempts to assess the impact of scholarly publications on the web used links as analogies of citations, a later strand of research directly used web-based citations (Vaughan & Shaw, 2003). The number of web-based citations of a given article can be estimated in many cases by searching for the article title as a phrase search in a commercial search engine such as Google. Mentions of journals can also be retrieved with Google searches, but the results are likely to be unreliable for the many journals that have common names. The advantage of web-based citation analysis over link analysis is that citations are probably more numerous than links and are more likely to correspond to a genuinely scholarly context. In comparison to citation counting in paper journals, web-based citations have the potential to reflect a wider range of types of use for scholarly work, such as online course reading lists.

Webometric analyses of web-based citations have tended to focus on comparisons with traditional bibliometric techniques (based on Web of Science [WoS] data) to assess the extent to which the two are measuring something similar. The first such study showed that the results of the two techniques correlated significantly for most WoS-indexed library and information science journals (Vaughan & Shaw, 2003). A follow-up study included a classification of types of web-based citation and extended the scope to encompass four science disciplines (Vaughan & Shaw, 2005). The findings revealed that only 30 percent of the web citations reflected intellectual impact (including class reading lists). Nevertheless, the significant correlation between WoS and web citations to articles was confirmed for most journals, with more web than WoS citations being found in total. Some additional patterns were identified, such as weaker correlations for non-U.K. and non-U.S. journals. Other studies have also compared web and traditional citations in more restricted settings, such as the CiteSeer computer science web digital library (Goodrum, McCain, Lawrence, & Giles, 2001), also finding significant correlations with WoS data. A significant difference in the case of CiteSeer was that computer science conference papers attracted significantly more web-based citations than journal articles did, in comparison with their WoS citations. It remains an open question whether the differences identified represent shortcomings in WoS data or web data or both. Nevertheless, it may be that the main application of web-based citation analysis is in providing a second data source with which to compare the WoS citation index. This is an important role, given the use of WoS data in important decisions such as promotion and funding.

Search Engine Evaluation

Web search engine evaluation is the strand of webometrics research that is perhaps most widely useful as background knowledge for information scientists. Traditional information retrieval systems seem to be highly accurate and reliable, but web search engines have many apparently counterintuitive properties because they are optimized for fast performance over huge data sets and for giving results that have a good chance of being useful for a wide audience. One counterintuitive feature of search engines is that the estimated hit counts displayed on results pages (e.g., results 1–10 of about 50,000) can vary widely between pages (Bar-Ilan, 1999; Rousseau, 1999). In general, it seems that when the estimate changes, it is revised downward, often by about 50 percent (Thelwall, 2008a). This appears to result from pages that are rejected because they match the search but are too similar in some way to other matching pages or because there are too many pages from the same website. This duplicate elimination process seems not to be done fully when the initial query is submitted but to be carried out in chunks as demanded.

A related, counterintuitive observation is that search engines sometimes seem to forget URLs over time, even when the pages continue to exist, and sometimes do not return pages matching a query even when the page is known (Bar-Ilan & Peritz, 2004; Mettrop & Nieuwenhuysen, 2001). Moreover, these overlooked pages can contain information that is not present in any returned page (Bar-Ilan & Peritz, 2004). Combining these observations with the known uneven and partial coverage of the web by major search engines, it is clear that if a search engine does not return a useful document for a given search, then one cannot assume that no such document exists. As a result, it is worth trying alternative searches or search engines.

Blog Search Engines

Another device with considerable potential use in social science research is the blog search engine. Blog entries are arranged in reverse chronological order. Because blogs appear to be kept by hundreds of millions of people they form a vast repository of opinions and records about aspects of everyday life, from the mundane to major news stories. This resource can easily be tapped via blog search engines. For example, Google Blog Search, Technorati, or IceRocket allow one to query millions of blogs via a Google-like keyword search. Blog posts are dated, and the results can be displayed chronologically, so a simple search can produce a snapshot of current public opinion about any topic. For example, companies can search for brand names to find customers' recent blogged opinions. More powerfully for social science research, date-specific queries can be issued to find blog posts from a specified period. For example, what did people think about Barack Obama before he declared his candidacy for the 2008 presidential election? Did anyone predict great things for him before 2007? Date-specific blog searching is the only technique available to get retrospective public opinion about a topic of interest that has not been included in an ongoing survey. A variant of the powerful blog-searching technique is the *blog graph*. Search engines such as blog pulse.com and technorati.com can produce graphs showing the proportion of blog posts mentioning a keyword over time (say, 6 months or 1 year). This graph can show trends in interest in a topic and can also be used to identify spikes of interest around particular dates, pointing to particularly significant events. Figure 11.1 shows when the Danish cartoons depicting the Prophet Mohammed attracted significant interest: 4 months after their publication. No other source of evidence could convincingly demonstrate the lack of initial interest in the topic. Reading blog posts around the start of the spike (January 26, 2006) reveals the two main causes: the boycott of Danish products in Saudi Arabia and the recall of the Saudi ambassador from Denmark (Thelwall, 2007).

Social Networks

Another new webometrics direction is the analysis of the contents of social network sites. This combination of webometrics and data mining involves extracting specific data from webpages, such as the number of days since the last login of each member. Figure 11.2 shows these data for MySpace for a random sample of members. Member IDs are given in ascending order; this graph shows that many members (the top line in the graph, about a third of all members) give up within a week of joining but that many others (the bottom line of the graph, also about a third) continue to use the site at least weekly (Thelwall, 2008b).

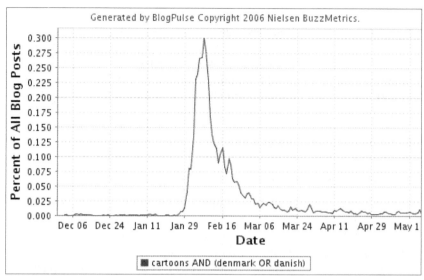

Figure 11.1   A blog trend graph of the cartoons debate: Volume of blog postings related to the Danish cartoons debate (Thelwall, 2007)

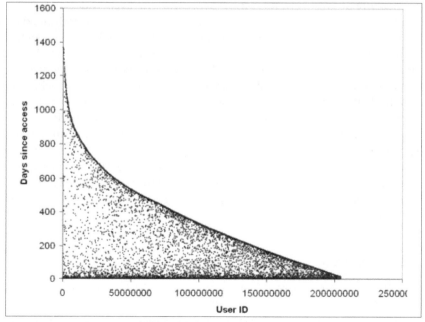

Figure 11.2   Last logon dates plotted against user IDs for random MySpace members (reproduced with permission from Thelwall, 2008b)

Also of interest is *friendship homophily:* the tendency of friends to share similar characteristics (e.g., race, age, religion, motivations for joining a site, marital status). This has been shown to exist in MySpace along many dimensions but with the notable exception of gender (Thelwall, 2009). Very different conclusions were found for a nonwebometric study of a different social network site, last.fm, however (Baym, 2008). This shows that findings for one social network site should not be assumed to apply to others. These two examples (last logon dates and homophily) illustrate just two of a wide range of potential measures that could be applied to social network sites.

Next Steps in Webometrics

There is still considerable scope for more methodological research to explore how best to use links and web citations and the contexts in which they are most useful. This kind of research should be carried out by information scientists who have an intellectual grounding in information issues, particularly citation analysis. Link analysis's main strength is that it can be applied in a wide variety of contexts, not just in its intellectual home of information science, but also more widely in the social sciences to help address problems that relate to the web or have a reflection in the web. Blog link analysis seems particularly promising in this regard because of the likely wide social background of bloggers. A second strength of link analysis is that both the data and the tools to gather it are free and the tools (either search engine searches or the link crawler) are easy to learn. These strengths make link analysis a practical new research tool. It would be logical for information scientists to use link analysis as part of collaborative research with other social scientists (Thelwall, Wouters, & Fry, 2008). The principal weakness of link analysis is that link creation is an unsystematic phenomenon and partly dependent upon factors that are not of interest in most research, such as the design choices of individual web authors. For large-scale research, such decisions tend to even out, but not necessarily on a smaller scale. Hence, unless links themselves are the object of study, they will often need to be used in conjunction with other data sources (e.g., citations) for triangulation in studies with small websites.

References

Adamic, L. A., & Adar, E. (2003). Friends and neighbors on the web. *Social Networks, 25*(3), 211–230.

Almind, T. C., & Ingwersen, P. (1997). Informetric analyses on the World Wide Web: Methodological approaches to "webometrics." *Journal of Documentation, 53*(4), 404–426.

An, L., & Qiu, J. P. (2004). Research on the relationships between Chinese journal impact factors and external web link counts and web impact factors. *Journal of Academic Librarianship, 30*(3), 199–204.

Association of College and Research Libraries. (2009). *Integrating scholarly communication into your library*. Chicago, IL: American Library Association. Retrieved November 11, 2010, from www.acrl.ala.org/scholcomm/node/21.

Bar-Ilan, J. (1999). *Search engine results over time: A case study on search engine stability*. Retrieved November 11, 2010, from www.cindoc.csic.es/cybermetrics/articles/v2i1p1.html.

Bar-Ilan, J. (2001). Data collection methods on the web for informetric purposes: A review and analysis. *Scientometrics, 50*(1), 7–32.

Bar-Ilan, J. (2004a). Blogarians: A new breed of librarians. *Proceedings of the Annual Meeting of the American Society for Information Science and Technology, 41*, 119–128.

Bar-Ilan, J. (2004b). A microscopic link analysis of academic institutions within a country: The case of Israel. *Scientometrics, 59*(3), 391–403.

Bar-Ilan, J. (2004c). Self-linking and self-linked rates of academic institutions on the web. *Scientometrics, 59*(1), 29–41.

Bar-Ilan, J., & Peritz, B. C. (2004). Evolution, continuity, and disappearance of documents on a specific topic on the web: A longitudinal study of "informetrics." *Journal of the American Society for Information Science and Technology, 55*(11), 980–990.

Baym, N. (2008). *Tunes that bind? Predicting friendship strength in a music-based social network*. Retrieved October 21, 2008, from www.onlinefandom.com/wp-content/uploads/2008/10/tunesthatbind.pdf.

BBC. (2005). Blog reading explodes in America. *BBC News*. Retrieved November 11, 2010, from news.bbc.co.uk/1/hi/technology/4145191.stm.

Björneborn, L. (2004). *Small-world link structures across an academic web space: A library and information science approach*. Copenhagen, Denmark: Royal School of Library and Information Science.

Björneborn, L., & Ingwersen, P. (2001). Perspectives of webometrics. *Scientometrics, 50*(1), 65–82.

Björneborn, L., & Ingwersen, P. (2004). Towards a basic framework for webometrics. *Journal of the American Society for Information Science and Technology, 55*(14), 1216–1227.

Blair, D. C. (1990). *Language and representation in information retrieval*. Amsterdam: Elsevier.

Borko, H. (1968). Information science: What is it? *American Documentation, 19*(1), 3–5.

Bradford, S. C. (1948). *Documentation*. London: Crosby Lockwood.

Bradford, S. C. (1953). *Documentation* (2nd ed.). London: Crosby Lockwood.

Brookes, B. C. (1969). Bradford's law and the bibliography of science. *Nature, 224*(5223), 953–956.

Burnett, R., & Marshall, P. (2002). *Web theory: An introduction*. London: Routledge.

Caldas, A. (2003). Are newsgroups extending "invisible colleges" into the digital infrastructure of science? *Economics of Innovation and New Technology, 12*(1), 43–60.

Capocci, A., Servedio, V. D. P., Colaiori, F., Buriol, L. S., Donato, D., Leonardi, S., et al. (2006). *Preferential attachment in the growth of social networks: The case of Wikipedia*. Retrieved November 11, 2010, from arxiv.org/abs/physics/0602026.

Cole, J. R., & Cole, S. (1973). *Social stratification in science*. Chicago: University of Chicago Press.

Committee Toward a National Collaboratory: Establishing the User-Developer Partnership, National Research Council. (1993). *National collaboratories: Applying information technology for scientific research*. Washington, DC: National Academies Press. Retrieved November 11, 2010, from www.nap.edu/catalog.php?record_id=2109.

Crane, D. (1972). *Invisible colleges: Diffusion of knowledge in scientific communities*. Chicago: University of Chicago Press.

Cronin, B. (2001). Hyperauthorship: A postmodern perversion or evidence of a structural shift in scholarly communication practices? *Journal of the American Society for Information Science and Technology, 52*(7), 558–569.

Diodato, V. (1994). *Dictionary of bibliometrics*. New York: Haworth Press.

Egghe, L. (1991). The exact place of Zipf's and Pareto's law amongst the classical information laws. *Scientometrics, 20*(1), 93–106.

Egghe, L. (2000). New informetric aspects of the internet: Some reflections, many problems. *Journal of Information Science, 26*(5), 329–335.

Egghe, L., & Rousseau, R. (1990). *Introduction to informetrics: Quantitative methods in library, documentation and information science*. Amsterdam: Elsevier.

Fedorowicz, J. (1982). The theoretical foundation of Zipf's law and its application to the bibliographic database environment. *Journal of the American Society for Information Science, 33*(5), 285–293.

Finholt, T. (2002). Collaboratories. *Annual Review of Information Science and Technology, 36*, 73–107.

Fry, J. (2006). Studying the scholarly web: How disciplinary culture shapes online representations. *Cybermetrics, 10*(1). Retrieved June 1, 2009, from www.cindoc.csic.es/cybermetrics/articles/v10i1p12.html.

Fuchs, S. (1992). *The professional quest for truth: A social theory of science and knowledge*. Albany: State University of New York Press.

Garrido, M., & Halavais, A. (2003). Mapping networks of support for the Zapatista movement: Applying social network analysis to study contemporary social movements. In M. McCaughey & M. Ayers (Eds.), *Cyberactivism: Online activism in theory and practice* (pp. 165–184). London: Routledge.

Gill, K. E. (2004). *How can we measure the influence of the blogosphere?* Paper presented at the WWW 2004 Workshop on the Weblogging Ecosystem: Aggregation, Analysis and Dynamics. Retrieved May 11, 2011, from citeseerx.ist.psu.edu/viewdoc/download?doi=10.1.1.124.2509+rep=rep1+type=pdf.

Goodrum, A. A., McCain, K. W., Lawrence, S., & Giles, C. L. (2001). Scholarly publishing in the internet age: A citation analysis of computer science literature. *Information Processing & Management, 37*(5), 661–676.

Granovetter, M. (1973). The strength of weak ties. *American Journal of Sociology, 78*, 1360–1380.

Gruhl, D., Guha, R., Liben-Nowell, D., & Tomkins, A. (2004). *Information diffusion through blogspace.* Paper presented at the WWW2004, New York. DOI: 10.1145/988672.988739.

Hajjem, C., Harnad, S., & Gingras, Y. (2005) Ten-year cross-disciplinary comparison of the growth of open access and how it increases research citation impact. *IEEE Data Engineering Bulletin, 28*(4), 39–47. Retrieved July 1, 2009, from eprints.ecs.soton.ac.uk/12906.

Harries, G., Wilkinson, D., Price, E., Fairclough, R., & Thelwall, M. (2004). Hyperlinks as a data source for science mapping. *Journal of Information Science, 30*(5), 436–447.

Harter, S., & Ford, C. (2000). Web-based analysis of e-journal impact: Approaches, problems, and issues. *Journal of the American Society for Information Science, 51*(13), 1159–1176.

Heimeriks, G., Hörlesberger, M., & Van den Besselaar, P. (2003). Mapping communication and collaboration in heterogeneous research networks. *Scientometrics, 58*(2), 391–413.

Heimeriks, G., & Van den Besselaar, P. (2006). Analyzing hyperlink networks: The meaning of hyperlink-based indicators of knowledge. *Cybermetrics, 10*(1). Retrieved June 1, 2009, from www.cindoc.csic.es/cybermetrics/articles/v10i1p1.html.

Hjørland, B., & Nicolaisen, J. (2005). Bradford's law of scattering: Ambiguities in the concept of "subject." *Proceedings of the 5th International Conference on Conceptions of Library and Information Sciences*, 96–106. Retrieved December 20, 2010, from vip.db.dk/jni/articles/hjorland&nicolaisen(2005).pdf.

Hulme, E. W. (1923). *Statistical bibliography in relation to the growth of modern civilization.* London: Grafton.

Ingwersen, P. (1998). The calculation of web impact factors. *Journal of Documentation, 54*(2), 236–243.

Kessler, M. M. (1963). Bibliographic coupling between scientific papers. *American Documentation, 14*(1), 10–25.

Kling, R., & McKim, G. (2000). Not just a matter of time: Field differences and the shaping of electronic media in supporting scientific communication. *Journal of the American Society for Information Science, 51*(14), 1306–1320.

Kumar, R., Novak, J., Raghavan, P., & Tomkins, A. (2004). Structure and evolution of blogspace. *Communications of the ACM, 47*(12), 35–39.

Larson, R. R. (1996). *Bibliometrics of the World Wide Web: An exploratory analysis of the intellectual structure of cyberspace.* Paper presented at the ASIS 59th annual meeting, Baltimore.

Li, X., Thelwall, M., Musgrove, P. B., & Wilkinson, D. (2003). The relationship between the WIFs or Inlinks of computer science departments in UK and their RAE ratings or research productivities in 2001. *Scientometrics, 57*(2), 239–255.

Li, X., Thelwall, M., Wilkinson, D., & Musgrove, P. B. (2005a). National and international university departmental web site interlinking, part 1: Validation of departmental link analysis. *Scientometrics, 64*(2), 151–185.

Li, X., Thelwall, M., Wilkinson, D., & Musgrove, P. B. (2005b). National and international university departmental web site interlinking, part 2: Link patterns. *Scientometrics, 64*(2), 187–208.

Lotka, A. J. (1926). The frequency distribution of scientific productivity. *Journal of the Washington Academy of Sciences, 16*(12), 317–324.

Lyman, P., & Varian, H. R. (2003). *How much information? 2003.* Retrieved November 11, 2010, from www.sims.berkeley.edu/how-much-info-2003.

Marlow, C. (2004). Audience, structure and authority in the weblog community. *International Communication Association Conference.* Retrieved November 11, 2010, from alumni.media.mit.edu/~cameron/cv/pubs/04-01.pdf.

Marshakova, I. V. (1973). A system of document connection based on references. *Scientific and Technical Information Serial of VINITI, 6*(2), 3–8.

Martyn, J. (1964). Bibliographic coupling. *Journal of Documentation, 20*(4), 236.

Mayr, P., & Tosques, F. (2005). *Google web APIs: An instrument for webometric analyses?* Retrieved November 11, 2010, from www.ib.hu-berlin.de/%7Emayr/arbeiten/ISSI2005_Mayr_Toques.pdf.

Mettrop, W., & Nieuwenhuysen, P. (2001). Internet search engines: Fluctuations in document accessibility. *Journal of Documentation, 57*(5), 623–651.

Mosteller, F., & Wallace, D. L. (1964). *Inference and disputed authorship: The Federalist.* Reading, MA: Addison-Wesley.

Nardi, B. A., Schiano, D. J., Gumbrecht, M., & Swartz, L. (2004). Why we blog. *Communications of the ACM, 47*(12), 41–46.

Narin, F. (1976). *Evaluative bibliometrics: The use of publication and citation analysis in the evaluation of scientific activity.* Cherry Hill, NJ: Computer Horizons.

Nature. (2006). *Nature's peer review debate.* Retrieved July 1, 2009, from www.nature.com/nature/peerreview/debate/index.html.

Nicolaisen, J. (2007) Citation analysis. *Annual Review of Information Science and Technology, 41,* 609–641.

Nisonger, T. E. (1998). *Management of serials in libraries.* Englewood, CO: Libraries Unlimited.

Ohly, H. P. (1982). A procedure for comparing documentation language applications: The transformed Zipf curve. *International Classification, 9*(3), 125–128.

Otte, E., & Rousseau, R. (2002). Social network analysis: A powerful strategy, also for the information sciences. *Journal of Information Science, 28*(6), 441–453.

Park, H. W. (2003). Hyperlink network analysis: A new method for the study of social structure on the web. *Connections, 25*(1), 49–61.

Park, H. W., & Thelwall, M. (2003). Hyperlink analyses of the World Wide Web: A review. *Journal of Computer-Mediated Communication, 8*(4). Retrieved November 11, 2010, from jcmc.indiana.edu/vol8/issue4/park.html.

Potter, W. G. (1988). "Of making many books there is no end": Bibliometrics and libraries. *Journal of Academic Librarianship, 14,* 238a–238c.

Price, D. J. D. (1963). *Little science, big science.* New York: Columbia University Press.

Price, D. J. D. (1965). Networks of scientific papers. *Science, 149*(3683), 510–515.

Price, D. J. D. (1970). Citation measures of hard science, soft science, technology, and non-science. In C. E. Nelson & D. K. Pollock (Eds.), *Communication among scientists and engineers* (pp. 3–22). Lexington, MA: Heath.

Price, D. J. D. (1975). *Science since Babylon* (enl. Ed.). New Haven, CT: Yale University Press.

Pritchard, A. (1969). Statistical bibliography or bibliometrics? *Journal of Documentation, 25*(4), 348–349.

Rider, F. (1944). *The scholar and the future of the research library.* New York: Hadham Press.

Rodríguez i Gairín, J. M. (1997). Valorando el impacto de la información en Internet: AltaVista, el "Citation Index" de la Red [Assessing the impact of information on the Internet: AltaVista, the "citation index" network.] *Revista Española de Documentación Científica, 20*(2), 175–181.

Rogers, E. M., & Kincaid, D. L. (1981). *Communication networks: Toward a new paradigm for research.* New York: Free Press.

Rousseau, R. (1997). Sitations: An exploratory study. *Cybermetrics, 1*(1). Retrieved November 11, 2010, from www.cindoc.csic.es/cybermetrics/articles/v1i1p1.html.

Rousseau, R. (1999). Daily time series of common single word searches in AltaVista and NorthernLight. *Cybermetrics, 2/3*, Retrieved July 25, 2006 from www.cindoc.csic.es/cybermetrics/articles/v2i1p2.html.

Small, H. (1973). Co-citation in the scientific literature: A new measurement of the relationship between two documents. *Journal of the American Society of Information Science, 24*(4), 265–269.

Smith, A. G. (1999). A tale of two web spaces: Comparing sites using web impact factors. *Journal of Documentation, 55*(5), 577–592.

Snyder, H. W., & Rosenbaum, H. (1999). Can search engines be used for web-link analysis? A critical review. *Journal of Documentation, 55*(4), 375–384.

Søndergaard, T. F., Andersen, J., & Hjørland, B. (2003). Documents and the communication of scientific and scholarly information: Revising and updating the UNISIST model. *Journal of Documentation, 59*(3), 278–320.

Sonnenwald, D. (2007). Scientific collaboration. *Annual Review of Information Science and Technology, 41*, 643–681.

Spang-Hanssen, H. (2001). How to teach about information as related to documentation? *Human IT, 5*(1), 125–143. Retrieved November 11, 2010, from www.hb.se/bhs/ith/1-01/hsh.htm.

Suber, P. (2007). *Open access overview.* Retrieved November 11, 2010, from www.earlham.edu/~peters/fos/overview.htm.

Tang, R., & Thelwall, M. (2003). U.S. academic departmental web-site interlinking: Disciplinary differences. *Library & Information Science Research, 25*(4), 437–458.

Tang, R., & Thelwall, M. (2008). A hyperlink analysis of US public and academic libraries' web sites. *Library Quarterly, 78*(4), 419–435.

Thelwall, M. (2004). *Link analysis: An information science approach.* San Diego, CA: Academic Press.

Thelwall, M. (2007). Blog searching: The first general-purpose source of retrospective public opinion in the social sciences? *Online Information Review, 31*(3), 277–289.

Thelwall, M. (2008a). Extracting accurate and complete results from search engines: Case study Windows Live. *Journal of the American Society for Information Science and Technology, 59*(1), 38–50.

Thelwall, M. (2008b). Social networks, gender and friending: An analysis of MySpace member profiles. *Journal of the American Society for Information Science and Technology, 59*(8), 1321–1330.

Thelwall, M. (2009). Homophily in MySpace. *Journal of the American Society for Information Science and Technology, 60*(2), 219–231.

Thelwall, M., Wouters, P., & Fry, J. (2008). Information-centred research for large-scale analysis of new information sources. *Journal of the American Society for Information Science and Technology, 59*(9), 1523–1527.

Thomas, O., & Willet, P. (2000). Webometric analysis of departments of librarianship and information science. *Journal of Information Science, 26*(6), 421–428.

UNISIST. (1971). *Study report on the feasibility of a World Science Information System by the United Nations Educational, Scientific and Cultural Organization and the International Council of Scientific Unions.* Paris: UNESCO. Retrieved November 11, 2010, from unesdoc. unesco.org/images/0006/000648/064862eo.pdf.

van Raan, A. F. J. (2001). Bibliometrics and internet: Some observations and expectations. *Scientometrics, 50*(1), 59–63.

Vasileiadou, E., & Van den Besselaar, P. (2006). Linking shallow, linking deep. How scientific intermediaries use the web for their network of collaborators. *Cybermetrics, 10*(1). Retrieved May 11, 2011, from dare.uva.nl/document/22526.

Vaughan, L., & Shaw, D. (2003). Bibliographic and web citations: What is the difference? *Journal of the American Society for Information Science and Technology, 54*(14), 1313–1322.

Vaughan, L., & Shaw, D. (2005). Web citation data for impact assessment: A comparison of four science disciplines. *Journal of the American Society for Information Science and Technology, 56*(10), 1075–1087.

Voss, J. (2005). Measuring Wikipedia. *Proceedings of the 10th International Conference of the International Society for Scientometrics and Informetrics,* 221–231.

Wasserman, S., & Faust, K. (1994). *Social network analysis: Methods and applications.* Cambridge, UK: Cambridge University Press.

Watts, D. J., & Strogatz, S. H. (1998). Collective dynamics of "small-world" networks. *Nature, 393,* 440–442.

Weinberg, A. (1961). Impact of large-scale science on the United States. *Science, 134,* 161–164.

White, H. D. (1981). "Bradfordizing" search output: How it would help online users. *Online Review, 5*(1), 47–54.

Wilkinson, D., Harries, G., Thelwall, M., & Price, E. (2003). Motivations for academic web site interlinking: Evidence for the web as a novel source of information on informal scholarly communication. *Journal of Information Science, 29*(1), 49–56.

Wyllys, R. E. (1981). Empirical and theoretical bases of Zipf's law. *Library Trends, 30*(1), 53–64.

Zipf, G. K. (1935). *The psycho-biology of language.* New York: Houghton-Mifflin.

Zipf, G. K. (1949). *Human behavior and the principle of least-effort.* New York: Addison-Wesley.

Zuccala, A. (2006). Author cocitation analysis is to intellectual structure as web colink analysis is to ...? *Journal of the American Society for Information Science and Technology, 57*(11), 1486–1501.

CHAPTER 12

Information Policy

12.1. What Is Information Policy?

This chapter considers three subjects related to information policy: economics of information, intellectual property (IP), and standardization and flow of information. Considerations of three major stakeholder groups—individuals, governments, and organizations—are reviewed for each subject area. Governments are considered separately from other organizations because their impact on information policy is so profound that they warrant consideration in their own right.

From the information policy perspective, the user or stakeholder who gathers, understands, and acts on information may be an individual, an organization, or a government. Members of any group of stakeholders will have diverse priorities and opinions regarding the effective disposition of information resources. Stakeholders each have an individual set of goals and criteria for making decisions, and they will develop their own strategies for deriving benefit from information. Formally or informally, each of these stakeholders develops mechanisms for managing information as a tool to achieve the desired goals. Information policy therefore assumes both the existence of information as a resource and the existence of stakeholders.

Information policy discussions highlight the multiple meanings of the word *information*. Braman (2006) posed four ways the term is understood:

1. As a resource

2. As a commodity

3. As a perception of pattern

4. As a societal force

When considered as a resource or commodity, information has broad microeconomic and macroeconomic impacts. When treated as a perception of pattern (i.e., as knowledge), information can provide enlightenment or strategic advantage. When considered as a societal force, information has broad political impacts and has caused innumerable changes in modern society.

From a political science perspective, which works well for information policy study, policy can be described as determining who gets how much of a resource. Government information policy is often created in response to information distribution or protection issues, especially when those issues have broad economic, social, or security ramifications. For example, information policies at the individual level might include personal email management practices or household rules regarding internet or telephone use by children. Information policies at the organizational level might include policies regarding confidentiality or collections management. Information policy decisions are largely dictated by the obligations and motivations of the policymakers, which are in turn shaped by a number of internal and external factors, especially the economic value of the information resource under management and the desire and ability of the information stakeholder to share the information.

Context also has a role in defining information policy. To be useful, information must be managed strategically. The kinds of information available, as well as the priorities of the policymakers and the decisions required in order to manage information collections for the benefit of users, vary depending on the nature of the collection and the motivations of owners of the information. Consider the examples of two organizations, the individual, and the government:

- A public library will develop information policies that are focused on achieving the library's goals, which the American Library Association (ALA; 2010) describes as "to promote the highest quality library and information services and public access to information." Collection management decisions, internet access policies, and periodical selections are examples of policy decisions that are all considered from the perspective of a body whose primary motivation is the encouragement of access to information.

- In contrast, the information policies of an institution that perceives information as a commodity will be developed with considerations of maximizing competitive advantage and minimizing the risk of undesirable data loss. Corporations use sophisticated data collection methods and leverage intellectual assets and IP in order to achieve advantage in the marketplace. The library's goal is to disseminate information, but the corporation aims to use information as an asset.

- Individuals may seek information with the intention of arming themselves with information for strategic advantage, for instance when making consumer decisions.

- Governments have always been both the source of and the destination for vast amounts of information; the policies directing how that information should be managed are tools of governance, as well as resources to be used for strategic gain. Furthermore, governments have traditionally been the source of information resources such as cryptography, national statistics, and standards. Governments are also key policymakers when decisions must be made regarding the dissemination of information, as in case of the consumer health information resource *MedlinePlus*, or in its restriction, as in the case of laws intended to protect the confidentiality of citizens' medical records (the Health Information Portability and Accountability Act, or HIPAA). Governments are also frequently the source of regulatory policy, as in the case of regulation of the broadcast and telephony infrastructure.

Shapiro and Varian (1997) described three areas of government information policy:

1. Governmental creation and dissemination of information (including funding research and creating and distributing statistics and records)

2. Development, regulation, and use of information infrastructure (including telephony and broadcast legislation, library policy, and internet censorship)

3. Institutional and legal infrastructure (including participation in international treaties and organizations, privacy rules, antitrust policy, standard settings, contract law, encryption and security, and IP policy)

The transition from viewing information as a "thing" for edification and improved understanding to viewing it as a commodity with economic and civic value has brought greater prominence to the study of information policy. Governments, organizations, and individuals receive a constant torrent of information; the ability to identify, organize, understand, and act on this intellectual capital has become crucial for even mundane tasks. Failure to use information effectively can result in lost opportunity, reduced productivity, and less effective competition in the global marketplace. In some ways information is unlike other economic assets (e.g., it is non-rivalrous and promiscuous—see next section); appreciating these characteristics has led to new policies in both economic and political spheres. Developing these policies is challenging because so many varied groups have interests and because the technology, and the social structures shaped by that technology, continue to evolve. Samuelson (2000) noted that policymakers in this arena need to recognize when existing policy can be adapted to modern versions of old challenges (as in the case of censorship) and when new laws must be created to deal with new policy challenges (as in the case of data mining and cybercrime).

Information policy assumes that information is a resource to be allocated, managed, and used by stakeholders. Therefore, information policy might be thought of as an established way of making decisions regarding the generation, acquisition, organization, storage, retrieval, use, or dissemination of information assets. Some policy issues relate specifically to the internet and do not pertain to government or other organizations; for example, administration and standards issues, as well as subjects related to the structure and administration of the internet. These issues are considered later in this chapter.

12.2. Economics of Information

Information Economic Policy
From a Governmental Perspective

Modern telecommunications technology has increased the utility of information as a resource and an asset. Technology has also encouraged people to treat information as a commodity with economic value but no other salient distinguishing characteristics: It has increased the *commoditization* of information.

These developments are not new; network technologies date to the mid-19th century, and more than half of all U.S. workers have been *knowledge workers* since the late 1950s. The U.S. Supreme Court recognized the economic value of "facts" in 1991 (*Feist Publications, Inc., v. Rural Telephone Service Co.*). Information has always had strategic value to individuals and organizations; after World War II, technological developments supported the rise of what has been called the "network society" (Castells, 1996), and fundamental changes in the nature of government (Braman, 2006). Rubin (2004) worried that, with the commoditization of information, the observation that some information has economic value might lead to the conclusion that all of it does. That is, excessive commoditization of information may have the potential to diminish the amount of information in the public sphere, to the detriment of the public in general and with particular harm to the economically disadvantaged.

On the other hand, there are those who maintain that because all information has economic value, policy should address the ability of individuals of limited means to have access to vital resources. Furthermore, without some way of ensuring the economic significance of the information infrastructure, the internet will suffer a *tragedy of the commons* downfall. (The tragedy of the commons demonstrates that individual needs can overwhelm the common good: The commons, open pasture for all the people in a village, will be overgrazed if each villager brings in as many sheep as possible.) That information has economic value, however, is not in dispute. The study of the economics of information has developed enormously since Stigler (1961) described the field as occupying a "slum dwelling in the town of economics" (p. 213). As the economic and social significance of information has been better understood, its perceived importance as a necessity for economic and political well-being has been more thoroughly recognized, and information policy has been perceived as necessary to the survival of the state (high policy).

Information has characteristics that make it fundamentally different from other commodities. Most important, information is *non-rivalrous*: The internalization of information by one user does not impede the ability of another to do the same. This property makes information unique among commodities; two people may use the same recipe to make bread, but the two people cannot buy the same loaf of bread. However, like bread, information can be sold; it has economic value. Unlike bread, information does not require a fixed physical form, and it is not bound by physical location.

Many researchers have suggested that the internet suffers from a tragedy of the commons market inefficiency. As Shapiro and Varian (1997) put it, "The key aspect of information for the purposes of economic analysis is that information is costly to produce, but very cheap to reproduce, especially in digital form" ("Information as a public good"). As a consequence, digital information becomes ubiquitous and thus almost free. Some people have suggested that it is most efficient to make information freely available. However, producing information is expensive, and these costs must be borne somewhere in the information production chain. Shapiro and Varian suggest that (government) information producers charge "at least incremental cost" for the use of information. Failure to provide compensation to information producers will reduce incentive for future innovation. Moreover, if the information infrastructure is treated as a free, public resource, it may be devalued and filled with the informational equivalent of rubbish and undesirable elements. The omnipresence of intrusive or disreputable advertising in some free online services and applications (and its absence in subscription-based services) provides a cautionary example.

Publishers' roles in the dissemination of information are changing rapidly, a situation sometimes perceived as challenging their continued existence. Some commentators argue that these concerns are unjustified, that the distribution of IP changes often, each time presenting information property creators and stakeholders the opportunity to access new revenue streams. For example, music publishers resisted the player piano and radio broadcast; and the entertainment industry had concerns about home video technology (*Sony Corp. of America v. Universal City Studios, Inc.*, the "Betamax case"). Technological restrictions on duplication and dissemination of information are often suggested in such cases. To date, however, such technologies have generally proven to be ineffective and perhaps even counterproductive. Rightsholders have sought policies to enforce their rights, either in the courts or through laws. In this way the government has been involved in information policies related to the enforcement of property rights and rights of contract.

Given information's entropic nature (in the sense of spreading and becoming uniform) and ease of reproduction, some scholars (such as Lessig, 2002) have suggested that information is a *public good*. Public goods are typically defined as being non-rivalrous and difficult to restrict to specified users. Advocates of *digital rights management* (DRM) and encryption technology maintain that information can be made exclusive, so that it would fail the definitional test of being a public good. However, technological measures to exclude unauthorized users from accessing information have so far not been able to provide security, limiting information rightsholders' abilities to enforce their exclusive rights. In any case, the characteristics that make information similar to a public good encourage economies of scale, with a small number of providers becoming the overwhelming source of a given product.

Policy implications related to the economics of information are significant. Taxation is one example: Should ecommerce be taxed, and if so, how (Goolsbee, 2000)? More profound economic considerations include the ramifications of information technologies on IP law, both domestically and internationally. The regulation of infrastructure such as the broadcast spectrum and the use of standards are also policy issues with significant economic impact. These issues will be addressed more fully later in this chapter. A mundane but significant issue that demonstrated the importance of government in the development of information policy is the passage of the Uniform Electronic Transactions Act, which described and affirmed the legal authority of electronic signatures and the validity of electronic contracts when one is engaging in ecommerce.

Information Economic Policy From an Organizational Perspective

Business and industry are important stakeholders in the information economy, and organizations often hold much of their value in the form of intellectual assets. Information and intellectual capital are the foundation of many organizations' economic well-being; such assets must be carefully managed and exploited to gain competitive advantage in the marketplace. Thus, business and industry have strong motivations to be concerned with both information development and management. This drive is reflected in the development of policies that help the business discover and exploit new information. Policies are developed and enacted in part so that there is an institutionwide understanding of how information is to be used; the development of policies for organization and access to information are a part of this policy development issue.

Orna (1999) discussed the issues an organizational information policy should address. First, the policy must include the basic obligations of the organization: guiding principles that form the organization's ethic and direction, and principles articulating goals regarding knowledge sharing and development for advancing the organization's objectives. The policy should also include strategic information use, such as

- Defining the knowledge required to achieve organizational goals, the information needed to maintain the knowledge, and how people in the organization need to use knowledge and information

- Auditing use of information and knowledge regularly to ensure that the organization has what it needs and is using it appropriately

- Providing a coordinated overview of all knowledge and information resources

- Safeguarding both current and historical information resources so that they will be accessible at all times

- Preserving the organization's "memory" in the knowledge base

Orna (1999) recommends that the draft policy should be

- Short

- Clearly linked to what the organization is trying to do and to where it is seeking to go

- Focused on key points

- Organized to provide a framework on which people can grow their ideas based on knowledge and experience

- Expressed in ways appropriate to its character and culture

- Visually well-designed and accessible

Orna (1999) concludes that information policy "should be used throughout the organization as a focus for thinking about how it uses knowledge and information" (p. 106).

The public is another important user group with interests in information policy; organizations advocating for the public good can be included in this group. The ALA is an example of a group that seeks to improve the informational lot of the general public. In contrast to the corporate sector's view of information as a source for commercial gain, the ALA focuses on distributing information as broadly as possible for the benefit of the general public. Such different priorities mean that the organizations will address questions of information management in distinct ways.

Questions of information policy relevant to public libraries are manifold; they range from patrons' privacy rights to accessibility issues to collections development and circulation and to the role of technology in the modern library. A recent example is the Children's Internet Protection Act, which ties federal funding for libraries to the presence of filtering software on publicly available computers connected to the internet. Opponents sued, and the U.S. Supreme Court upheld the law, ruling that filtering software did not represent a threat to availability of information to the public.

12.3. Intellectual Property

Intellectual property (IP) is products of the human mind and creativity that are protected by law. IP has all of the characteristics of any other economic asset; it can be bought, sold, and rented; insured; and used as collateral. Patents, copyright, and trademarks are the most widely recognized kinds of IP. The U.S. Patent and Trademark Office (www.uspto.gov) is the government body responsible for granting the rights associated with these products. IP rights are exclusive rights granted to their holder; they allow the holder to dictate which parties will be excluded from the reproduction, distribution, or sale of protected works. In general, to qualify for IP protection, a product must be an original creation. Protection occurs at the moment of *fixation* (recorded in tangible form) in the case of copyrightable works and through registration with the Patent and Trademark Office for novel creations and logos.

IP is an asset in organizations and businesses; it is created as *intellectual capital* and then recorded and disclosed internally and to the public, transforming it from a private (but legally unrecognized) intellectual asset to publicly disclosed IP. From the perspective of business, intellectual capital is the sum of all knowledge in an enterprise: the knowledge and skills of the employees; processes; and all recordings, designs, and inventions. Intellectual capital is what is left after an enterprise has been stripped of all its tangible assets (see the discussion of knowledge management in Chapter 10). It has been said that intellectual capital is the part of a company that walks out the door every evening. *Intellectual assets* are information assets that have been recorded and made available to the organization; they have been shared beyond the minds of their creators, moving from the world of thought to the physical plane. *Intellectual capital management* is the process of converting (through documentation) the knowledge of the employee, transforming intellectual capital into intellectual assets. Intellectual assets include software, methods, manuals, reports, publications, databases, patents, trademarks, copyrights, and domain names. The economics of IP are significant: In 2009, intangible assets represented 81 percent of the total market value of the Standard & Poor's 500 companies (Poltorak & Lerner, 2011).

A Brief History of IP Law

Historical Roots of Copyright

IP law has its roots in antiquity; patents were originally monopolies granted by a head of state as a reward. Such boons were extended to favored subjects and could be applied to a wide variety of goods, including playing cards, stamps, and tea. Because patents were granted by a head of state, the legal reach of these monopolies was largely limited to that particular nation. Then and now, a key aspect of the law of IP is the question of international enforceability of IP rights. Modern IP law is shaped by early attempts to develop international protections. The Berne Convention of 1896 (or more formally, the International Union for the Protection of Literary and Artistic Works) was a treaty guaranteeing that signatories would respect other nations' copyright holders as their own. The Berne Convention was updated seven times in the 20th century. Although it was a model of modern international law when created, factors such as economic globalization, international politics, and modern issues regarding IP rights enforcement have necessitated the development of other IP-oriented bodies such as the World Intellectual Property Organization.

The Trade-Related Aspects of Intellectual Property Rights (TRIPS) agreement is a recent response to perceived limitations of the Berne Convention. TRIPS has stronger provisions for the enforcement of IP rights, and nations must abide by TRIPS in order to join the World Trade Organization. The TRIPS agreement dictates that the IP rights of foreigners must be as comprehensive as those of residents. Additionally, TRIPS demands compliance with Articles 1 through 21 of the Berne Convention, protection of computer programs as literary creations, and rental rights for computer and cinematographic works.

Other significant laws regarding copyright include the Geneva Phonograms Convention (which the U.S. joined in 1974), protecting member states and residents against the unauthorized reproduction of sound recordings. In addition, the Brussels Convention of 1974 legislates against the unauthorized access to and use of satellite signals. The World IP Organization adopted these two treaties as international law in 1996; consequently, computer programs are protected as legal works, data compilations are protected as intellectual creations, and provisions are made for the distribution and rental of computer, film, and audio works. Further, all signatories must institute legal protection of technologies related to distribution and rights management. In the U.S., these obligations are fulfilled through the Digital Millennium Copyright Act (DMCA).

The DMCA exists to protect encryption and DRM schemes by prohibiting technologies whose purpose is to deconstruct, disable, or remove technological measures intended to limit copying and distribution. The law has proved controversial. Some opponents have argued that the measures are technologically ineffective; others have noted the law's potential chilling effect on research on encryption and rights technologies by anyone other than major industrial shareholders. It is certainly true that the DMCA has not prevented removal of DRM technologies and distribution of content, particularly outside the U.S. It is also likely that the prohibition of public research on these technologies has weakened DRM in general because proprietary schemes are rapidly broken and workarounds developed to defeat technologies that the entertainment industry developed at considerable time and expense (Reuters, 2002). Further, the continued use of DRM has resulted in some public embarrassment for the entertainment industry, as in the case of the Rootkits installed by DRM technology included on some Sony products (Doctorow, 2005).

Historical Roots of Patents

Legal protection for patents has existed in the U.S. since the passage of the Patent Act of 1790. The U.S. Constitution (Article I, section 8) grants Congress the authority "to promote the progress of science and useful arts, by securing for limited times to authors and inventors the exclusive right to their respective writings and discoveries"; modern U.S. patent law is based on the Patent Act of 1953. Some scholars have argued that many patents date to the ancient Greeks (as a cook's reward for a culinary triumph). However, the Venetian legislation of 1474 requiring that new, useful innovations be registered so that they might be protected for a period of 10 years is generally regarded as the antecedent of modern patent law.

No global agreement exists regarding patents. The variable enforceability of patent rights internationally has been an incentive for nations to find some system to enforce rights; the U.S. has joined numerous such agreements. The 1883 Paris Convention for the Protection of IP was an early attempt to internationalize patent and trademark rights by mandating that signatory nations treat the rights of other states with the same deference that they would treat their own. The Paris Convention also established a framework and time frame for registering patents. The modern TRIPS agreement contains provisions dictating that signatories (almost every nation in the World Trade Organization) will conform to legal requirements of patentability such as term of the patent and novelty and nonobviousness.

Historical Roots of Trademarks

Trademarks are also an ancient form of IP protection, literally marks to designate someone's product or property. Trademarks are intended both to facilitate commerce and to guarantee quality; a consumer will (ideally) come to associate a trademark with consistency and quality and will be able to make better decisions based on confidence in the excellence of products bearing a given trademark. One of the oldest forms of marking is the branding of livestock, and the term *brand* (as in a maker's mark) derives from that early meaning (Devil's Rope Museum, 2007). Other marks may have been applied by tradesmen to sign work; this way of establishing that a product had been manufactured by a member of a guild provided assurance that it conformed to established standards of quality. In the U.S., the 1947 Lanham Act was passed to remedy perceived shortcomings in previous laws, greatly expanding eligibility and protections for trademarks.

Copyright

Copyright is legal protection for works of authorship, covering everything from books to choreography to architecture. Copyright protection arises automatically when an original work of authorship is fixed in a tangible means of expression. The work can incorporate pre-existing material and still be original. When pre-existing material is incorporated, the copyright on the new work covers only the original material contributed by the author. (The U.S. Copyright Law is available online at www.copyright.gov/title17.) Copyright law exists to remedy a perceived market failure concerning products of the mind: that intellectual works are non-rivalrous (consumption by one individual does not preclude consumption by another, as opposed to tangible goods such as apples) and difficult to exclude (it is difficult to exclude the public from access to the property). These conditions reduce the cost of the product to the consumer, possibly to the point that the creator of the good would not be rewarded for his or her efforts. To ensure that a creator is fairly compensated, a legal system of rights has been created regarding the distribution, reproduction, display, and sale of the product. The copyright holder also has rights regarding the development of derivative works such as screenplays or translations. A copyright owner has five exclusionary rights: reproduction, modification, distribution, public performance, and public display.

The U.S. Copyright Act of 1976 allows copyright to be extended to any work of authorship, including literary works; musical works; dramatic works; pantomime and choreography; pictorial, graphic, and sculptural works; motion pictures and other audiovisual works; sound recordings; and architectural works. Copyright is extended to any work as soon as it is "fixed in any tangible medium of expression," in the words of the Act and (unlike patents and trademarks) no formal registration is required—although registration has advantages. Copyright covers expressions of ideas, not ideas themselves. Copyright now extends for 70 years past the lifetime of the creator, 96 years for corporate works for hire. These long terms are recent extensions; earlier versions of U.S. copyright law had more limited terms of protection. Infringement of copyright is a long-standing issue; tales of the outrage of Robert Louis Stevenson and Mark Twain because of rampant international piracy are frequently cited. Infringement of copyright generally involves the unauthorized reproduction and distribution of copies of a work for which the creator receives no remuneration. The protections of copyright law give creators recourse in such circumstances, allowing them to stop unauthorized distribution and seek compensation for loss of revenue. However, in some circumstances copyrighted works may be used without the explicit permission of rightsholders; examples of the protected uses of works include *first sale*, which allows libraries to lend copyrighted materials, and *fair use*, which allows the use of material for time shifting (*Universal v. Sony*), critique, satire (*Rose music v. Acuff*), and educational purposes. A four-fold test is used to determine whether fair use is justified:

1. The character of the use

2. The nature of the work used

3. The amount of material used

4. The potential economic impact of the use

In general, the use of nonfiction or reference work is less likely to be deemed as infringing than is the use of original, creative material. Similarly, the use of material for educational purposes is generally acceptable. Use of small amounts of material is more likely to be acceptable than use of large excerpts or whole works. Finally, the potential impact of the use on the economic value of the original work must be considered. If the work that uses the copyrighted material is not likely to satisfy a user's desire for the original (and thus infringe on a potential sale of the original work), the use is more likely to be deemed fair.

Users can determine whether a work is copyrighted with ease; the U.S. government maintains a searchable directory of copyrighted works (www.copyright.gov/records). A rule of thumb is that if a work was created after 1938, it is likely protected by copyright law. Technology has greatly facilitated infringement in recent times. Any informational product may be transformed into a digital format and reproduced rapidly at almost no cost. Attempts to prevent such conversion and storage are hampered by legal reverse engineering to counter the protections and by the legitimate needs of the public to make archival or time-shift copies of material they have legally acquired. Rightsholders have repeatedly attempted to eliminate or limit the unauthorized distribution of copyrighted works, but with little success. In the face of such failures, organizations of rightsholders, such as the Recording Industry Association of America and the Motion Picture Association of America, have undertaken a controversial campaign of litigation and legislative change. Such actions are perceived by many as an attempt to undermine or eliminate fair use and first sale exceptions to copyright law; the efforts have resulted in massive negative publicity and boycotts. Ironically, history shows that the recording industry has repeatedly fought the development of novel distribution technologies, including the player piano, radio, and the videocassette recorder; has lost the fight; and has then benefitted because the technology proliferated, enabled more consumers to access creative works, and increased sales.

Some scholars have suggested that the contemporary IP environment is no longer appropriate for traditional copyright protections. The negligible cost and ease of distribution of electronic documents has dramatically reduced the value of copies, although not the cost of producing the original. Rightsholders face a future in which they must find new ways of generating revenue from their IP or re-evaluate the economic incentive underlying the creative impulse. Alternatives to traditional copyright have been suggested, including the *collective commons*. Under the collective commons, rights-holders may choose which of their rights they wish to enforce. For example, an author may decide to distribute the product freely, with the proviso that any copies give appropriate attribution. Another alternative to traditional copyright is found in *open source*. Traditionally associated with the Linux operating system, open source allows users to modify and distribute code and other IP. Because open source software is maintained by a community of users, bugs and security flaws tend to be identified and dealt with more quickly than those found in proprietary systems (where the knowledge of a security vulnerability may go unremedied for some time). The disadvantage of both schemes is that the potential for profit is much reduced; however, broader distribution may lead to greater overall sales and may consequently prove to be a feasible economic model. In spite of industry criticisms, open source software accounts for a significant portion of the server community, numerous governments have adopted it for their computer systems, and the percentage of users relying on open source software on their home comput-ers rises annually. Regardless of their profitability, it has become evident that alternatives to traditional copyright schemes are becoming more attractive to users at every level.

Patents

A patent is a monopoly granted to a rightsholder in exchange for disclosure of the design of a novel, useful, and nonobvious innovation. The patent is granted for a limited time, typically 20 years past the filing date. The right conferred by the patent grant is, in the language of the statute (Contents and term of patent; provisional rights) and of the grant itself, "the right to exclude others from making, using, offering for sale, or selling" the inven-tion in the U.S. or "importing" the invention into the country. What is granted is not the right to make, use, offer for sale, sell, or import, but in the language of the statute, "the right to exclude others from making, using, offering for sale, or selling the invention." Enforcement of these rights is the responsibility of the patentholder; the U.S. Patent and Trademark Office grants but does not enforce patentholders' rights. Patent applications are available from the office's website, which also offers public search capabilities; novelty is a condition of patentability and would-be registrants may search the USPTO databases for "prior art."

There are three types of patents: utility, design, and plant.

- *Utility patents* may be granted for invention or discovery of any new and useful process, machine, article of manufacture, or composition of matter, or any new and useful improvement thereof.

- *Design patents* may be granted for invention of a new, original, and ornamental design for an article of manufacture. Examples include bottles and fonts.

- *Plant patents* may be granted for the invention or discovery and asexual reproduction of any distinct and new variety of plant.

U.S. patent law also allows patents for synthetic genes, cell lines, organisms, software, and algorithms. Patents for software are controversial because all software is ultimately based on mathematical processes, and mathematics and mathematical equations are not patentable under the law. Some scholars justify the non-patentability of math on the basis that natural phenomena and abstract ideas cannot be patented, and others say that mathematics is not a process, article, or composition of matter. Software patent critics also maintain that computer software design builds on previous design and that the patenting of algorithms and processes has a detrimental effect on innovation. Some critics argue that the patent review process is not sufficiently robust to address the suitability of these products for protection and that as a result, many frivolous or inappropriate protections have been granted. Countless legal battles have been fought over software patents, and numerous frivolous patents have been found by courts to be invalid (Electronic Frontier Foundation, 2009). This area of law is evolving with the technologies and products it treats; policy and regulatory issues surrounding these topics are likely to persist and to have broad implications for years to come.

Trademarks

Trademarks are words, names, symbols, or devices used by owners to identify their goods and services as distinct from those of others. Similar to trademarks, yet distinct from them, are *trade secrets*, defined as "information, including a formula, pattern, compilation, program device, method, technique, or process, that ... derives independent economic value ... from not being generally known ... and ... is the subject of efforts that are reasonable under the circumstances to maintain its secrecy" (National Conference of Commissioners on Uniform State Laws, 1985, §1(4)).

The purpose of trademarks and trade secrets is similar to that of patents: to provide protection for distinctive designs. Trademarks are also intended to simplify the challenges that consumers face in the marketplace. Trademarks acquire protection through use; a design that is never publicly used is not protected. On the other hand, designs that remain in public view are protected as long as the design is in use. This system of enforcement is intended to prevent competitors from falsely representing the provenance of goods. However, a mark may lose protection should it become a generic term, synonymous with the product itself (examples of this phenomenon include Xerox, Kleenex, and Heroin).

Trademarks can be formally established through a federal registration process codified in the federal statute known as the Lanham Act. Federal registration confers protection in all U.S. states and gives the right to the holder to use the official trademark (®, for a registered trademark; distinguished from the unregistered trademark symbol, ™) imprimatur, an assurance of quality to the consumer. Application for trademark protection can be obtained from the Patent and Trademark Office's website. Applicants submit the mark, along with a list of products on which the mark has been used. The application is then examined by an attorney from that office to establish that the mark is sufficiently distinctive (that it does not too closely resemble an already-protected mark). If the mark is approved, a public notification is published in the *Official Gazette of the Patent and Trademark Office* (www.uspto.gov/web/trademarks/tmog).

12.4. Information Standards

As articulated by the International Organization for Standardization (2009b), standards are important because they help to guarantee desirable characteristics such as safety, reliability, and interchangeability in goods and services. In addition to helping ensure quality and consistency, standards are perceived as being important to innovation and dissemination of technologies. Standards can provide strong benefits for business, innovators, consumers, and governments by allowing greater market competition and faster spread of technologies and markets. (Examples of standards that have allowed interoperability and technological expansion are the ubiquitous Open Systems Interconnection reference model and the transmission control protocol/internet protocol suite of protocols, which are the foundations of the internet.) The International Organization for Standardization (ISO; the acronym does not correspond to its name in most languages but is known universally and means *equal* in Greek) tests for "conformity assessment," the practice of ensuring that products, services, systems, and materials meet the specifications of appropriate standards before they reach the markets. As the organization indicates on its website (www.iso.org/iso/casco_2005.pdf), "ISO guides and standards for conformity assessment represent an international consensus on best practice. Their use contributes to the consistency of conformity assessment worldwide and so facilitates trade" (p. 4). Standards allow for better market penetration and enhanced competition. Such standards can be controversial, as in the case of the Microsoft OOXML standard, which some industry players such as IBM (2008) deem unacceptable.

Global Standards

The ISO is a nongovernmental organization intended to form consensus standards among various stakeholders, including industry, individuals, and governments. With 157 subscriber nations, ISO is the largest developer of standards and norms for a variety of areas (it has published more than 17,000 standards), ranging from traditional activities such as agriculture and construction through mechanical engineering, manufacturing and distribution, transport, medical devices, and information and communication technologies (International Organization for Standardization, 2009a).

ISO develops standards for products and ideas at work in the marketplace by consulting with experts in industry, business, and research to develop consensus. Such standards tend to evolve with technology and are subjected to periodic review (typically every 5 years) in order to stay current and relevant.

National Information Standards

The National Information Standards Organization (NISO; 2010) is a nonprofit standards organization that "identifies, develops, maintains, and publishes technical standards to manage information in our changing and ever-more digital environment. NISO standards apply both traditional and new technologies to the full range of information-related needs, including retrieval, re-purposing, storage, metadata, and preservation." NISO is certified by the American National Standards Institute (ANSI) and is ANSI's designated representative to the ISO. ANSI is a private, not-for-profit organization whose purpose is to develop and assess conformity standards in many areas, including information handling and management, and from many sources, including academia, industry, and government bodies such as the National Institute for Standards and Technology. ANSI is also involved in the accreditation of organizations that assess conformity to standards, such as NISO. Examples of standards pertinent to the field of information science include accepted norms for healthcare information, information security, and cryptography. ANSI does not set standards itself but accredits consensus proposed by others. One example of a standard panel administered by ANSI is the Healthcare Information Technology Standards Panel (www.hitsp.org), a body whose purpose is to produce a set of standards to enable interoperability among healthcare software applications. Topics addressed by this panel include interoperability between electronic health record and laboratory systems, emergency health records, and medication management interoperability specifications.

As articulated in its mission statement, "NISO fosters the development and maintenance of standards that facilitate the creation, persistent management, and effective interchange of information so that it can be trusted for use in research and learning" (National Information Standards Organization, 2010). NISO produces white papers, recommended practices, technical reports, and publications intended to promulgate standards and consensus for a wide variety of undertakings and disciplines in the fields of information management. Developing standards involves peer review and public commentary, which is open to any NISO voting member. Once approved, such standards become American National Standards. One exemplar of the work of this body can be found in ANSI/NISO standard Z39.85, which defines descriptors (known as metadata) for information across disciplines. This standard identifies 15 core elements (title, creator, subject, description, date, format, source, and other characteristics that describe the nature and form of the document, rather than its content); these are used to define and describe documents in such a way that users and systems from disparate fields may use them with ease.

The standards and practices regarding information storage and access shape society in profound and subtle ways; the importance of policy decisions regarding information cannot be overestimated. The U.S. government has many branches and institutions that define information standards; one such group is the National Institute of Standards and Technology (NIST), a branch of the Department of Commerce; its purpose is to define measurements and technology standards to increase U.S. competitiveness. NIST is also responsible for the publication of federal information processing standards codes, which are used as standards for legal and statistical definition of people and places. Such information policies dictate Congressional districting, resource allocation, and taxation policies. Another branch of the NIST is the National Vulnerability Database (nvd.nist.gov), the repository of Security Content Automation Protocol, the standards that are used to list software vulnerabilities and determine their impact. Such assessment tools are intended to develop and enhance a secure and robust national information infrastructure. Information policy is sometimes defined *de jure*, as in the case of the standards for handling healthcare records. The 1996 HIPAA legislation sets strict (some would say onerous) limitations on the use and dissemination of personal health information. A summary of the privacy rules that HIPAA guarantees is available online (www.hhs.gov/ocr/privacy/hipaa/understanding/summary/privacysummary.pdf). Coincident with the development of these standards and practices has been the development of digitally stored personal medical information embodied by the electronic health record, which has had a profound impact on information access and use policies and practices throughout the healthcare industry.

Professional Organizations and Standards

In addition to organizations such as NISO and ISO, professional organizations are often active in the development and promulgation of standards. Such bodies and standards abound; the following are intended as examples of such bodies and their approaches to the development of information policy. These organizations approach the development of information policy from a variety of levels and perspectives; the role of these bodies in shaping the development of policy is as important as the role that government plays. For example, the Institute of Electrical and Electronics Engineers (IEEE) is a developer of standards for many industries and is recognized by other standard-making bodies such as the ISO and the World Trade Organization. The IEEE is active in the development of standards across a broad range of disciplines, including information technology, telecommunications, and healthcare. The Association for Computing Machinery is a venerable professional organization of technologists and, like the IEEE, is a major contributor of standards with impact on the computing field. It seeks to foster innovation in the computer sciences by educating leaders and the public for the benefit of society.

Similarly, the ALA, mentioned in the first section of this chapter, is active in the development of standards; it prepares and publishes standards on the accreditation of programs to educate librarians. The Association of College and Research Libraries (ACRL) is a professional association of academic librarians committed to the improvement of scholarly libraries and institutions. A division of the ALA, ACRL releases white papers, guidelines, and standards on diverse topics such as materials selection, information literacy, and promotion of library professionals. These recommendations shape the daily practices and policies of libraries in the U.S. and serve as models for librarians in other countries; many ACRL standards have been translated into other languages. Professional organizations and their policy statements, standards, and guidelines are ubiquitous; their impact is widespread.

The World Wide Web Consortium (www.W3C.org) is an international non-profit standards body that seeks to "lead the World Wide Web to its full potential by developing protocols and guidelines that ensure long-term growth for the web." Since its inception in 1994, the W3C has published more than 100 standards in the form of W3C Recommendations. The goal of the organization is the long-term success and development of the web and its attendant technologies and the distribution of the web and its benefits to all of humanity. Standards published by the W3C cover such topics as metadata standards, XML definitions and standards, and the development of the elusive Semantic Web. Recently, the head of the W3C (Tim Berners-Lee) has advocated the development of a content evaluation system for the web that would apply credibility ratings to web-based information in an effort to marginalize bogus information online.

12.5. (Free) Flow of Information

The Universal Declaration of Human Rights (United Nations, 1948) asserts the following:

> Everyone has the right to freedom of opinion and expression; this right includes freedom to hold opinions without interference and to seek, receive and impart information and ideas through any media and regardless of frontiers. (Article 19)

This moving statement captures the concept of free flow of information, at once noble in principle and exceptionally difficult to practice. The discussion of information policy in this chapter has taken a Western, even U.S.-centric, perspective. When information professionals and others have attempted to extend these ideas worldwide, they have encountered objections on the basis of cultural, economic, and national security concerns, among others. The controversy about Danish cartoons depicting the Prophet Mohammed (see Chapter 11) is an example.

An increasingly global economy and the spread of computer and communication technologies make complete isolation increasingly difficult. Nevertheless, many groups and nations have attempted to impede the flow of information. For example:

- Google's mission to help web searchers find whatever they are looking for has been challenged by the need to comply with the laws on information access in various countries; some question how the company can abide by its corporate motto, "don't be evil" (McHugh, 2003). Concerns over censorship (among other things) led to Google's withdrawal from China (Drummond, 2010).

- The Great Firewall of China (officially the Golden Shield Project) has been reported to block or redirect internet addresses and web searches (MacKinnon, 2008).

- Iranian bloggers have made Persian one of the most popular languages on the blogosphere, even though the government places limits on what may be said (Sreberny & Khiabany, 2008).

- In response to a request from an offshore bank, a U.S. district court ordered the removal of the domain name for Wikileaks.org, an organization allowing whistle-blowers to make anonymous posts about corruption (Electronic Frontier Foundation, 2008).

- The Swedish website *The Pirate Bay* is "one of the world's largest facilitators of illegal downloading" (Sarno, 2007); it indexes and tracks BitTorrent (peer-to-peer file-sharing protocol) files. Access has been blocked from several European countries and through Facebook.

Groups such as the International Freedom of Expression eXchange (www.ifex.org), OpenNet Initiative (opennet.net), and Reporters Without Borders (www.rsf.org) maintain websites to bring attention to cases of censorship and challenges to information access.

As these examples suggest, challenges to the free flow of information connect with information policy issues of economics, IP, and standardization in many ways. Work on information policy is closely tied to the co-construction of the technical and the social aspects of information systems (see Chapter 10).

References

American Library Association. (2010). *About the ALA*. Retrieved November 11, 2010, from www.ala.org/ala/aboutala/offices/pio/mediarelationsa/factsheets/aboutala.cfm.

Braman, S. (2006). The micro- and macroeconomics of information. *Annual Review of Information Science and Technology, 40*, 3–52.

Castells, M. (1996). *The rise of the network society*. Walden, MA: Blackwell.

Devil's Rope Museum. (2007). *Typical brand designs*. Retrieved November 11, 2010, from www.barbwiremuseum.com/Typical_Brand_Designs.htm.

Doctorow, C. (2005, November 12). Sony anti-customer technology roundup and time-line. *BoingBoing.net*. Retrieved November 11, 2010, from www.boingboing.net/2005/11/14/sony-anticustomer-te.html.

Drummond, D. (2010, March 22). A new approach to China: An update. *The Official Google Blog*. Retrieved November 11, 2010, from googleblog.blogspot.com/2010/03/new-approach-to-china-update.html.

Electronic Frontier Foundation. (2008). Bank Julius Baer & Co v. Wikileaks. *Electronic Frontier Foundation*. Retrieved November 11, 2010, from www.eff.org/cases/bank-julius-baer-co-v-wikileaks.

Electronic Frontier Foundation. (2009). *Intellectual property*. Retrieved November 11, 2010, from www.eff.org/issues/intellectual-property.

Goolsbee, R. (2000). In a world without borders: The impact of taxes on internet commerce. *Quarterly Journal of Economics, 115*(2), 561–576.

IBM. (2008). *IBM announces new I.T. standards policy.* Retrieved August 4, 2009, from www-03.ibm.com/press/uk/en/pressrelease/25186.wss.

International Organization for Standardization. (2009a). *The scope of ISO's work.* Retrieved November 11, 2010, from www.iso.org/iso/about/discover-iso_the-scope-of-isos-work.htm.

International Organization for Standardization. (2009b). *Why standards matter.* Retrieved November 11, 2010, from www.iso.org/iso/about/discover-iso_why-standards-matter.htm.

Lessig, L. (2002). *The future of ideas: The fate of the commons in a connected world.* New York: Vintage.

MacKinnon, R. (2008). Flatter world and thicker walls? Blogs, censorship and civic discourse in China. *Public Choice, 134*(1–2), 31–46.

McHugh, J. (2003, January). Google vs. evil. *Wired, 11.01.* Retrieved November 11, 2010, from www.wired.com/wired/archive/11.01/google_pr.html.

National Conference of Commissioners on Uniform State Laws. (1985). *Uniform trade secrets act.* Retrieved November 11, 2010, from euro.ecom.cmu.edu/program/law/08-732/Trade Secrets/utsa.pdf.

National Information Standards Organization. (2010). *About NISO.* Retrieved November 11, 2010, from www.niso.org/about.

Orna, E. (1999). *Practical information policies* (2nd ed.). Aldershot, UK: Gower.

Poltorak, A., & Lerner, P. (2011). *Essentials of intellectual property* (2nd ed.). New York: Wiley.

Reuters. (2002, May 20). CD crack: Magic marker indeed. *Wired.* Retrieved November 11, 2010, from www.wired.com/science/discoveries/news/2002/05/52665.

Rubin, R. (2004). *Foundations of library and information science* (2nd ed.). New York: Neal-Schuman Publishers.

Samuelson, P. (2000). *Five challenges for regulating the global information society.* Retrieved November 11, 2010, from people.ischool.berkeley.edu/~pam/papers/5challenges_feb22_v2_final_.pdf.

Sarno, D. (2007, April 29). The internet sure loves its outlaws. *Los Angeles Times.* Retrieved November 11, 2010, from www.latimes.com/entertainment/news/la-ca-webscout29apr29,0,1261622.story?coll=la-home-entertainment.

Shapiro, C., & Varian, H. R. (1997, July 30). *US government information policy.* Retrieved November 11, 2010, from people.ischool.berkeley.edu/~hal/Papers/policy/policy.html.

Sreberny, A., & Khiabany, G. (2008). Internet in Iran: The battle over an emerging public sphere. In M. Mclelland & G. Goggin (Eds.), *Internationalizing internet studies: Beyond Anglophone paradigms.* New York: Routledge.

Stigler G. J. (1961). The economics of information. *Journal of Political Economy, 69*(3), 213–225.

United Nations. (1948). *Universal declaration of human rights.* Retrieved November 11, 2010, from www.un.org/en/documents/udhr.

CHAPTER 13

The Information Professions

13.1. Introduction

This chapter considers the institutional roots and professional expectations of those who choose careers in information science and technology. Historically, libraries, archives, and museums have encountered and in some ways resolved many of the issues that face today's information professional. A review of the roles these "memory institutions" perform and how they interact permits consideration of their various professional responsibilities and challenges. We consider the values of information professionals and how these values are demonstrated in their sense of mission. The chapter concludes with a discussion of the complexities of ethics in the information professions.

13.2. Memory Institutions

As individuals and as members of society, we preserve and use information from the past to inform and enlighten the present days and plan for the future. Libraries, museums, and archives have evolved over many generations to help preserve and support the use of recorded information. They are sometimes called "memory institutions because they organize and provide access to our cultural records" (Hjerppe, 1994).

These organizations are adapting to the challenges of maintaining digital as well as physical records. They are also responding to calls for improving access to their growing collections from parts of society that did not have access in the past. And, to the extent that they rely on public funding, libraries, museums, and archives are increasingly aware of their accountability to the people and societies that support them. Developments in information and communication technologies continue to influence these institutions' activities, their potentials, and their users' expectations.

This synopsis presents current developments and information practices in each type of memory institution: libraries, museums, and archives. The final section includes suggested sources for historical perspective and additional information on these important social institutions.

Libraries

Library (from the Latin word *liber*, for *book*) can mean a collection of information resources and associated services or the building in which these things are housed. Modern libraries' collections include books as well as many other materials: maps, sound and video recordings, databases, and other electronic resources. Librarians determine what to add to the collections and how to catalog resources so that they are accessible; librarians are also trained to help people identify the kinds of information they need and to assist in locating the best sources for the information required.

Public libraries are usually supported by taxes and open to the general public. This broad mandate to develop collections and provide services for all—"regardless of age, education, ethnicity, language, income, physical limitations or geographic barriers"—reflects librarians' "core values of the library community such as equal access to information, intellectual freedom, and the objective stewardship and provision of information," to quote the American Library Association (2010).

Some public libraries and many academic libraries have developed and continue to maintain large and historic collections that support scholars and researchers. Their resources and services often go into greater depth than those of most public libraries; many collect primary source material (such as manuscripts or historical documents), as well as published works (such as books, periodicals, and their electronic counterparts). These libraries are part of the cycle of scholarly communication: Scholars and researchers contribute new ideas, which are made available via publications; publications are acquired by libraries; and scholars and researchers use library resources to develop new ideas (see Chapter 11).

Special libraries support corporations, government agencies, specialized academic units, or other organizations with in-depth collections and services. Special librarians often work closely with researchers in their employing organization, such as banks, medical schools, news, or the pharmaceutical industry. Users of these libraries also contribute to scholarly communication.

School libraries, sometimes called media centers, provide materials and services for students and teachers in elementary and secondary schools. A school library aims to support and enhance the curricular goals of the school.

All libraries are major sources of information for their clients; public and research libraries often have commitments to society at large, as well. As guardians of the public's access to information, their roles are changing rapidly with the revolutionary developments of the digital world. Libraries are becoming virtual, in that information technologies allow people to reach the information they need from almost any place.

Museums

The International Council of Museums (2006) defines a museum as "a non-profit making permanent institution in the service of society and of its development, open to the public, which acquires, conserves, researches, communicates and exhibits, for purposes of study, education and enjoyment, the tangible and intangible evidence of people and their environment" (International Council of Museums, under "Glossary").

Museums provide opportunities for lifelong learning and are stewards of our cultural heritage. They engage with schools, families, and communities, connecting the whole of society to the cultural, artistic, historical, natural, and scientific understandings that constitute our heritage. Museums collect and conserve tangible objects—animate and inanimate—for the benefit of future generations (Institute of Museum and Library Services, 2008). Examples include both governmental and private museums of anthropology, art history and natural history, aquariums, arboreta, art centers, botanical gardens, children's museums, historic sites, nature centers, planetariums, science and technology centers, and zoos (American Association of Museums, 2009).

Because of the uniqueness of the items they collect, museums have special responsibilities to work closely with the communities from which their collections originate, as well as the communities they serve. Museums are held to a standard of stewardship that includes respect for rightful ownership, permanence, documentation, accessibility, and responsible disposal of items collected (International Council of Museums, 2006).

Archives

Archives are the records a person or organization creates or receives and preserves because of their enduring value (Pearce-Moses, 2005). For a corporation or a state or nation, these include administrative files, business records, memos, official correspondence, meeting minutes—sometimes referred to as the by-products of the organization's activities. The material in an archive may be written text on paper, photographs, sound recordings, electronic records, or other formats. In an archive these permanent records are maintained using principles of provenance (keeping separate records from different sources, to preserve their context), original order, and collective control.

Archives constitute the memory of nations and of societies, shape their identity, and are a cornerstone of the information society. By providing evidence of human actions and transactions, archives support administration and underlie the rights of individuals, organizations, and states. By guaranteeing citizens' rights of access to official information and to knowledge of their history, archives are fundamental to democracy, accountability, and good governance (International Council on Archives, 2008).

Archivists assess, collect, organize, preserve, maintain control over, and provide access to archival information. The primary duty of archivists is to maintain the integrity of the records in their care and custody. They must consider the legitimate, but sometimes conflicting, rights and interests of employers, owners, data subjects, and users—past, present, and future (International Council on Archives, 1996). "Archivists keep records that have enduring value as reliable memories of the past, and they help people find and understand the information they need in those records" (Pearce-Moses, 2006, p. 3).

Information Science Perspectives

Memory institutions focus on accumulating, analyzing, and disseminating a variety of information to diverse populations and cultures. Libraries, museums, and archives have developed principles for handling their specific kinds of "informative objects" or documents. These principles reflect the different nature and tasks of the various institutions. Their different experiences have contributed to the development of generalized knowledge in information science. This knowledge is then given back to those institutions in order to improve their functions.

Libraries, archives, and museums perform complementary functions. They collect and preserve unique records of our world, records of individual and organizational lives, and the published record of human communication. Librarians, archivists, and museum professionals understand what to acquire for these collections and how to preserve them for future generations. The rapid growth of electronic resources, especially web-based content, has challenged these professionals to develop and maintain collections of new kinds.

The convergence of media and technologies toward digital storage and access implies that old and well-established divisions of responsibility based on the nature of objects handled will change—*published documents* and *unique objects* have to be reconsidered. From an abstract perspective, these different institutions are performing the same task: handling information. Their approaches and perspectives, however, differ. For example, archivists emphasize the principle of *provenance* (knowing an item's origin and history of ownership). Information professionals must be aware of the various specialized principles and be prepared to adopt them when needed; this understanding is especially useful in dealing with digital resources.

New areas of expertise within information science are developing to respond to the challenges of developing and maintaining collections of new kinds, one of which is digital preservation. Digital preservation is customarily described as "a set of activities aimed toward ensuring access to digital materials over time." Because information objects are not usable if they cannot be accessed and understood in the future, preservation aims to ensure their availability, understandability, authenticity, viability, and renderability.

Libraries, museums, and archives are making more of their collections available over the internet. Digital libraries, virtual museums, and electronic archives greatly extend access to these collections, in line with a memory institution's commitment to support education and enjoyment. Marty (1999) observed that information professionals have yet "to analyze and understand the social dimension that emerges when advanced information technology is integrated into an organizational context" (p. 1084). The stage is set for a social informatics perspective on how digital access and collaborative technologies affect memory institutions and people's memories.

Connections With Computer Science

The stewardship of cultural heritage increasingly demands competence with computer and information technologies; and computer scientists have become increasingly aware of the need to understand and take responsibility for the work and consequences of these technologies. The prominent computer scientist Edsger Dijkstra remarked that "computer science is no more about computers than astronomy is about telescopes" (Dijkstra 1972)—highlighting the value of studying the theory and practice of what computers can do, not just the instruments themselves.

Although early work in computer science emphasized the machines and their architecture, the importance of software soon became obvious as programming became easier. The computer moved from being merely a high-speed calculator to become a ubiquitous presence essential for research, business, and leisure. Many of the information scientists who see computer science as their principal profession are members of the Association for Computing Machinery (ACM; www.acm.org). The ACM's special interest groups of particular interest to information scientists include SIGIR (Information Retrieval), SIGCHI (Computer-Human Interaction), and SIG-CAS (Computers and Society).

13.3. Values

Freedom, equal access, and neutrality are fundamental, but contested, values in information science; they are the topics of many of today's great debates. For instance, people's "right-to-know" has been supported by both hackers and the American Library Association. Some would argue that private matters must be protected from public disclosure, and corporations would affirm that no one has either a right to know or a right to access proprietary information unless it was purchased on the open market.

Equity of access is a common, although not universal, value for information professionals. Government-funded agencies (including public libraries) often have equal access as a goal. An individual's access to information may be limited because of poor literacy skills, economic disadvantages, or physical or learning disabilities. Location can also reduce access: rural communities have less or slower access to the internet, enhancing the effect of the so-called *digital divide* (Chen & Wellman, 2003).

Neutrality is also a divisive concept. Some interpret neutrality to mean detachment and indifference to the content of what is collected, organized, preserved, and disseminated; from this perspective, the neutral information provider does not discriminate and thus promotes democracy. Others believe that, conversely, a skilled professional demonstrates neutrality by skillfully screening content to provide authoritative answers for information seekers.

It is evident that politics and economics are playing an increasingly influential role in the design, planning, and implementation of information services and the values driving these choices. The contested area of *intellectual freedom* demonstrates the complexity of upholding a fundamental value.

Intellectual Freedom

The right to intellectual freedom is stated in Article 19 of the Universal Declaration of Human Rights: "Everyone has the right to freedom of opinion and expression; this right includes freedom to hold opinions without interference and to seek, receive and impart information and ideas through any media and regardless of frontiers" (United Nations, 1948).

Several professions, including education and librarianship, promote the safeguarding of this right. For instance, the International Federation of Library Associations and Institutions (1999) states that "the right to know is a requirement for freedom of thought and conscience; freedom of thought and freedom of expression are necessary conditions for freedom of access to information" (paragraph 3). And the Canadian Library Association (1985) holds that everyone in that country has "the fundamental right ... to have access to all expressions of knowledge, creativity, and intellectual activity, and to express their thoughts publicly" (paragraph 1).

European and North American writers debate how traditional intellectual freedoms will be identified and preserved in the digital age: digital liberties have been described that include access to technology, free exchange of ideas, the right to privacy, culture sharing, knowledge and skill development, and emancipation through empowerment.

Some of the values supporting intellectual freedom may be culturally influenced and sometimes at odds with some sensitive and proprietary indigenous knowledge. This is evident in anthropological research: Newly empowered native peoples have found their own voices and claimed the right of repatriation of artifacts, together with the knowledge associated with their religious rituals, in order to regain full ownership of their mysteries.

The concept of intellectual freedom has also expanded to software development, access, and use. For instance, advocates of free and open source software contend that computer users have the right to replace proprietary software (used under restrictive licensing terms and conditions) with free software (considered a superior model for software development). This approach to social, ethical, and technical issues has resulted in efforts to pass legislation encouraging use of free software by government agencies in various countries, including the U.S.

13.4. Information Ethics

Issues related to information ethics impinge on technology, government publication and legislation, graphic display, computer security, database management, disinformation, peer review, privacy, censorship, cyberspace, and information liability; these may be approached from sociological, philosophical, theoretical, and applied perspectives (McFarland & Company, 2009). Mason, Mason, and Culnan (1995) described four areas of interest in the field of information ethics: privacy, accuracy, property, and accessibility. From a global perspective, Froehlich (1997) identified access, ownership, cultural orientation, and ethical priorities as being key to the consideration of the ethics of information.

In business settings information has vital strategic and therefore economic value. It is an asset to be developed, managed, and leveraged for advantage. Personal information, consumer information, and health information, for example, are generated by individuals and have economic value as well. The increased importance of ebusiness and user-generated content online reduced personal privacy and information security. Online applications greatly simplify the task of finding people in the physical world. Computer processing power, storage capacity, and interconnectivity often make violations of personal property and information remarkably easy, and incompetent use or abuse of information at either the organizational or personal level can have significant economic and social consequences. The confluence of personal information (a form of personal property), communication technology, and the base urges of capitalism create ethical dilemmas that may be novel or may represent issues from antiquity recast in modern trappings. As is the case with the other policy aspects of information science, questions of information ethics have personal, institutional, and social dimensions; and they may be considered at both the political and the legal level.

Organizations and professional societies develop codes of ethics or conduct as guidelines for members. These declarations of principles provide a rubric for mission development as well as a model for defining high standards and identifying excellence. Most such professional creeds articulate responsibilities to society and to practitioners and tend to be positive rather than prohibitive in nature. Major issues pertaining to the unethical use of information include, but are by no means limited to, the following:

- Fraud and identity theft

- Protection of and access to personal information from a security standpoint

- Abuse of personal privacy and data mining for commercial or law enforcement reasons

- The protection of personal information such as financial and health information from public disclosure

- Censorship

The ASIST Professional Guidelines (American Society for Information Science and Technology, 1992) provide an example:

> ASIS&T recognizes the plurality of uses and users of information technologies, services, systems and products as well as the diversity of goals or objectives, sometimes conflicting, among producers, vendors, mediators, and users of information systems.
>
> ASIS&T urges its members to be ever aware of the social, economic, cultural, and political impacts of their actions or inaction.
>
> ASIS&T members have obligations to employers, clients, and system users, to the profession, and to society, to use judgement and discretion in making choices, providing equitable service, and in defending the rights of open inquiry.

Responsibilities to Employers/Clients/System Users:

- To act faithfully for their employers or clients in professional matters

- To uphold each user's, provider's, or employer's right to privacy and confidentiality and to respect whatever proprietary rights belong to them, by limiting access to, providing proper security for and ensuring proper disposal of data about clients, patrons or users

- To treat all persons fairly

Responsibility to the Profession

To truthfully represent themselves and the information systems which they utilize or which they represent, by

- Not knowingly making false statements or providing erroneous or misleading information

- Informing their employers, clients or sponsors of any circumstances that create a conflict of interest

- Not using their position beyond their authorized limits or by not using their credentials to misrepresent themselves

- Following and promoting standards of conduct in accord with the best current practices

- Undertaking their research conscientiously, in gathering, tabulating or interpreting data; in following proper approval procedures for subjects; and in producing or disseminating their research results

- Pursuing ongoing professional development and encouraging and assisting colleagues and others to do the same

- Adhering to principles of due process and equality of opportunity

Responsibility to Society

To improve the information systems with which they work or which they represent, to the best of their means and abilities by

- Providing the most reliable and accurate information and acknowledging the credibility of the sources as known or unknown

- Resisting all forms of censorship, inappropriate selection and acquisitions policies, and biases in information selection, provision and dissemination

- Making known any biases, errors and inaccuracies found to exist and striving to correct those which can be remedied

To promote open and equal access to information, within the scope permitted by their organizations or work, and to resist procedures that promote unlawful discriminatory practices in access to and provision of information, by

- Seeking to extend public awareness and appreciation of information availability and provision as well as the role of information professionals in providing such information

- Freely reporting, publishing or disseminating information subject to legal and proprietary restraints of producers, vendors and employers, and the best interests of their employers or clients

Information professionals shall engage in principled conduct whether on their own behalf or at the request of employers, colleagues, clients, agencies or the profession.

Some ethical issues related to the use and abuse of information date from antiquity, such as the persistent issues of censorship and identity theft. Technological developments have exacerbated some concerns, but the fundamental issues are constant. Other issues, such as data mining and the use of technologies such as radio frequency identification and global positioning system tracking have raised new questions about the nature of privacy and anonymity. In many cases, modern ethical questions are not new but have become more pressing and relevant because of fundamental technological trends. Technological factors that contribute to or exacerbate problems in the information society include the exponential growth of processing power and storage capacity of information handling technology (computers and network devices), increased incidental data production by individuals (daily living now results in a much more detailed data trail than it did 25 years ago), and increasingly sophisticated and wide-reaching data analysis tools.

Because using today's information and communication technologies can provide significant economic value, some entities are highly motivated to refine their techniques in order to increase profit by selling ever more detailed information about individuals. Such data aggregators and brokers are controversial; however, many of their sources of information have always been publicly available and have simply become more convenient with the advent of widespread information networks. For example, a search of home sales and tax records once required a trip to the local or state records office; today a much larger search can be done in less time from any device with access to the appropriate data repositories. The practice has not changed, but its speed and convenience have.

Any discussion of information ethics must first consider what constitutes ethical behavior. Ethics comprises the precepts that free individuals use in making choices to guide their decisions and behaviors. Without undertaking a study of the history of ethics, it is useful to consider the most commonly used ethical principle in Western civilization: Immanuel Kant's *categorical imperative*, a moral test that asks the question: If everyone behaved in this way, could the organization or society in general survive? It can also be seen as a restatement of the Golden Rule, "Do unto others as you would have them do unto you."

Smith (1997) noted two dominant philosophical approaches to information ethics: *utilitarian* (largely based on the work of John Stuart Mill) and *deontological* (largely based on Kant's work). Mitcham and Huning (1986) considered epistemological and metaphysical issues surrounding information. Mason and colleagues' (1995) textbook, *Ethics of Information Management*, explored the life cycle of information, including ethical considerations regarding information dissemination and integrity and their impact on society in general. Spinello (1995) examined concerns about personal information rights such as informed consent, privacy, and intellectual property. Questions of information ethics are often considered in terms of basic ethical tests:

- *The slippery slope*: This ethical test asks whether an act's rightness or wrongness is defined by its magnitude. (If I make an analog copy of a recording for a child, is that different from distributing the recording on the internet? Alternatively, is it more moral to take a $1 bribe than a $10,000 bribe?)

- *Utilitarianism*: As described by Mill, the rightness of an act is determined entirely by its consequences, or in more colloquial terms, "The end justifies the means." Such a calculus is common in business and government, in which net benefit is measured against potential liability to determine a course of action.

- *Risk aversion*: This test asks, "What are the consequences to me from this action?" The potential negative effects of a decision are weighed against potential benefits. This line of thought may take its most famous form in Pascal's argument for belief in God, paraphrased as follows: To believe in God and to be wrong costs one nothing. However, if one does not believe in God and is wrong, then the penalty is infinite. Thus, it is better to believe than not.

- *The no-free-lunch rule*: This rubric for making ethical decisions assumes that any tangible property is owned by someone unless explicitly stated otherwise. It is a test that asks, What is the likelihood that taking this action will deprive someone else of his or her property?

Laudon and Laudon (2007) described five moral issues of importance to an information society:

1. Individual information rights: What are the rights of the individuals with regard to information about themselves or created by themselves? Concerns include data mining of records and protection of personal information such as telephone numbers or medical records.

2. Intellectual property rights and obligations: How can creative works or inventions of an intangible nature be protected in the

digital marketplace? In short, how can intellectual property rights be maintained in an environment in which such creations are neither rivalrous (can be possessed by more than one person) nor excludable (people who have not paid can be prevented from having access)? (These questions are explored in more detail in Chapter 11.)

3. Accountability and control: Who is responsible or accountable in the event that data or information is lost and personal privacy or other social harms result? The legal concepts of responsibility, accountability, and liability all come into play with regard to this aspect of information ethics.

4. System quality: What public standards exist to ensure the reliability and quality of the information in information systems? Issues in this area include the rights of individuals to access and correct information about them and to seek justice in the event that information is lost or misused.

5. Quality of life: What institutions and values will be preserved in a society in which all information generated by an individual is available through some electronic source? Examples include the extent to which individuals have an expectation of privacy in their daily lives and the role of the library in a changing information-based economy.

Social ethical norms play a major role in understanding ethical decisions. For example, although U.S. law contains no explicit right to privacy, individuals have historically had what Justice Blackmun (1986, p. 199) described as "the right to be left alone," based on the principles detailed in the First and Fourth Amendments to the U.S. Constitution. In particular, First Amendment protections relating to speech and assembly, and the Fourth Amendment's protection of the individual from unreasonable search and seizure, have been held to protect the individual from unwanted scrutiny.

In a society in which the protection of personal property has become the paramount social value, any product generated by an individual that has negotiable worth is deemed worthy of protection. Consequently, records and personal information may be protected from public disclosure for personal reasons or for economic ones.

Numerous laws exist to protect individuals and to address ethical dilemmas created by the presence of vast amounts of information available instantly anywhere in the world to billions of highly unpredictable users. Examples of policies (laws) that exist to protect the individual include the Financial Privacy Act of 1974 and the Health Insurance Portability and Accountability Act, which protects medical records from unauthorized disclosure. Restricting content available to minors has long been a justification for censorship; modern incarnations include the Communications Decency Act and the Children's Internet Protection Act. Attempts to legislate other aspects of information use in society that have ethical dimensions include the development of the Digital Millennium Copyright Act, which (among other things) restricts research into encryption technologies in an attempt to make copy protection a viable technology by eliminating users' ability to examine those technologies legally. To conclude, the accelerative aspects of information technology continue to blur the distinctions between disciplines, making information ethics a complex and evolving area of inquiry.

Issues such as the role that information plays in creating a better society and the ethical implications of the digital divide, ownership, access, censorship, and privacy domestically and globally continue to be complex and vexatious. Simple guidelines rather than prohibitions seem to be the more effective approach to making ethically sound decisions for the individual and society. One approach, adopted by the American Library Association, is that information should be made available to all people. How individuals use (or choose not to use) such information to their advantage affects everyone, but the ethical considerations then fall to the individual rather than to policymakers. Such an approach leads to a multiplicity of outcomes, but if information has one unifying trait, it is that its significance and utility are directly proportional to the number of users.

Like information use, information ethics is dependent on the activities of individuals, or in the parlance of moral philosophers, *free moral agents*. People have developed uses for networked information that are far beyond the original expectations of authors or telecommunications workers; it is the freedom to make decisions based on information that leads to innovation and diversity of opinion. Such decisions necessarily entail ethical concerns. Top-down mandates dictating how information should be used not only stifle innovation and intellectual freedom, but such behavior also tends to be strongly culturally biased and leads to conflict at the moral, personal, societal, and global levels. Individuals must have access to information for the sake of good government, innovation and economic growth, and personal development. The role of the individual in creating a better society is affected by access to information and the ability to transform it into knowledge. Wise policymakers will bear in mind that intellectual freedom is a powerful social force, and policy decisions should be geared toward expanding the freedoms and rights of the engines of innovation—information users.

13. 5. Links to Professional Associations

Here are links to several important professional associations:

- American Association of Museums, www.aam-us.org

- American Library Association, www.ala.org

- American Society for Information Science and Technology, www.asis.org

- ARMA International, www.arma.org

- Association for Computing Machinery, www.acm.org

- International Council on Archives, www.ica.org

- International Council of Museums, www.icom.museum

- Society of American Archivists, www.archivists.org

- Special Libraries Association, www.sla.org

References

American Association of Museums. (2009). *What is a museum?* Retrieved November 11, 2010, from www.aam-us.org/aboutmuseums/whatis.cfm.

American Library Association. (2010). *Access to information.* Retrieved November 11, 2010, from www.ala.org/ala/issuesadvocacy/access/accesstoinformation/index.cfm.

American Society for Information Science and Technology. (1992). *ASIST professional guidelines.* Retrieved December 21, 2010, from http://www.asis.org/professionalguidelines.html.

Blackmun, J. (1986). Bowers v. Hardwick (478 U.S. 186).

Canadian Library Association. (1985). *Position statement on intellectual freedom.* Retrieved November 11, 2010, from www.cla.ca/Content/NavigationMenu/Resources/Position Statements/Statement_on_Intell.htm.

Chen, W., & Wellman, B. (2003) *Charting and bridging digital divides: Comparing socio-economic, gender, life stage and rural-urban internet access and use in eight countries.* Sunnyvale, CA: AMD Global Consumer Advisory Board. Retrieved November 11, 2010, from www.finextra.com/Finextra-downloads/featuredocs/International_digital_divide.pdf.

Dijkstra, E. W. (1972, August). Speech accepting the ACM Turing Award. Quotation retrieved April 24, 2011, from www.quotes.net/quote/12595.

Froehlich, T. (1997). *Survey and analysis of legal and ethical issues for library and information services.* UNESCO Report (Contract No. 401.723.4) for the International Federation of Library Associations. IFLA Professional Series. Munich, Germany: G. K. Saur.

Hjerppe, R. (1994). A framework for the description of generalized documents. *Advances in Knowledge Organization, 4,* 173–180.

Institute of Museum and Library Services. (2008, December). *Exhibiting public value: Government funding for museums in the United States.* Retrieved November 11, 2010, from www.imls.gov/pdf/MuseumPublicFinance.pdf.

International Council of Museums. (2006). *Code of ethics.* Retrieved November 11, 2010, from www.icom.museum/ethics.html.

International Council on Archives. (1996). *Code of ethics.* Retrieved November 11, 2010, from www.ica.org/sites/default/files/Ethics-EN.pdf.

International Council on Archives. (2008). *Welcome to ICA.* Retrieved May 11, 2011, from www.ica.org/102/about-ica/an-introduction-to-our-organization.html.

International Federation of Library Associations and Institutions. (1999). *IFLA statement on libraries and intellectual freedom.* Retrieved November 11, 2010, from www.ifla.org/en/publications/ifla-statement-on-libraries-and-intellectual-freedom.

Laudon, K. C., & Laudon, J. P. (2007). *Management information systems: Managing the digital firm* (10th ed.). Upper Saddle River, NJ: Pearson.

Marty, P. F. (1999). Museum informatics and collaborative technologies: The emerging socio-technological dimension of information science in museum environments. *Journal of the American Society for Information Science, 50*(12), 1083–1091.

Mason, R. O., Mason, F. M., & Culnan, M. J. (1995). *Ethics of information management.* Thousand Oaks, CA: Sage.

McFarland & Company, Inc. (2009). *JIE* call for submissions. Retrieved November 11, 2010, from www.mcfarlandpub.com/jiesubmissions.html.

Mitcham, C., & Huning, A. (1986). *Philosophy and technology II: Information technology and computers in theory and practice.* Dordrecht, Netherlands: Reidel.

Pearce-Moses, R. (2005). *A glossary of archival and records terminology.* Chicago: Society of American Archivists. Retrieved November 11, 2010, from www.archivists.org/glossary/term_details.asp?DefinitionKey=156.

Pearce-Moses, R. (2006, March/April). Identity and diversity: What is an archivist? *Archival Outlook.* Retrieved November 11, 2010, from www.archivists.org/periodicals/ao_back issues/AO-Mar06.pdf.

Smith, M. M. (1997). Information ethics. *Annual Review of Information Science and Technology, 32,* 339–366.

Spinello, R. A. (1995). *Ethical aspects of information technology.* Englewood Cliffs, NJ: Prentice Hall.

United Nations. (1948). *Universal declaration of human rights.* Retrieved November 11, 2010, from www.un.org/en/documents/udhr.

CHAPTER 14

Information Theory

14.1. Introduction

"Theory is not dry abstraction but the body of concerns, methods, and research problems a discipline develops over time. [It provides] not only intellectual content, but exposure to conventions governing choice of research problems, methods, materials, and equipment to use." This is how Pierce (1992, p. 641) presented the case for theory; she was writing as a sociologist who had taken the requisite introduction to theory course (which the students called "Dead Germans") in that field and lamented the absence of theory in information science.

One might have thought that, for so important a field, a general theory would be easy to identify. Although much has been written on various information systems (online databases, libraries, etc.), the attention is often limited to one type of system, restricted by technology (usually to computer-based systems), or focused on one function (such as retrieval) and disregards the broader context. Writings specifically on theory have often focused on logic, probability, and physical signals. In addition, the field has only gradually recognized that the word information is used by different people to denote different things.

In the 1950s *information theory* was developed from the statistical theory of communication. As information science developed, researchers and practitioners have also considered more socially oriented theories such as network theory and social epistemology. Philosophers have also taken an interest in the provocative challenges of our field.

14.2. Shannon and Weaver's Information Theory

American electrical engineer Claude Shannon worked for the Bell Telephone Laboratories, investigating how messages in a system are transmitted and received, including how unwanted noise in a system can interfere with communication. In 1948 he published a journal article on the topic, which was later expanded into a book, *The Mathematical Theory of Communication* (Shannon & Weaver, 1949), co-authored with Warren Weaver. They depicted a generic communication system and quantified entropy (a measure of uncertainty) in both the selection of the message to be transmitted and the transmission of the message itself. In this model, a message originates at a source; the message is sent by a transmitter along a channel to a receiver; then the message arrives at a destination (see Figure 14.1; also Figure 2.2 from Chapter 2's Shannon-Weaver discussion):

- The information source produces (or selects) the message or the sequence of messages to be transmitted to the destination.

- The transmitter converts the message into a signal suitable for transmission over the channel.

- The channel is the medium that is used to transmit the signal.

- Noise is any interference with the signal during transmission.

- The receiver is a device that reconstructs (either exactly or approximately) the message from the received signal.

- The destination is the person (or thing) for which the message is intended.

Shannon and Weaver present a formula to characterize S, the entropy or uncertainty (randomness, complexity, unpredictability, surprise) of a message: $S = \sum p_i \ln p_i$. The amount of information in a message is measured in units called *bits*, short for binary digits (two states). Thus the researcher can determine the minimum number of bits required to send a given message (signal) and the maximum rate (bits per second) at which a given communication channel can transmit information reliably.

The Shannon-Weaver model acknowledges the constraint of *channel capacity*, a measure of the ultimate speed or rate at which a channel can

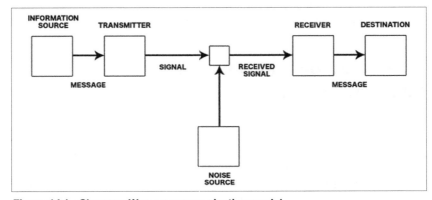

Figure 14.1   Shannon-Weaver communication model

transmit information reliably. The capacity of a particular system can be approached but never exceeded. A transmission channel's capacity is measured in *bits per second*. With a properly designed transmitter, a message can be transmitted perfectly reliably at any speed up to the channel's capacity. However, if the capacity is exceeded, the message received at the destination will contain errors.

Shannon and Weaver introduced the concept of *entropy* (from the second law of thermodynamics) to describe the information content of a message. The information content from most sources may vary from message to message—some messages are more likely than others. The unlikely messages convey the most information; messages that are highly probable convey less information.

The amount of information is the negative of the logarithm of a sum of probabilities. Thus, the amount of information is equal to entropy. Shannon and Weaver caution that *information* at this level should not be equated with the semantic content of a message (the "everyday" notion of information), only with the *probability* that a given message (or unit information) would be sent.

For Shannon and Weaver, information theory had primarily a theoretical value. However, it has had a major impact on the design of practical data communication and storage systems, such as telephone and computer networks. The theory can be applied to both the transmission and the storage of messages because storage is fundamentally transmission in time.

Norbert Wiener's Contributions

Norbert Wiener's (1948) book *Cybernetics, or Control and Communication in the Animal and the Machine* is also foundational to information theory. Wiener integrated the concepts of amount of information, entropy, feedback, and background noise derived from findings regarding the role of bioelectric signals in biological systems, including humans. The brain and nervous system coordinate information to determine which actions will be performed; control mechanisms for self-correction in machines (for example, guided missiles) serve a similar purpose. This principle of *feedback* is the fundamental concept of automation; Wiener noticed that it is also a key feature of life forms: The simplest plants and the most complex animals change their actions in response to their environment.

According to Wiener, in any system where a transformation occurs, control is maintained in response to inputs and outputs. The inputs are the result of the environment's influence on the system, and the outputs are the influence of the system on the environment. In a feedback loop, information about the result of a transformation or an action is sent back to the input of the system.

If new data facilitates and accelerates the transformation in the same direction as the preceding results, then it is positive feedback, and its effects are cumulative. If the new data produces a result in a direction opposite to that of previous results, it is negative feedback, and its effects stabilize the system. In the first case, there is exponential growth or decline; in the second there is maintenance of the equilibrium. The destructive behavior of positive loops is controlled by negative loops. According to Wiener, this control is essential for a system to maintain itself over time.

As with Shannon and Weaver, entropy is the key concept that characterizes information: "The notion of the amount of information attaches itself very naturally to a classical notion in statistical mechanics: that of entropy. Just as the amount of information in a system is a measure of its degree of organization, so the entropy of a system is a measure of its degree of disorganization" (Wiener, 1948, p. 18). Wiener also defines information in terms of probability. But unlike Shannon and Weaver, he describes the amount of information as the negative of entropy.

The Reception of the Shannon-Weaver Theory in Information Science

Shannon and Weaver's use of the term *information* in their theory of communication has intrigued information scientists since the 1950s. Kline (2004) found that the Shannon-Weaver model has been used in information science in three ways: 1) as a scientific foundation for the field, 2) as a metaphor to analyze broad topics, and 3) as a mathematical tool to design information-retrieval systems.

Wersig (2003) termed the "development stage [of information theory] from 1948 to the 1970s the 'Shannon and Weaver phase'" (p. 313), which was followed in the 1970s by the era of the cognitive approach. The Shannon-Weaver theory has been used to model video (moving image documents) by Watt (1979), O'Connor (1991), and Kearns (2003). Because sound and music resemble video in being a set of time-varying signals, information theory can be applied to them as well. Some authors, such as Cawkell (1990), still find standard information theory to be useful in information science and as a metaphor (Shaw & Davis, 1983).

14.3. Network Theory

Network theory studies information networks (e.g., the World Wide Web), technical networks (the internet, railways, airline routes), biological networks (the human genome), and social networks (human relationships) (Newman, 2003). Networks are systems of nodes and links; network theory is the study of the interconnections found in networks. It is an empirical discipline; it studies real-world networks in natural settings.

Small worlds theory is the dominant network theory; it was developed from the mathematical discipline of graph theory in response to a desire to study the perception that social interconnections are increasing across the globe ("small worlds"). *Social network theory* focuses specifically on the unique characteristics of social networks.

Network theory is relevant to the communication and use of information because communication often involves networks: computer networks; networks of libraries and library resources; the social networks of information scientists and information seekers. Network theory improves understanding of network structures and behaviors and creates models that help explicate network properties. Network theory suggests that there is a degree of order in the universe and that there are common patterns.

Nodes (also known as *vertices*) are points in a network where a message can be created, received, or repeated. A *hub* is a specific type of node that has many links flowing out from it; an *authority* is another type of node, with many links flowing into it. *Links* (also known as *connectors*, *branches*, and *edges*) transmit messages and connect nodes. *Local links* connect relatively close nodes; *long distance links* connect nodes that are far away from each other. Real-world networks are "scale-free" (the connectivity of the nodes follows a power law, with just a few being highly linked): they tend to be clustered, and they are dynamic (i.e., display growth and preferential attachment). Because of this dynamic nature, early nodes have more time to acquire links than latecomers do, hence the preferential attachment.

Empirical observation tells us that networks are ubiquitous. In an interconnected universe, we inhabit multiple networks simultaneously: social networks, information networks, and technical and biological networks. Network theory offers the best opportunity of understanding such networks.

The 80/20 Rule

The 80/20 rule describes inequalities found in many social situations. It has been applied to business management, citation analysis, criminology, and web analysis. For example, business managers describe the 80/20 rule as "Murphy's Law of Management": 80 percent of profits are the result of 20 percent of employees, 80 percent of problems are caused by 20 percent of customers, 80 percent of decisions are made in 20 percent of meeting time, 80 percent of efforts are wasted and 20 percent are productive (Barabási, 2002, p. 662).

Citation analysts report that 80 percent of citations cite 20 percent of scientists; criminologists note that 80 percent of crime is committed by 20 percent of criminals; film critics find that 80 percent of films are made by 20 percent of actors; and web analysts report that 80 percent of web links are directed to 20 percent of webpages. In libraries, 80 percent of circulation is attributable to 20 percent of library holdings. The 80/20 rule is known as Pareto's law (named for Italian economist Vilfredo Pareto).

The 80/20 rule displays a property key to understanding complex, scale-free networks: *exponential distribution*. The continuous decreasing curve described by the rule typifies the distribution of real-world networks such as the internet, the neural networks of the brain, and the human genome. Take the web, for example; a bell curve distribution would suggest most webpages would be equally popular. However, we find instead that relatively few pages are popular and most are not. This indicates an exponential distribution in which many small events coexist with a few large ones.

The exponential distribution is a mathematical indication of the interconnected universe and suggests that complex networks within the universe are not entirely random. In other words, there is a degree of order in the universe.

Small Worlds Theory

Small worlds theory is a popular network theory that developed from the branch of mathematics called graph theory, now called network theory. Paul Erdös (1913–1996), a Hungarian mathematician, discovered that no matter how many nodes there may be in a network, a small percentage of randomly placed links is always enough to tie the network together into a more or less completely connected whole. More surprisingly, the percentage required dwindles as the network gets larger. For example, a network of 300 nodes can be linked in almost 50,000 ways, but if no more than 2 percent of those links are in place, the network will be completely connected.

Network theorists found that real-world networks were not random at all but followed predictable patterns of order and growth. Although graph theory studies random networks exclusively, small worlds theory studies the scale-free networks found in the real world; thus, it is the study of the interconnections that form real-world networks.

Perhaps the single most influential piece of research in small worlds theory is Mark Granovetter's (1973) article "The Strength of Weak Ties." Granovetter found that the links in social networks could be divided into *strong ties* (between family members, friends, co-workers, colleagues) and *weak ties* (between casual or rare acquaintances). Strong ties tend to form clusters and have little effect on the overall connectivity of the network. It is the weak ties that are most important to the formation of real-world networks. Granovetter called these weak links *bridges*; they act as crucial ties that bind the social network together. As a real-world example, Granovetter found that only 16 percent of people he interviewed got their jobs through strong contacts, whereas 84 percent found their jobs through contacts they saw occasionally or rarely.

Network Theory's Contributions

Starting with a completely ordered network, in which each node links to its neighbor and its next nearest neighbor, Watts and Strogatz (1998) reconnected the links randomly and found that the new links contributed to six degrees of separation; that is, in a network with just 2 percent randomly generated links, most nodes can be reached from other nodes by traversing relatively few links. At the same time, the random links have little noticeable impact on the degree of local clustering. Barabási (2002) and Newman (2003) explored small worlds theory as a way to explain the apparent order and connectivity of the information networks of the World Wide Web and the technical networks of the internet.

Network theory improves understanding of network structures and behaviors, creates models that help explicate network properties, and helps in predicting future behavior of networks. As an emerging discipline, there are significant research opportunities (Newman, 2003), especially in the prediction of network behavior. Technologically mediated communication depends on communications networks such as the internet, satellite, radio, and television; improved understanding of networks can increase the effectiveness of communication.

14.4. Social Epistemology

Goldman (2001) defines social epistemology as "the study of the social dimensions of knowledge or information." Schmitt (1998) calls it "the conceptual and normative study of the relevance to knowledge of social relations, interests and institutions. It is thus to be distinguished from the sociology of knowledge, which is an empirical study of the contingent social conditions or causes of what is commonly taken to be knowledge. Social epistemology revolves around the question of whether knowledge is to be understood individualistically or socially" (p. 1).

When Jesse Shera (1970) introduced the term, he contrasted social epistemology with classical epistemologies, especially empiricism and logical positivism, which conceived of the individual's perception as "given." All verbal reports, thus all literature, were considered "second hand knowledge" (Wilson, 1983). If individual perception and thinking are not given, but depend on language, theories, views, and background knowledge, then the distinction between individual and social knowledge is seriously blurred.

From a structuralist perspective, for example, concepts are formed by languages, and there is no one-to-one relation between meanings in different languages. Hjelmslev (1943/1961) contends that each language put arbitrary borders on reality (other theories find that symbolic systems tend to capture functional aspects in the things people perceive). It follows that the individual does not see a tree objectively. What is seen—or at least what is being reported as seen—depends on the conceptual structure in the language used.

Many philosophies have argued that knowledge is fundamentally social. This is more or less the case with, for example, activity theory, critical theory, feminist epistemology, hermeneutics, Marxism, paradigm theory, pragmaticism, semiotics, social constructivism (and social constructionism), and structuralism. Social epistemology emphasizes problems related to the social organization of knowledge or the organization of cognitive labor. It is thus closely related to problems in information science.

Social Epistemology and Information Science

As noted, Shera (1970) was one of the first to use the phrase social epistemology in information science; he, in turn, credits his associate Margaret Egan with selecting the term. Shera described social epistemology as "the study of knowledge in society. … The focus of this discipline should be upon the production, flow, integration, and consumption of all forms of communicated thought throughout the entire social fabric" (p. 86). He was particularly interested in the affinity between social epistemology and librarianship.

Shera's social view of libraries and information science had little influence at the time. Around 1990 the social perspective gained strength, bringing about what Cronin (2008) called "the sociological turn in information science" (p. 465). The emergence of social informatics (see Chapter 10) is further evidence of the trend.

A Paradigm Shift in Information Science?

Philosopher and historian of science Thomas Kuhn introduced the concept of a *paradigm shift* to describe a radical change in how scientists comprehend and advance their field. Kuhn (1996) defines a paradigm as a set of theories, ideas, abstractions, and beliefs that "provide models from which spring particular traditions of scientific research" (p. 10). His examples of paradigm shifts, which are primarily from the physical sciences, include Aristotelian dynamics, Copernican astronomy, Newtonian optics, and Einstein's theories of relativity. A paradigm shift is a crisis brought on by conflict between two or more paradigms and in which the "fittest" paradigm survives. There is no synthesis; Kuhn claims that paradigms are incommensurable (incompatible), hence the crisis; the resulting change is comparable to a revolution.

Kuhn distinguishes between mature and immature fields of scientific research. Immature fields are marked by many rival schools. Because no common body of belief exists in such schools, nothing can be taken for granted. Thus, scientists in the immature fields are compelled to engage in metaphysical and methodological debate. Without a shared framework of beliefs, the immature fields of science pursue knowledge rather randomly and have no standard by which to assess the value of various data.

Many in information science see a paradigm shift in the turn from a systems view to a user view (as evidenced in Belkin's *anomalous states of knowledge*, Dervin's *sense-making*, Kuhlthau's *information search process*, Schamber's *notion of relevance*, and Taylor's *information need*; Pettigrew & McKechnie, 2001). But, according to Kuhn, such a shift occurs between two or more incommensurable paradigms. That systems and user viewpoints are problematic is a reasonable belief, but it is not evident that the two views are incommensurable. It may be more meaningful to consider both views as mutually dependent: Without information systems, there are no information users, and without the needs of information users, there is no purpose for information systems.

Although some information science researchers discern clear boundaries between information systems and users (Allen, 1996), other educators and practitioners adopt an "interpretivist" philosophical framework that considers reality as primarily a social construction (Williamson, 2002). This suggests that the discipline is willing to question the interpretation of its own boundaries.

Some authors have investigated library and information science from the point of view of its paradigms (or metatheories, views, philosophical or epistemological positions). Ellis (1996, pp. 23–36) discussed paradigm in information retrieval research and presented "the archetypal approach," as well as "the cognitive approach." Hjørland (2002) has used a critique of individualistic approaches to suggest the need for a sociocognitive, domain-oriented paradigm; similarly, Tuominen, Talja, and Savolainen (2002, 2003) argue for a "social constructionist" paradigm or viewpoint in the field.

14.5. Philosophy of Information

Philosophers (and information scientists with philosophical perspectives) have found interesting topics for investigation in the philosophy of information. Floridi (2002) defined this area as the philosophical field concerned with "the critical investigation of the conceptual nature and basic principles of information, including its dynamics, utilization, and sciences, and the elaboration and application of information-theoretical and computational methodologies to philosophical problems" (p. 123).

Relations Between Philosophy and Information Science

Philosophical questions about information science are most often addressed by people working within the field, such as textbook authors, historians of information science, or theoretically minded information scientists. Some researchers in information science have made connections with the developing field of philosophy of information (e.g., Herold, 2004), and some information scientists have backgrounds in philosophy—among them are Bernd Frohmann, Elaine Svenonius, and Patrick Wilson. Philosophers (some not formally trained as such) who are frequently cited in information science include Thomas Kuhn, Karl Popper, Charles Sanders Peirce, Jürgen Habermas, and Michel Foucault.

Some researchers in information science work from a particular philosophical position. Hope Olson (1997), for example, has adopted a feminist view (a feminist philosophy); Rafael Capurro (1986) works from a hermeneutical perspective; and Birger Hjørland (1997) employs a family of views associated with cultural, historical activity theory.

Any theoretical view within information science also implies philosophical questions about the field. Two classical areas in philosophy are important for information science: 1) ontology and metaphysics, and 2) epistemology (theory of knowledge); these are introduced in the next two subsections. Other important areas include philosophy of science, philosophy of language, philosophy of mind, and ethics.

Ontology and Metaphysics

Popperian cosmology (Popper, 1972) divides the universe into three interacting subuniverses:

- World 1: the world of physical objects and events, including biological entities

- World 2: the world of mental objects and events

- World 3: the world of the products of the human mind

This view is an alternative to Cartesian dualism, according to which the universe is composed of two essential substances: the thinking being and the physical world. Popperian cosmology maintains the view that physical and mental states exist and interact. To this he added World 3 (objective knowledge), which information scientists such as Brookes (1980) have considered the domain of information science (a view that has been criticized by Hjørland, 1997, and Rudd, 1983). The theory of *integrative levels* provides an alternative metaphysical theory. Its origin can be traced at least as far back as the positivism of Auguste Comte, and it is clearly set out in Spencer's (1862) *First Principles*. The Classification Research Group adopted the theory; Mills and Ball (2007) claim that it is the basis for the Bliss Bibliographic Classification:

> Bliss Bibliographic Classification ... is an internationally accepted detailed general classification which is based on clear and comprehensive principles for both its overall structure (main-class order) and the internal structure of each and every class. The former is based on the theory of integrative levels first advanced by Comte. The second is based on the revolutionary theory of faceted classification developed by Ranganathan and elaborated by the ... (British) Classification Research Group. (back cover)

Epistemology

Epistemology, the theory of knowledge, is important for information science, as it is in any science or research field. It is closely connected to the different approaches or paradigms; epistemological views are essentially built into the research methods accepted by the field. In information science the importance is doubled: epistemology underlies the approaches used to study information, and it concerns views of this information itself. Because *knowledge* and *information* are often used interchangeably in information science, it is obvious that the theory of knowledge must also be important for the theory of information.

Epistemologies may be characterized by the kind of information that is found relevant. Hjørland (2002) outlined relevance criteria in four basic epistemological theories (see Table 14.1).

Each of these epistemological positions has strong arguments against the others. The classical rationalist argument against empiricism is that observations cannot play the sole role (or even the major role) in acquiring knowledge because one cannot experience anything that is not already anticipated in the inborn capacity to sense and form concepts. Our knowledge about colors, for example, cannot come from experience alone because the ability to discriminate colors is a prerequisite to experiencing them.

The inherent weakness in the epistemological positions may lead to skepticism or methodological anarchism. Common sense shows, however, that science is successful in producing knowledge. Thus it is possible to produce valuable knowledge, and some principles and methods simply are better than others in describing how this is done. This consideration may contain an argument for a pragmatic philosophy.

The epistemological positions outlined here are ideal types: they cannot exist in pure form, but different persons or documents may be more or less influenced by one or another of the views. Different views of knowledge

Table 14.1 Relevance criteria in four epistemological theories (Hjørland, 2002)

Theory	Relevant	Not Relevant
Empiricism	Observations, sense data; Induction from collections of observational data; Intersubjectively controlled data	Speculations, knowledge transmitted from authorities ("book" knowledge); Data about the observers' assumptions and pre-understanding
Rationalism	Pure thinking, logic, mathematical models, computer modeling, systems of axioms, definitions and theorems	Low priority is given to empirical data because such data must be organized in accordance with principles that cannot come from experience
Historicism	Background knowledge about pre-understanding, theories, conceptions, contexts, historical developments, and evolutionary perspectives	Low priority is given to decontextualized data of which the meanings cannot be interpreted; Intersubjectively controlled data is often seen as trivia
Pragmatism	Information about goals, values, and consequences involving both the researcher and the object of research (subject and object)	Low priority (or outright suspicion) is accorded to claimed value-free or neutral information; For example, feminist epistemology is suspicious of the neutrality of information produced in a male-dominated society

underlie the various approaches or paradigms in all fields of knowledge. The social sciences in particular have adopted many different approaches. In information science, for example, the facet-analytic tradition in classification research is connected to rationalism; the experimental information retrieval tradition and bibliometrics have mainly been dominated by empiricism and positivism (Hjørland, 1997). Hjørland attempted to base information science on activity theory, which is related to both pragmatism and (critical) forms of realism.

Epistemology is important for information science not only in relation to the research methods adopted. Because the field focuses on communicating knowledge, information science can be seen as applied epistemology. Any activity related to selecting, organizing, seeking, or communicating knowledge is basically an epistemological activity. Thus, any explanation of why scientists cite the paper they do must take into consideration the epistemological preferences of the citers (Hjørland, 2002).

As in other social sciences, the information science view of knowledge tends to be dominated by empiricism and positivism. There are, however, attempts to inform the field by, for example, activity theory, feminist epistemology, hermeneutics, postmodernism, and social constructionism. Such attempts are pertinent, but they risk remaining in a metatheoretical position without sufficient connection to specific problems. Hjørland has suggested that the methods of classification inside and outside information science are basically connected to the four epistemological positions presented in Table 14.1 and that epistemological knowledge helps to identify strengths and weaknesses in different approaches to classification. Other information science problems have similar relations to epistemology.

14.6. Conclusion

As an interdisciplinary field, information science continues to draw on theoretical insights from many sources. The persistence and continuing utility of both mathematical models and social perspectives demonstrate the variety of challenges in understanding and finding coherent solutions for the real-world problems that information scientists encounter. The emerging interest in how philosophy can address these problems provides yet another source of insight.

References

Allen, B. (1996). *Information tasks: Toward a user-centered approach to information systems.* San Diego, CA: Academic Press.

Barabási, A. L. (2002). *Linked: The new science of networks.* Cambridge, MA: Perseus.

Brookes, B. C. (1980). The foundations of information science, Part 1: Philosophical aspects. *Journal of Information Science, 2*(3/4), 125–133.

Capurro, R. (1986). *Hermeneutik der Fachinformation.* Munich, Germany: Karl Alber.

Cawkell, A. E. (1990). The boundaries of information science: Information theory is alive and well. *Journal of Information Science, 16*(4), 215–216.

Cronin, B. (2008). The sociological turn in information science. *Journal of Information Science, 34*(4), 465–475.

Ellis, D. (1996). The dilemma of measurement in information retrieval research. *Journal of the American Society for Information Science, 47*(1), 23–36.

Floridi, L. (2002). What is the philosophy of information? *Metaphilosophy, 33*(1/2), 123–145.

Goldman, A. (2001). History of social epistemology. *Stanford encyclopedia of philosophy.* Retrieved November 11, 2010, from plato.stanford.edu/entries/epistemology-social/#1.

Granovetter, M. S. (1973). The strength of weak ties. *American Journal of Sociology, 78*(6), 1360–1380.

Herold, K. (Ed.) (2004). The philosophy of information. (Special Issue.) *Library Trends, 52*(373–665).

Hjelmslev, L. (1961). *Prolegomena to a theory of language* (F. J. Whitfield, trans.). Madison: University of Wisconsin Press. (Original work published in 1943).

Hjørland, B. (1997). *Information seeking and subject representation: An activity-theoretical approach to information science.* Westport, CT: Greenwood.

Hjørland, B. (2002). Epistemology and the socio-cognitive perspective in information science. *Journal of the American Society for Information Science and Technology, 53*(4), 257–270.

Kearns, J. (2003). Dancing with entropy: Form attributes, children, and representation. *Journal of Documentation, 60*(2), 144–163.

Kline, R. R. (2004). What is information theory a theory of? Boundary work among information theorists and information scientists in the United States and Britain during the Cold War. In W. B. Rayward & M. E. Bowden (Eds.), *The history and heritage of scientific and technical information systems: Proceedings of the 2002 Conference* (pp. 15–28). Medford, NJ: Information Today.

Kuhn, T. S. (1996). *The structure of scientific revolutions* (3rd ed.). Chicago, IL: University of Chicago Press.

Mills, J., & Ball, C. (2007). *Bliss bibliographic classification. Class W. The arts.* Munich, Germany: Sauer.

Newman, M. E. J. (2003). *The structure and function of complex networks.* Retrieved November 11, 2010, from arxiv.org/abs/cond-mat/0303516v1.

O'Connor, B. C. (1991). Selecting key frames of moving image documents: A digital environment for analysis and navigation. *Microcomputers for Information Management, 8*, 119–133.

Olson, H. A. (1997). The feminist and the emperor's new clothes: Feminist deconstruction as a critical methodology for library and information studies. *Library & Information Science Research, 19*(2), 181–198.

Pettigrew, K. E., & McKechnie, L. (2001). The use of theory in information science research. *Journal of the American Society for Information Science and Technology, 52*(1), 62–73.

Pierce, S. J. (1992). Dead Germans and the theory of librarianship. *American Libraries, 23*(8), 641–643.

Popper, K. R. (1972). *Objective knowledge: An evolutionary approach.* Oxford, UK: Clarendon Press.

Rudd, D. (1983). Do we really need World III? Information science with or without Popper. *Journal of Information Science, 7*, 99–105.

Schmitt, F. F. (1998). Social epistemology. In E. Craig (Ed.), *Routledge encyclopedia of philosophy.* London: Routledge. Retrieved August 12, 2009, from www.rep.routledge.com/article/P046.

Shannon, C., & Weaver, W. (1949). *The mathematical theory of communication.* Urbana: University of Illinois Press.

Shaw, D., & Davis, C. H. (1983). Entropy and information: A multidisciplinary overview. *Journal of the American Society for Information Science, 34*(1), 67–74.

Shera, J. (1970). *Sociological foundations of librarianship.* New York: Asia Publishing House.

Spencer, H. (1862). *A system of synthetic philosophy (Vol. 1: First principles)*. Retrieved November 11, 2010, from praxeology.net/HS-SP.htm.

Tuominen, K., Talja, S., & Savolainen, R. (2002). Discourse, cognition and reality: Toward a social constructionist metatheory for library and information science. *Proceedings of the Fourth International Conference on Conceptions of Library and Information Science* (pp. 271–283). Greenwood Village, CO: Libraries Unlimited.

Tuominen, K., Talja, S., & Savolainen, R. (2003). Multiperspective digital libraries: The implications of constructionism for the development of digital libraries. *Journal of the American Society for Information Science and Technology, 54*(6), 561–569.

Watt, J. (1979). Television form, content attributes, and viewer behavior. In M. J. Voight (Ed.), *Progress in communication* (pp. 51–89). Norwood, NJ: Ablex.

Watts, D. J., & Strogatz, S. H. (1998). Collective dynamics of "small-world" networks. *Nature, 393*, 440–442.

Wersig, G. (2003). Information theory. In J. Feather & P. Sturges (Eds.), *International encyclopedia of library and information science* (pp. 310–319). London: Routledge.

Wiener, N. (1948). *Cybernetics, or control and communication in the animal and the machine*. New York: MIT Press.

Williamson, K. (2002). *Research methods for students, academics and professionals: Information management and systems* (2nd ed.). Wagga Wagga, New South Wales, Australia: Center for Information Studies.

Wilson, P. (1983). *Second-hand knowledge: An inquiry into cognitive authority*. Westport, CT: Greenwood Press.

Glossary

abstract. A summary of a statement, speech, document, or information object. The International Organization for Standardization defines an abstract as "an abbreviated, accurate representation of the contents of a document, without added interpretation or criticism and without distinction as to who wrote the abstract."

American Documentation Institute (ADI). See American Society for Information Science and Technology (ASIST).

American National Standards Institute (ANSI). A nonprofit organization of government agencies, companies, universities, and individuals that oversees the creation, promulgation, and use of standards of all types. It is the official U.S. representative to the International Organization for Standardization (ISO). ANSI accredits other organizations, such as the National Information Standards Organization (NISO), in the development of standards in certain technical areas. See also International Organization for Standardization (ISO); National Information Standards Organization (NISO).

American Society for Indexing (ASI). A nonprofit membership organization founded in 1968 to promote excellence in indexing and increase awareness of the value of well-written indexes.

American Society for Information Science and Technology (ASIST). Established as the American Documentation Institute (ADI) in 1937; name changed to American Society for Information Science (ASIS) in 1968 and again to ASIST in 2000. It is a personal membership organization.

anomalous state of knowledge (ASK). A term meaning an individual's state of knowledge is inadequate to resolve a particular problematic situation. The inadequacy might result from lack of knowledge or uncertainty regarding which concept would be appropriate in the situation. The concept was developed originally by Nicholas Belkin.

Association for Computing Machinery (ACM). Founded in 1947, an international scientific and educational organization dedicated to advancing the art, science, engineering, and application of information technology. It is a personal membership organization.

authority control. In indexing and cataloging, the selection of unambiguous forms of names and titles to be used in place of forms that may cause confusion.

background noise. Extraneous signals (or noise) that interfere with sound transmission or quality and cannot be separated from the desired signal.

Berne Convention for Protection of Literary and Artistic Works. An international agreement governing copyright that was first accepted in Berne, Switzerland, in 1886 and requires its signatories to recognize the copyright of works of authors from other signatory countries (known as members of the Berne Union) in the same way as it recognizes the copyright of its own nationals. The U.S. became a signatory in 1989.

bibliographic control. A variety of activities and processes that enable the identification, description, selection, and use of all types of information resources (books, journals, videos, films, images, archival materials, museum objects, etc.) in an information system, such as a library or archive. See also *surrogate record*; *metadata*.

bibliometrics. Statistical methods to quantify and describe written communication.

Boolean logic. A complete system for logical operations. In information retrieval (search engine and database queries), the Boolean operators OR, AND, and NOT are employed to clarify the formation of sets in search queries. Named for mathematician George Boole.

Bradford's law of literature scatter. In bibliometrics, the observation that a small number of journals in a given field publishes most of the core articles.

Chartered Institute of Library and Information Professionals (CILIP). Established in the U.K. in 2002 through a merger of the Institute of Information Scientists (IIS), which was founded in 1958, and the Library Association (LA), which was founded in 1877.

Classification Research Group (CRG). Founded in the U.K. in 1952, a group actively involved in studying and developing classification systems. It has been an important contributor to classification research, particularly facet analysis and relational operators, since its founding.

cloud computing. Internet-accessible computing resources (storage, software) supplied by a third party on an as-needed basis.

competitive intelligence. Information that an organization collects about organizations considered to be competitors. See also *strategic intelligence*.

computer hardware. All the physical components of a computer, including peripherals such as a printer.

computer operating system. A program that manages computer hardware and how the user interacts with the system.

computer software. The instructions or programs that control the operations of computer hardware.

content analysis. Systematic and objective description of the content of a text, or information object, usually for the purpose of providing additional understanding of the meaning of the information.

contextual analysis. Analysis of texts or other information objects in conjunction with the traditions, customs, and practices in which they were developed and used. See also *hermeneutic analysis.*

controlled vocabulary. A subset of natural language with less nuance and more precision, achieved with a thesaurus, for example, by carefully defining accepted terms and allowing use only of terms from the thesaurus to represent the subjects in a document.

Cross Language Evaluation Forum (CLEF). Supported by the European Commission, this body promotes research and development in multilingual information access by developing an infrastructure for the testing and evaluation of information retrieval systems operating in European languages. Test suites of reusable data are provided to system developers for benchmarking purposes. See also *Text REtrieval Conference (TREC).*

data. Facts that result from observations; also signs, symbols, and figures that usually require context or interpretation for full meaning.

data mining. The process of detecting meaningful patterns from data. It is used in marketing studies, security or surveillance, profiling, and fraud protection, for example, in which extensive digital data resources exist. It may be performed on a sample of data or on a complete file of data.

descriptor. A word of phrase from a controlled vocabulary (usually a thesaurus) that can be used to depict subject content of an information item.

digital divide, global digital divide. An expression of the gap that exists between people, societies, or nations that have effective access to digital information and technology and those that do not.

digital library. A system to store and retrieve large, complex collections of digital data (text, sound, images, video) and to maintain the cyberinfrastructure to support access.

digital literacy. Attitudes, understanding, and skills to handle and communicate information and knowledge effectively, in a variety of media and formats, especially in digital or electronic format.

discourse analysis. Identification of implicit assumptions in the use of language by investigating the relationships among a text, its discursive practices, and the larger social context. It assumes that the resources and strategies used to produce texts are characteristics of a community rather than unique to a discursive event.

documentation. The process of systematically collecting, organizing, storing, retrieving, and disseminating information in any format to facilitate research or preserve institutional memory. Also, an early term used to describe the field of study that involved these processes, used especially in Europe but also in the U.S.

Dublin Core. A metadata element set in the fields of library and information science that is intended to be used for cross-domain information resource description. It consists of two levels: simple and qualified. It is named for Dublin, Ohio, home of OCLC, Inc., and managed by the Dublin Core Metadata Initiative (DCMI).

empiricism. In philosophy, the doctrine that all knowledge is derived from experience. It emphasizes the role of experience and perception as opposed to innate ideas. In the philosophy of science, it emphasizes those aspects of scientific knowledge that rely on evidence. See also *logical positivism.*

encryption. Transformation of data, using an encryption coding system, so that it cannot be read unless the reader has a decoding key, or cipher. Frequently used for sensitive commercial and military data.

entropy. In physics, a measure of the unavailable energy in a thermodynamic system; or, a statistical measure of the amount of disorder in a closed system. In computer science, communications, and information science, a measure of the efficiency of a system, such as a code or language, in transmitting information. See also *negentropy.*

enumerative classification. A classification system that attempts to provide a structure, or organization, that lists (enumerates) classifications for every possible topic. See also *faceted classification; hierarchical classification.*

faceted classification. Initial analysis identifies aspects, or facets, of a topic, and indexers describe each document in relation to the facets. The information searcher then combines the facets to construct a description of the documents to be retrieved. See also *enumerative classification*; *hierarchical classification*.

feedback. The return of a portion of the output (or energy) of a process or system to the input, usually used to maintain performance or to control the system or process; the return of information about a process or an activity, sometimes aiding in system or process evaluation.

firewall. Hardware or software that separates one or more computers from a network (such as the internet) and denies access to unauthorized users.

folksonomy. A collaboratively developed and maintained classification system; also known as collaborative tagging, social classification, social indexing, and social tagging.

Functional Requirements for Bibliographic Records (FRBR). Developed by the International Federation of Library Associations and Institutions in 1995, a metadata schema and entity relationship model that presents a generalized view of the bibliographic universe and intended to be independent of any cataloging code or implementation. See also *metadata*; *Dublin Core*.

hermeneutic analysis. An approach to understanding textual data; either the parts or the whole of a text can be examined to discover hidden meanings in individually or socially constructed realities. Hermeneutic analysis holds that interpretation is contextual, depending on the moment of interpretation and the horizon brought to it by the interpreter.

heuristic evaluation. Assessment of the interface for a computer system by a small group of evaluators using a list of recognized usability principles, called *heuristics*.

hierarchical classification. A classification system, or scheme, whose organization is based on a specific order, such as general to specific; biological classification of living organisms is an example. See also *enumerative classification*; *faceted classification*.

homonyms, homophones, and homographs. *Homonyms* is the more general term for words that are spelled or pronounced in the same way but that have different meanings. Homophones have the same pronunciation but different spellings (e.g., *oar* and *ore*). Homographs are words or symbols written the same way but meaning different things (e.g., *bank*).

human-computer interaction (HCI). Study of the design, evaluation, and implementation of interactive computer systems and the conditions surrounding their use.

indexing. The process of representing a part or the whole of a document or information object in a separate record (or index) for the purpose of retrieval.

information. A collection of facts (or symbols or signs) provided with context. See also *data, knowledge, wisdom.*

information analysis. Careful study or investigation of the component parts of an information object (text, pictures, sounds) and their relations in making up the whole item.

information and communications technologies (ICTs). The combination of computers, hardware, software, and communications networks to handle information.

information architecture. The process of organizing, representing, and designing an information object, website, database, or information system that allows people to find easily the information they need.

information behavior. All human actions involved with information, including information seeking, unintentional or passive behaviors (such as glimpsing or encountering information), and purposive behaviors that do not involve seeking, such as actively avoiding certain types of information.

information literacy. The ability to recognize information needs, locate and evaluate the quality of information sources, store and retrieve information, and make effective and ethical use of information to create and communicate knowledge. See also *digital literacy.*

information need. An individual's or group's perception that information of some type is required to accomplish a desired goal.

information seeking. A conscious effort, or process, to acquire information in response to a need or gap in one's knowledge.

information visualization. The graphical presentation of abstract, usually nonspatial, data in order to improve understanding.

Institute for Scientific Information (ISI). Private corporation that created citation indexes to the literature of science, social science, and arts and humanities; it was acquired by Thomson Reuters, and its work continues as the *Web of Science.*

International Council of Archives (ICA). Established in 1948, this nongovernmental organization brings together professional archival associations and individual archivists interested in researching, developing, and sharing their full range of archival expertise. It works for the protection and enhancement of the memory of the world and to improve communication while respecting cultural diversity.

International Council of Museums (ICOM). Established in 1946, this nongovernmental organization of museums and museum professionals promotes the conservation, continuation, and communication to society of the world's natural and cultural heritage, present and future, tangible and intangible.

International Federation for Information and Documentation (FID). (Fédération Internationale de Documentation). Founded in 1895 as the International Institute of Bibliography (IIB) by Paul Otlet and Henri LaFontaine, FID underwent several name changes. It played a critical role in the early development of ideas and practices in documentation and information science and technology. It was dissolved in 2002.

International Federation of Library Associations and Institutions (IFLA). Founded in 1927, describes itself on its website as the "global voice of the library and information profession" (www.ifla.org). Headquarters are at the Royal Library of The Netherlands.

International Organization for Standardization (ISO). The world's largest developer and publisher of standards for a wide variety of products and services, including all areas related to information science and technology. ISO cooperates with national standards organizations, such as NISO in the U.S. ISO standards ensure desirable characteristics of products and services, such as quality, environmental friendliness, safety, reliability, efficiency, and interchangeability. (ISO is not an initialism; the name is based on the Greek word *isos*, meaning *equal*.)   See also *National Information Standards Organization (NISO)*.

keyword index. The most important words from a document, extracted and placed in an index to represent the document's content. The terms may be extracted from any part of the document manually or by computer. See also *KWIC index, KWOC index*.

knowledge. Created from facts, information, truths, or principles through study or investigation that supply meaning. See also *data, information, wisdom*.

KWIC (Key Word In Context) index. The process of extracting and placing in an index (usually alphabetical) keyword(s) from a text and retaining some portion of the context of each term. Most KWIC indexes are compiled semi-automatically with a computer.

KWOC (Key Word Out of Context) index. Like a KWIC index, a computer algorithm selects keywords and a portion of the surrounding text to be placed in an index. Each keyword (index term) is displayed in the left-hand margin, above the index entries for that term (the result looks more like a typical book index).

latent semantic analysis. Uses mathematical models to find connections (such a co-occurrence in a document and word proximity) or concealed meanings among the words in a database.

literary warrant, user warrant. Creators of a controlled vocabulary, such as a thesaurus, use literary warrant to include terms that appear in the documents to be indexed and user warrant to include terms that the intended users might employ.

logical positivism (or **logical empiricism**). A school of philosophy that combines empiricism with rationalism, the idea that scientific knowledge includes a component not derived from observation. Logical positivists insist that a statement (or proposition) is meaningful only if there is a process by which it can be shown to be true or false.

Lotka's law of author productivity. In bibliometrics, the observation that a small number of authors account for most of the journal articles in a field.

markup languages. Based on the publishing industry's practice of using codes to signify such things as headings and type face, markup is now common in computer text processing. SGML (standard generalized markup language) was the first to be standardized by the International Organization for Standardization; its derivatives are used in most computer text processing programs and on webpages. The three major types are presentational, procedural, and descriptive.

metadata. Literally, data about data. The descriptive information (e.g., title, author, subjects covered, location as a webpage) about an information resource in an information system. Metadata schemas exist for different kinds of information resources or objects, such as libraries, archives, spreadsheets, geographic information, and images; eXtensible Markup Language (XML) is frequently used on the web. See also *bibliographic control; Dublin Core; markup languages; surrogate record.*

National Information Standards Organization (NISO). A nonprofit organization founded in 1939 and accredited by the American National Standards Institute to identify, develop, and publish technical standards to manage information. NISO standards apply both traditional and new technologies to information-related needs, including retrieval, repurposing, storage, metadata, and preservation. See also *American National Standards Institute (ANSI); International Standards Organization (ISO).*

National Institute of Standards and Technology (NIST). Formerly the National Bureau of Standards, an agency of the U. S. Department of Commerce and the first federal physical sciences research laboratory, established in 1901. NIST co-sponsors the annual TREC conferences. See also *Text REtrieval Conference (TREC)*.

natural language. Words or signs people develop and use for everyday communication, written or oral.

negentropy. Term coined by Brillouin for *negative entropy;* in statistics and information theory, it is a measure of distance to normality for any signal. Sometimes used in organizational theory and risk management to describe the amount of energy needed to achieve and maintain organizational stability.

normalization. The process of removing redundant information from a relational database. See also *relational database*.

Open Systems Interconnection (OSI) reference model. Defines the seven layers at which computer network components can connect.

paradigm. An example serving as a pattern. Thomas Kuhn used the term *paradigm shift* to describe a basic change in assumptions, leading to new patterns of scientific thought that produce scientific revolutions.

Pareto's law (or principle). Named for Vilfredo Pareto, Italian economist, to describe a general rule of thumb about many skewed empirical distributions (e.g., 80 percent of a library's circulation comes from 20 percent of the collection; 80 percent of sales come from 20 percent of customers); also known as the 80/20 rule. It is not a scientific law but a pattern.

post-coordinate indexing. In information retrieval, the terms used to describe the contents of an information object (or document) are single words; the searcher combines them when doing a search on a multi-word concept; for example, *automatic* AND *indexing*. Separate entries for each word would appear in the index.

pre-coordinate indexing. In information retrieval, the terms used to describe the contents of an information object (or document) are combined by the indexer instead of the person searching for the information. For example, the indexer uses the pre-coordinated term *automatic indexing* instead of separate index entries for *automatic* and *indexing*. This type of index is usually found in back-of-the-book indexes, most library catalogs, and many bibliographic databases.

proximity searching. Specifying in a search query that search terms must appear as a phrase or within a specified number of characters of each other.

relational database. A database that organizes data in two-dimensional tables. Tables contain *records*, which have one or more *fields*, and each field has a specific *type* and a specific *value*.

representation of information. The process of identifying a shorter or smaller word, term, phrase, or image that brings to mind, stands for, or typifies the content of a book, manuscript, image, webpage, or other source of information. Examples are subject headings, terms from a thesaurus, classification symbols or numbers, or an abstract.

semantic ambiguity. This occurs when the meaning of a word or phrase is diffuse, vague, or unclear and must be resolved by context (e.g., "time flies like an arrow"). With lexical ambiguity, a word has multiple meanings in the same language (e.g., *bank*). Syntactical ambiguity occurs when a phrase or sentence may be parsed in different ways (e.g., "he ate the potato chips on the bed"). See also: *homonyms, homophones, and homographs.*

Semantic Web. Metadata and other technologies are used to describe the meanings (semantics) and relationships of data on the World Wide Web. It extends and enhances the human-readable hyperlinks on the web. This allows computer applications to connect and make use of the data, with the appearance of "understanding."

semiotics, semiology. In philosophy, the general study of symbolic systems, including language. Semiotics pursues the systematic study of signs and the production of meanings from sign systems, including how social reality is created and shared within a community. *Social semiotics* is the study of signs within the context of discourse analysis or content analysis. See also *content analysis; discourse analysis.*

social informatics. The study of the social aspects of computers, telecommunications, and related technologies. It examines issues such as the ways that these technologies shape organizational and social relations or the ways in which social forces influence the use and design of information and communication technologies.

strategic intelligence. Development and deployment of the knowledge an organization requires about the outside world in order to meets the organization's objectives. The emphasis is often on secret information and success over competitors. See also *competitive intelligence.*

structuralism. A method or approach that attempts to analyze a specific field (literary theory, linguistics, sociology, anthropology, etc.) as a complex system of interrelated parts.

surrogate record. Descriptive information, usually in the form of a citation, catalog entry, abstract, or metadata on a webpage, about an information resource that replaces (substitutes for) the actual information resource itself. These records in an information system (e.g., an online catalog or a search engine) are what the user actually searches. See also *bibliographic control*; *metadata*.

syndetic structure. Cross-references in a thesaurus or subject headings list to identify the preferred term and help the user to find or connect that term or to suggest additional descriptors.

tagging. The process of indexing an information object by choosing terms from natural language, with no restrictions on the format of the descriptions. See also *metadata*; *indexing*.

term truncation. Only part of a word in a search statement is entered in a search query, and a special character (such as *) indicates that all subsequent characters in that word are to be ignored in matching the query term to the data file. Example: *war** would retrieve all records containing the terms war, wars, warfare, warring, and warlike; however, it would also retrieve warren, warn, warns, and warning, so one must use truncated terms carefully.

Text REtrieval Conference (TREC). A series of conferences begun in 1992, co-sponsored by the National Institute of Standards and Technology (NIST) and the U.S. Department of Defense, to support information retrieval research by providing the infrastructure for large-scale evaluation of retrieval methods. NIST provides a test set of documents and questions; participants run their own retrieval systems on the data and return to NIST a list of the retrieved top-ranked documents for evaluation. See also *Cross Language Evaluation Forum (CLEF)*.

TCP/IP (transmission control protocol/internet protocol). A standard that allows dissimilar computers to send and receive data from each other.

United Nations Educational, Scientific and Cultural Organization (UNESCO; Unesco). A United Nations specialized agency supporting international work, including for libraries and information science and technology.

Universal Decimal Classification Consortium (UDC Consortium). A self-funded, noncommercial organization that directs the development and dissemination of the Universal Decimal Classification (UDC).

user-centered design. An approach to information system or website design focusing on user requirements at every stage of the design process. Similar terms are *cooperative design, participatory design, contextual design*.

user warrant. See *literary warrant.*

virtual private network (VPN). A secure channel for data transmission created through encryption and "tunneling."

wisdom. The highest level in the data-information-knowledge-wisdom pyramid; wisdom is created from shared insights and knowledge. See also *data, information, knowledge.*

World Intellectual Property Organization (WIPO). A United Nations specialized agency created in 1967 to encourage creative activity and to promote the protection of intellectual property throughout the world. It administers an intellectual property application and registration system known as the International Bureau.

Zipf's law of word frequency. In bibliometrics, the observation that speakers and writers use a few words very frequently and that most words are seldom used.

Index

A

ablative case, 45
aboutness, 4, 48–53, 60, 63, 115
absolute judgment limits, 135
abstracts/abstracting, 22, 53–57
acceptance of information systems, 98
access cost, information, 136
access to information, 119, 211, 212, 219
accountability for damage cost by information loss/theft, 218
accusative case, 44–45
ACM (Association for Computational Machinery), 23, 202, 211, 220
ACRL (Association of College and Research Libraries) standard development, 202
active hubs, 85
active information seeking behavior, 27
activity theory, 28–29, 234
adaptive information systems, 134
address bus, 81
address resolution protocol, 86
administrative metadata, 71, 73
Advancement of Learning (Bacon), 67

Advice on Establishing a Library (Naudé), 18
Aesthetics and Computation Group, 123–124
affect extraction/analysis, 50
ALA. *See* American Library Association
alphabetic writing, 44
American Association of Museums, 220
American Documentation Institute, 21
American Library Association (ALA)
  on core values of librarians, 208
  ethics, approach to, 219
  history, 19
  information policy interests, 191
  intellectual freedom, definition, 120
  standard development, 202
  website, 220
American Library Journal, 19
American National Standards Institute (ANSI), 87, 200–201
American Society for Indexing, 60
American Society for Information Science and Technology (ASIST), 16, 21, 23, 214–216, 220

More Titles of Interest from Information Today, Inc.

Information Need

A Theory Connecting Information Search to Knowledge Formation

By Charles Cole

In *Information Need*, Charles Cole digs deep into the need that motivates people to search for information and articulates a theory of information need as the basis for designing IR systems that engage the user's knowledge/belief system. He describes how such systems use signals from the user's own information environment to reduce overload, improve search results, and enhance the usefulness of information delivered on mobile devices. He explains the benefits for disadvantaged sectors of society and profiles a working system. An important text for researchers and students in information science, computer science, and HCI, and for anyone interested in IR theory, practice, and systems design.

May 2012/224 pp/hardbound/ISBN 978-1-57387-429-8
ASIST Members $47.60 • Nonmembers $59.50

Introductory Concepts in Information Science, Second Edition

By Melanie J. Norton

Melanie J. Norton presents a unique and carefully researched introduction to the practical and theoretical concepts of information science and examines the impact of the Information Age on society and its institutions. Topics new to the second edition include indexing, information repositories, and digital libraries.

224 pp/hardbound/ISBN 978-1-57387-394-9
ASIST Members $39.60 • Nonmembers $49.50

Information Representation and Retrieval in the Digital Age, Second Edition

By Heting Chu

This second edition of Heting Chu's popular work on information representation and retrieval (IRR) features numerous updates and revisions, including coverage of taxonomies, folksonomies, ontologies, social tagging, Search/Retrieve Web Service, and next generation OPACs. She reviews key concepts and major developmental stages of the field, and then systematically examines information representation methods, IRR languages, retrieval techniques and models, and internet retrieval systems. In addition, she explains the retrieval of multilingual, multimedia, and hyper-structured information and explores the user dimension and evaluation issues.

320 pp/hardbound/ISBN 978-1-57387-393-2
ASIST Members $39.60 • Nonmembers $49.50

Digital Inclusion
Measuring the Impact of Information and Community Technology

Edited by Michael Crandall and Karen E. Fisher

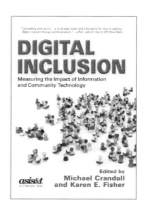

Through an examination of efforts by community technology organizations in Washington State, *Digital Inclusion* offers a model for educating policy makers about the actual impacts of such efforts, along with suggestions for practical implementation. The case studies and analyses presented here will be of critical interest to community technology centers, libraries, government service agencies, and any other organization (or funder) that uses technology to deliver services to the information poor.

200 pp/hardbound/ISBN 978-1-57387-373-4
ASIST Members $47.60 • Nonmembers $59.50

Computerization Movements and Technology Diffusion

From Mainframes to Ubiquitous Computing

Edited by Margaret S. Elliott and Kenneth L. Kraemer

"Computerization movement" (CM), as first articulated by Rob Kling, refers to a special kind of social and technological movement that promotes the adoption of computing within organizations and society. Here, editors Margaret S. Elliott and Kenneth L. Kraemer and more than two dozen noted scholars trace the successes and failures of CMs from the mainframe and PC eras to the emerging era of ubiquitous computing. The empirical studies presented here show the need for designers, users, and the media to be aware that CM rhetoric can propose grand visions that never become part of a reality and reinforce the need for critical and scholarly review of promising new technologies.

608 pp/hardbound/ISBN 978-1-57387-311-6
ASIST Members $47.60 • Nonmembers $59.50

Theories of Information Behavior

Edited by Karen E. Fisher, Sanda Erdelez, and Lynne (E. F.) McKechnie

This unique book presents authoritative overviews of more than 70 conceptual frameworks for understanding how people seek, manage, share, and use information in different contexts. Covering both established and newly proposed theories of information behavior, the book includes contributions from 85 scholars from 10 countries. Theory descriptions cover origins, propositions, methodological implications, usage, and links to related theories.

456 pp/hardbound/ISBN 978-1-57387-230-0
ASIST Members $39.60 • Nonmembers $49.50

Information Nation

Education and Careers in the Emerging Information Professions

By Jeffrey M. Stanton, Indira R. Guzman, and Kathryn R. Stam

Information and IT are central to virtually every industry in which the US plays a leadership role, yet colleges have failed to attract and produce a new generation of information professionals to meet the growing need. Here, three educators ask, "Why?" They look at barriers to inclusion and retention, analyze the forces that prevent high school and college students from getting the interdisciplinary skills, and tell the stories of a diverse group of students who are thriving in new majors and new jobs.

256 pp/softbound/ISBN 978-1-57387-401-4/$35.00

Understanding and Communicating Social Informatics

A Framework for Studying and Teaching the Human Contexts of Information and Communication Technologies

By Rob Kling, Howard Rosenbaum, and Steve Sawyer

Here is a sustained investigation into the human contexts of ICTs, covering both research and theory. The authors demonstrate that the design, adoption, and use of ICTs are deeply connected to people's actions as well as to the environments in which ICTs are used. They offer a pragmatic overview of social informatics, articulating its fundamental ideas for specific audiences and presenting important research findings.

240 pp/hardbound/ISBN 978-1-57387-228-7/$39.50